PROJECTIVE PLANE GEOMETRY

HOLDEN-DAY SERIES IN MATHEMATICS

Earl A. Coddington and Andrew M. Gleason, Editors

PROJECTIVE PLANE GEOMETRY

JOHN W. BLATTNER

PROFESSOR OF MATHEMATICS
SAN FERNANDO VALLEY STATE COLLEGE

HOLDEN-DAY, INC.
SAN FRANCISCO, CAMBRIDGE, LONDON, AMSTERDAM

Library of Congress Catalog Card Number: 69-10047

Printed in the United States of America

To
My Father and Mother

PREFACE

Projective geometry deserves a prominent place in the college mathematics curriculum for several reasons.

(1) Its study enhances one's understanding of affine, Euclidean, and non-Euclidean geometries.

(2) The subject can be developed from a simple axiomatic base, yet contains many beautiful and surprising theorems.

(3) Projective space is the natural setting for algebraic geometry.

Even more significant is the fact that projective geometry offers an eminently suitable vehicle for the introduction of many of the basic concepts of modern mathematics in a reasonably concrete, hence reasonably painless, environment. Thus, the present text has been written for a course intended to be a useful adjunct to courses in abstract algebra as well as to other geometry courses.

To achieve this aim of relevance to the modern curriculum, consistent use is made of the concept of function. The presence of functions is felt not only in the proofs of many theorems, but also in the axiomatic structure itself, a structure that has been greatly influenced by Artin's elegant book *Geometric Algebra* [1]. (Throughout the text, references to the bibliography at the end of the book are made by numbers in brackets.) The function approach to geometry is at once simple, appealing, and powerful.

The main subject matter is developed rigorously from an axiomatic foundation. The axioms are introduced in three sets, with the consequences of each set being worked out in some detail before the next set is brought forth. No axiom is introduced without a preliminary examination of its meaning in a familiar context. Much of this work is necessarily less rigorous than the central body of material. The distinguishing name "Proposition" (rather than "Theorem") is used for the required results of Euclidean geometry to serve as a reminder that their demonstrations are dependent upon information not all of which is contained in this book. While the emphasis of the book is on synthetic geometry, one of the principal goals, and the one that most intimately relates the geometry to abstract algebra, is the construction of coordinate systems in Desarguesian planes (Chapter 4). From here it is but a short step to the analytic methods of projective geometry, so thoroughly treated elsewhere. (The analytic method is used in Chapter 5 whenever its use effects a genuine economy.)

The numbering of chapters and sections is self-explanatory. All definitions, lemmas, theorems, examples, propositions, and important equations are numbered consecutively within each section, while figures are numbered consecutively within each chapter. There are numerous exercises at the end of each section, divided into A and B sets; the B exercises tend to be more difficult. When an exercise is referred to in the text only by its number (for example, exercise 3), it is an exercise at the end of that same section; otherwise, chapter and section numbers will precede the number of the exercise being referenced (for example, Exercise 2.5.6). Suggestions for many of the exercises are furnished at the end of the book; these are intended to be only suggestions, not complete solutions. The symbol ▮ is used to denote the end of a proof, definition, or example.

I would like to thank John Lindsay, Efrem Ostrow, Sister M. Clarice, O.P., Malcolm Soule, Philip Treisman, and Paul Yale for their comments and criticisms, which have had a highly beneficial influence on the final manuscript.

John W. Blattner

Northridge, California

TABLE OF CONTENTS

CHAPTER 1

Introduction to Projective Geometry

CHAPTER 2

Transformations of Projective Planes

CHAPTER 3

Desarguesian Planes

CHAPTER 4

Coordinates in a Desarguesian Plane

CHAPTER 5

Pappian Planes

Chapter 1

INTRODUCTION TO PROJECTIVE GEOMETRY

1.1. Functions

When we say that two plane figures are congruent, we probably share with Euclid the intuition that one of the figures can be rigidly moved until it coincides with the other. If requested to clarify the idea of a rigid motion, we could explain it in terms of translations, rotations, and reflections of $\mathcal{E}_2$, the Euclidean plane. For example, after examining Figure 1.1, we might assert that there is a translation of $\mathcal{E}_2$ that sends triangle ABC into position I and a rotation of $\mathcal{E}_2$ about the point C' that subsequently moves the triangle into position II. From this analysis we would conclude that triangles ABC and $A'B'C'$ are congruent.

An approach to geometry in which one obtains results by the method of transforming one figure into another might be called a dynamic approach; we are about to embark on a dynamic approach to projective geometry. In order to establish a logically acceptable foundation for the intuitive notion of a transformation of one figure into another, it suffices to interpret a transformation as a *function.* Besides underlying our study of projective geometry, the function concept is without doubt one of the most important ideas in all of mathematics. In defining a function we shall use the words *set* and *correspondence* (or *relation*), which we take as primitive terms, not requiring definition, though we shall briefly discuss the latter term.

Suppose that $\mathcal{S}_1$ and $\mathcal{S}_2$ are nonempty sets. The essential characteristic of a correspondence, or relation, from $\mathcal{S}_1$ to $\mathcal{S}_2$ is that it pairs

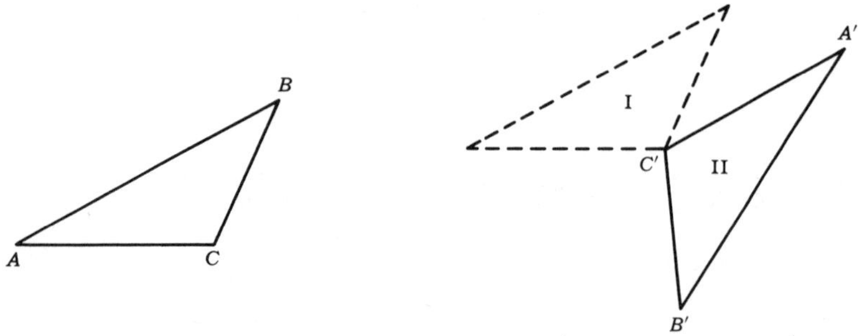

Figure 1.1

with each element of $\mathcal{S}_1$ some subset (perhaps the empty subset) of elements of $\mathcal{S}_2$. If X is in $\mathcal{S}_1$, each element of $\mathcal{S}_2$ that is paired with X is said to be related (or to correspond) to X under the correspondence. It is convenient to use the symbol $\sim$ to represent a relation and to write $Y \sim X$ if (and only if) Y is one of the elements of $\mathcal{S}_2$ that is related *to* X. Observe that a correspondence has a direction—*from* $\mathcal{S}_1$ *to* $\mathcal{S}_2$. Thus, from the statement $Y \sim X$ it does not ordinarily follow that $X \sim Y$.

As an example, let $\mathcal{S}_1$ be the set of all citizens of the United States and $\mathcal{S}_2$ the set of all colleges in the United States. Consider the correspondence from $\mathcal{S}_1$ to $\mathcal{S}_2$ that relates to each citizen those colleges that he has attended. There are citizens who have no colleges related to them, having attended none, and there are citizens who have more than one college related to them. Moreover, each college is related to many different citizens.

The foregoing discussion and example show the generality of the concept of correspondence. A function is a special kind of correspondence, characterized by the following definition.

Definition 1.1.1. Let $\mathcal{S}_1$ and $\mathcal{S}_2$ be nonempty sets. A *function* α, from $\mathcal{S}_1$ to $\mathcal{S}_2$, is a correspondence from $\mathcal{S}_1$ to $\mathcal{S}_2$ that pairs with each element of $\mathcal{S}_1$ one and only one element of $\mathcal{S}_2$.

The set $\mathcal{S}_1$ is the *domain,* and the set $\mathcal{S}_2$ is the *codomain,* of α. If X is an element of $\mathcal{S}_1$, the unique element of $\mathcal{S}_2$ that is paired with X (by α) is denoted by $X\alpha$ and is called the *image* of X under α, or the *value* of α at X. The set of all elements of $\mathcal{S}_2$ that are images (of elements of $\mathcal{S}_1$) under α is the *range* of α. ∎

A function will sometimes be called a *transformation* or a

mapping. When X is in the domain of the function α, we shall say that α transforms, maps, or sends X into $X\alpha$. These terms suggest the dynamic attitude toward functions that it is hoped the student will acquire. Throughout the book the following notational conventions will be adhered to.

(1) Script capital letters, such as $\mathcal{F}$, $\mathcal{S}$, will denote sets.
(2) Points will be designated by italic capitals, such as A, P, X.
(3) Lines will be indicated by small script letters, such as k, ℓ, m.
(4) Numbers will be represented by small italic letters, such as a, n, x.
(5) Greek letters will denote functions.

We now present three examples of functions, and the reader is urged to construct others.

Example 1.1.2. Let $\mathcal{S}_1$ be the set with elements A, B, C, D; we write $\mathcal{S}_1 = \{A, B, C, D\}$. Let $\mathcal{S}_2 = \{1, 2, 3, 4, 5\}$, and let α be the function from $\mathcal{S}_1$ to $\mathcal{S}_2$ that transforms A into 3, B into 2, C into 5, and D into 2. We write $A\alpha = 3$, $B\alpha = 2$, $C\alpha = 5$, and $D\alpha = 2$. This function illustrates several important points. For one thing, the range of a function need not be the entire codomain. For another, two different elements of the domain may be transformed into the same element of the range (as the elements B and D in this example). Finally, the concept of function is extremely general and transcends the common idea of a rule given by a formula. ▮

Example 1.1.3. Let $\mathcal{S}_1$ be the set of all nonnegative real numbers, and let $\mathcal{S}_2 = \mathcal{S}_1$. (That is, $\mathcal{S}_2$ is the same set as $\mathcal{S}_1$.) Let β be the function from $\mathcal{S}_1$ to $\mathcal{S}_2$ defined by $x\beta = \sqrt{x}$ for each nonnegative real number x. If x is a positive number, it has two distinct real square roots, and we follow the convention that $\sqrt{x}$ designates its positive square root. Indeed, it should be observed that *some* definite agreement is necessary in order that the equation $x\beta = \sqrt{x}$ define a function at all, because of the requirement that a function have a unique value at each point of its domain. In this example the domain of β is the same as the codomain of β. When a function ϕ has a set $\mathcal{S}$ for both its domain and codomain, ϕ is said to be a function *on* $\mathcal{S}$. Thus, in the statement, "ϕ is a function on $\mathcal{S}$," the domain and codomain of ϕ are both given as the set $\mathcal{S}$. ▮

Example 1.1.4. (Translations of $\mathcal{E}_2$) A *translation* of $\mathcal{E}_2$ (the Euclidean plane) is a function on (the set of points of) $\mathcal{E}_2$ that transforms an arbitrary point X into a point at a fixed distance and in a fixed direction from X. From this definition it is evident that a translation is completely determined by the specification of the image of one given point. Figure 1.2 illustrates the effect of a translation τ upon several points. Also, referring to Figure 1.1, we see that the triangle

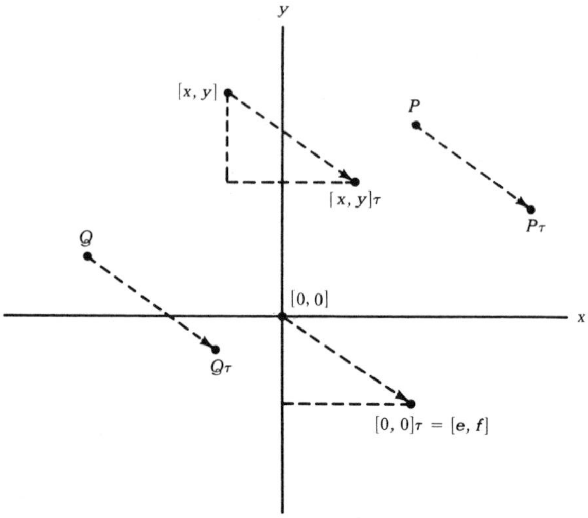

Figure 1.2

in position I corresponds to triangle ABC under a certain translation of the plane.

The task of understanding a translation is assisted by having an analytic expression for it. Let us introduce a Cartesian coordinate system into $\mathcal{E}_2$, and let us suppose that the translation τ sends the origin, $[0, 0]$, of this system into the point $[e, f]$. Then, an arbitrary point $[x, y]$ is transformed by τ into the point $[x + e, y + f]$ (Figure 1.2), so that τ is defined by the equation $[x, y]\tau = [x + e, y + f]$. This equation may also be written in the form

1.1.5. $[x, y]\tau = [x, y] + [e, f]$,

where the intended method of adding $[e, f]$ to $[x, y]$ is to add their first coordinates, and, in like manner, to add their second coordinates. Because of Equation 1.1.5 we call τ the translation by $[e, f]$. ▮

When we write $A = B$, we mean that A and B are the same point. When we write $\mathcal{S}_2 = \mathcal{S}_1$, we mean that $\mathcal{S}_2$ and $\mathcal{S}_1$ contain exactly the same elements; hence they are the same set. What do we mean when we say that two functions are equal? Since the definition of function requires that there be a domain, a codomain, and a correspondence from one to the other, we cannot consider that two functions are equal unless they agree with respect to all three ingredients.

Definition 1.1.6. The functions α and β are *equal* (written $\alpha = \beta$, or $\beta = \alpha$) if and only if the domain of α is the same as the domain of β, the codomain of α is the same as the codomain of β, and $X\alpha = X\beta$ for every X in the common domain of α and β. ▌

For instance, the function γ, from the set of nonnegative *integers* to the set of nonnegative real numbers defined by $x\gamma = \sqrt{x}$, is *not* equal to the function β of Example 1.1.3, because γ and β have different domains. On the other hand, the function δ, on the nonnegative real numbers, defined by $x\delta = (x^2)^{1/4}$ *is* equal to the β of Example 1.1.3, even though the definitions of δ and β employ formally different algebraic expressions.

Referring once more to Figure 1.1, we note that the triangle ABC of that figure is transformed into triangle $A'B'C'$ by a translation of $\mathcal{E}_2$ followed by a rotation; we say that the transformation involved is a *composite* of a translation and a rotation. More generally, suppose that the codomain of the function α is a subset of the domain of β; if X is in the domain of α, then $X\alpha$ is in the domain of β, and the application of β to $X\alpha$ yields $(X\alpha)\beta$. The composite of two functions, defined next, is merely a formalization of this idea of applying first one function and then the other.

Definition 1.1.7. If α is a function from $\mathcal{S}_1$ to $\mathcal{S}_2$, and if β is a function from $\mathcal{S}_3$ to $\mathcal{S}_4$, where $\mathcal{S}_2$ is a subset (perhaps all) of $\mathcal{S}_3$, then the *composite* of α and β, in that order, written $\alpha\beta$, is the function from $\mathcal{S}_1$ to $\mathcal{S}_4$ defined by $X(\alpha\beta) = (X\alpha)\beta$ for each X in $\mathcal{S}_1$. ▌

Since $X\alpha$ of the above definition is in $\mathcal{S}_3$ (because it is in the subset $\mathcal{S}_2$ of $\mathcal{S}_3$), β can be applied to it, and the value $(X\alpha)\beta$ is uniquely determined because α and β are functions. Therefore, $\alpha\beta$ *is* a function. Note that the sufficient condition that $\alpha\beta$ be defined is that the codomain of α be included in the domain of β. It is clear that composition can be repeated to give $(\alpha\beta)\gamma$, $[(\alpha\beta)\gamma]\delta$, etc., provided that the functions involved satisfy the obvious codomain-domain conditions. On the basis of the last two definitions, a fundamental property of the repeated composition of functions can be established.

Theorem 1.1.8. (Associative Law of Composition) For $i = 1, 2, 3$, let α_i be a function from $\mathcal{S}_i$ to $\mathcal{S}_i'$, and suppose that $\mathcal{S}_1'$ is a subset of $\mathcal{S}_2$, and that $\mathcal{S}_2'$ is a subset of $\mathcal{S}_3$. Then, $(\alpha_1\alpha_2)\alpha_3$ and $\alpha_1(\alpha_2\alpha_3)$ are both defined, and they are equal.

Proof: Since $\mathcal{S}_1'$ is a subset of $\mathcal{S}_2$, $\alpha_1\alpha_2$ is defined and has codomain $\mathcal{S}_2'$. Since $\mathcal{S}_2'$ is a subset of $\mathcal{S}_3$, $(\alpha_1\alpha_2)\alpha_3$ is defined. Likewise, $\alpha_2\alpha_3$ is defined because $\mathcal{S}_2'$ is included in $\mathcal{S}_3$, and $\alpha_2\alpha_3$ has domain $\mathcal{S}_2$. Then, $\alpha_1(\alpha_2\alpha_3)$ is defined because $\mathcal{S}_1'$ is included in $\mathcal{S}_2$. Thus, both $(\alpha_1\alpha_2)\alpha_3$ and $\alpha_1(\alpha_2\alpha_3)$ are defined, and both are seen to have domain $\mathcal{S}_1$ and codomain $\mathcal{S}_3'$. By the definition of equality of functions (1.1.6), it remains to be proved that $X[(\alpha_1\alpha_2)\alpha_3] = X[\alpha_1(\alpha_2\alpha_3)]$ for every X in $\mathcal{S}_1$. Repeated applications of the definition of composite function (1.1.7) yield:

$$\begin{aligned} X[(\alpha_1\alpha_2)\alpha_3] = [X(\alpha_1\alpha_2)]\alpha_3 &= [(X\alpha_1)\alpha_2]\alpha_3 \\ &= (X\alpha_1)(\alpha_2\alpha_3) = X[\alpha_1(\alpha_2\alpha_3)] \,. \qquad \blacksquare \end{aligned}$$

Theorem 1.1.8 and mathematical induction combine to provide the *general associative law* (exercise 6), which states that in any meaningful composite of functions the factors can be associated in any manner without affecting the result. We shall make use of the general associative law whenever the need arises.

Exercise 1.1.A

1. Let α, β, γ be functions such that $\alpha = \beta$ and $\beta = \gamma$. Prove that $\alpha = \gamma$.

2. Let $\mathcal{S} = \{A, B, C, D\}$, and let α be the function on $\mathcal{S}$ defined by $A\alpha = B$, $B\alpha = B$, $C\alpha = D$, and $D\alpha = A$. Also, let β be the function on $\mathcal{S}$ defined by $A\beta = A$, $B\beta = D$, $C\beta = B$, and $D\beta = C$. Describe fully the functions $\alpha\beta$ and $\beta\alpha$. Are $\alpha\beta$ and $\beta\alpha$ equal?

3. Show that the range of the function β of Example 1.1.3 is the entire codomain.

4. In $\mathcal{E}_2$ let τ be the translation by $[e, f]$ and σ the translation by $[g, h]$.

(a) Prove that $\tau\sigma$ is the translation by $[e + g, f + h]$.

(b) Prove that $\tau\sigma = \sigma\tau$.

5. Let $\mathcal{R}$ be the set of all real numbers. Does the equation $x\alpha = \tan x$ define a function α on $\mathcal{R}$? Why?

Exercise 1.1.B

6. (General Associative Law) For each i from 1 to n ($n > 2$), let α_i be a function from $\mathcal{S}_i$ to $\mathcal{S}'_i$. Suppose that $\mathcal{S}'_i$ is a subset of $\mathcal{S}_{i+1}$ for each i from 1 to $n - 1$.

(a) Prove that the composite of $\alpha_1, \alpha_2, \ldots, \alpha_n$, in that order, is defined for any association of the factors.

(b) Prove that the composite function of part (a) is the same for any association of the factors. (We say that two functions are the same if they are equal.)

7. Let $\mathcal{S}_1$ be the set of all real numbers, and let $\mathcal{S}_2$ be the closed interval of real numbers between -1 and 1, inclusive. Let α be the function from $\mathcal{S}_1$ to $\mathcal{S}_2$ defined by $x\alpha = \sin x$ for each real number x, and let β be the function from $\mathcal{S}_2$ to $\mathcal{S}_1$ defined by $y\beta = \sin^{-1} y$ (or arcsin y) for each y in S_2.

(a) Is it true that $x(\alpha\beta) = x$ for every x in $\mathcal{S}_1$?

(b) Is it true that $y(\beta\alpha) = y$ for every y in $\mathcal{S}_2$?

8. An *isometry* of $\mathcal{E}_2$ is a function on $\mathcal{E}_2$ that preserves distances. That is, if P and Q are any points of $\mathcal{E}_2$ and μ is an isometry, then the distance between $P\mu$ and $Q\mu$ is the same as the distance between P and Q. Prove that if μ is an isometry, and if P and Q are different points of $\mathcal{E}_2$, then $P\mu \neq Q\mu$.

9. Prove that a translation of $\mathcal{E}_2$ is an isometry (defined in exercise 8).

10. Let ℓ be a certain straight line and $\mathcal{C}$ a certain circle in $\mathcal{E}_2$. Let μ be an isometry (defined in exercise 8).

(a) Prove that the images under μ of all points on ℓ lie on a straight line ℓ'. Prove also that all points on ℓ' are images, under μ, of points on ℓ.

(b) Prove that the images under μ of the points of $\mathcal{C}$ all lie on a circle $\mathcal{C}'$, with the same radius as $\mathcal{C}$. Prove also that all points of $\mathcal{C}'$ are images, under μ, of points of $\mathcal{C}$.

1.2. The Extended Euclidean Plane

Projective geometry had its origin in questions of perspective drawing and how things are seen. We can easily recapture the spirit of the early development of the subject by considering the way in which an image is projected upon a screen. For simplicity, we suppose that our world is the two-dimensional one of the Euclidean plane $\mathcal{E}_2$. In Figure 1.3 the line segment ℓ represents a screen, the point O is a source of light, and the object whose image is to be projected upon ℓ consists of the set of points of the line segment k. The figure shows how the rays from O project P into P' and Q into Q'. By relating to each point of k its image on ℓ (if there is an image), we establish a correspondence from the points of the segment k to the points of ℓ. If the object k is suitably positioned with respect to O and ℓ, the correspondence so established is a function; that is, to each point of k there corresponds exactly one point of ℓ. However, it is clear that there are some positions of k for which only a partial image (as in Figure 1.3), or no image at all, is formed.

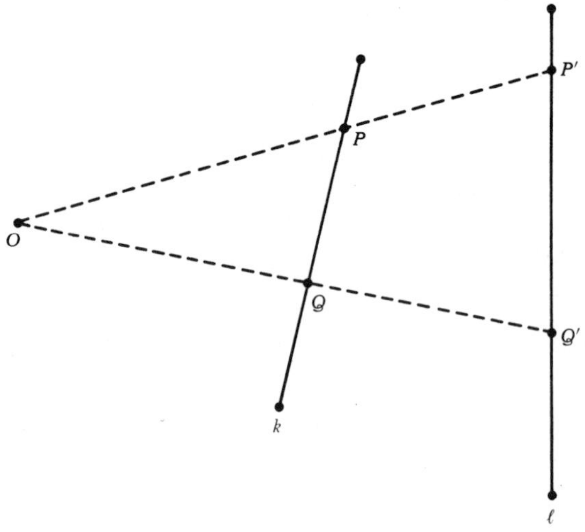

Figure 1.3

To adapt the idea of image projection to geometry, we need to free it of the physical limitations of light rays, objects, and screens. Consider the situation depicted in Figure 1.4. Here, k and ℓ are distinct lines of $\mathcal{E}_2$, and O is a point of $\mathcal{E}_2$ that is not on either k or ℓ. A correspondence $\sim$ from the points of k to the points of ℓ is defined as follows.

> If X is any point of k, let x be the line through O and X. If X' is the point of intersection of x and ℓ, then $X' \sim X$. If x does not intersect ℓ, then no point of ℓ is related to X by $\sim$.

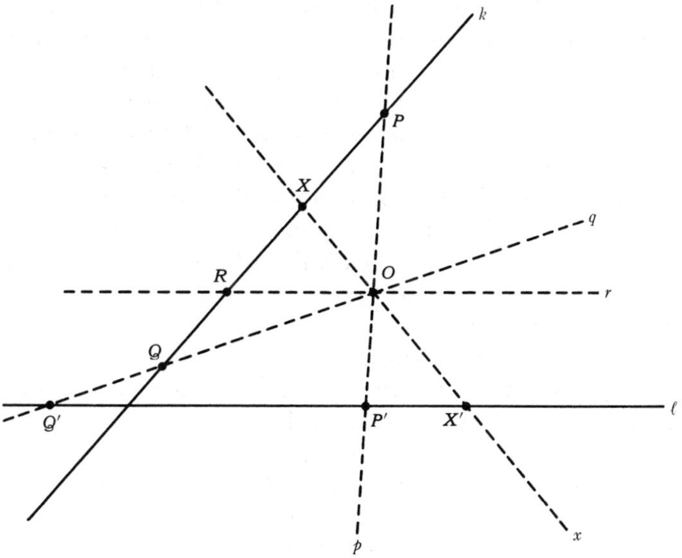

Figure 1.4

The correspondence so defined is called a *central projection* from k to ℓ, with *center* O. Thus, for a central projection the "object," the "screen," and the projecting "light rays" are complete lines of $\mathcal{E}_2$.

Although a central projection produces an image for any position of the object k (not on O), we are still dissatisfied, for the image formed usually is deficient by one point. When the lines k and ℓ are parallel, the central projection from k to ℓ with center O is a function (exercise 1), and the image is complete. However, if k and ℓ intersect (as in Figure 1.4), and if R is the point where the line through O parallel to ℓ meets k, then R has no image under the central projection. In this case, we might say that R is a "vanishing point." The vanishing of point R results from the existence of nonintersecting lines; if every two distinct lines in $\mathcal{E}_2$ were to meet, there would be no vanishing point, and every central projection would be a function.

It happens that a simple device affords the extension of $\mathcal{E}_2$ to a geometric structure in which every two lines *do* intersect. The idea of this device is easily grasped by anyone who has observed that in a perspective drawing two parallel lines (such as the two rails of a long, straight section of railroad track) are sometimes represented as two lines that would meet if extended. Specifically, the plan is to attach "ideal" points to the lines of $\mathcal{E}_2$ in such a way that any two parallel lines will meet in a common ideal point. To implement this plan, we proceed as follows: Choose a point A in $\mathcal{E}_2$. To each line ℓ on A, adjoin a single ideal point I_ℓ; the ideal points so adjoined are to be all different. If I_ℓ is any one of the ideal points, and ℓ the line to which it is adjoined, we stipulate that I_ℓ is to be adjoined also to every line of $\mathcal{E}_2$ that is parallel to ℓ, and to no other line. Since every line that is not on A is parallel to exactly one line on A, we see that one ideal point has been adjoined to each line of the plane, that any two parallel lines have the same ideal point, and that any two nonparallel lines have distinct ideal points.

What effect does the addition of ideal points to $\mathcal{E}_2$ have on the geometry? For one thing, it is not possible consistently to define distance from an ordinary point to an ideal point. Since we have in view a body of results that do not depend upon the distance structure of $\mathcal{E}_2$, we are willing to give up that structure. However, in our construction we have lost one property that *is* significant for our purposes—the property that any two distinct points determine a line; for, no line of $\mathcal{E}_2$ has two ideal points. This loss is easily recouped by the adjunction to $\mathcal{E}_2$ of a single line (the "ideal" line), stipulated to contain all the ideal points, but no other points.

We have augmented $\mathcal{E}_2$ by the adjunction of ideal points and an ideal line subject to the following conditions.

(1) To each line of $\mathcal{E}_2$ has been adjoined exactly one ideal point.

(2) The ideal points adjoined to any two parallel lines of $\mathcal{E}_2$ are the same.

(3) The ideal points adjoined to any two distinct, intersecting lines of $\mathcal{E}_2$ are different.

(4) The ideal line contains all ideal points, but no other points.

$\mathcal{E}_2$ so enlarged is called the *extended Euclidean plane* and is denoted by $\mathcal{E}_2^*$. It is easily shown (exercise 2) that $\mathcal{E}_2^*$ has the following incidence properties.

1.2.1. (a) Any two distinct points determine a unique line that contains them both.

(b) Any two distinct lines have a unique point of intersection.

Returning to the idea of central projection, we again consider the configuration of Figure 1.4, but this time in $\mathcal{E}_2^*$. Using the incidence properties 1.2.1, one can show that the central projection constructed just as before is now a function (exercise 3); it is important to notice that this result depends only upon properties 1.2.1. In Section 1.3, properties 1.2.1 will reappear as axioms for a projective plane. We observe that in the statements of these properties there is no mention of ideal elements, nor is there a hint of any distinguished role played by certain points and lines. Thus, there will be no special points or lines in a projective plane. Ideal elements were adjoined to $\mathcal{E}_2$ so that any two lines (of $\mathcal{E}_2^*$) would intersect, but this universality of meeting of two lines will be guaranteed from the outset by an axiom for our projective planes, the study of which is properly begun in the next section.

Exercise 1.2.A

1. Prove that a central projection between two distinct parallel lines in $\mathcal{E}_2$ is a function.

2. Prove that $\mathcal{E}_2^*$ has the incidence properties 1.2.1.

3. Let $\mathcal{P}$ be any set of points and lines satisfying the incidence properties 1.2.1, and let k and ℓ be distinct lines of $\mathcal{P}$. Let O be a point of $\mathcal{P}$ not on either k or ℓ. Show that a central projection from the points of k to the points of ℓ, with center O, can be defined, and that it is a function.

4. In $\mathcal{E}_2$ a parallel projection from a line k to a line ℓ can be defined in much the same way as a central projection, except that the projecting lines, instead of passing through a certain center O, are all parallel to a certain line m that intersects both k and ℓ.

(a) Draw a figure illustrating a parallel projection in $\mathcal{E}_2$.
(b) Show that a parallel projection in $\mathcal{E}_2$ is a function.
(c) Show that a parallel projection in $\mathcal{E}_2$ can be considered to be a special case of a central projection in $\mathcal{E}_2^*$.

Exercise 1.2.B

5. Consider the Euclidean plane $\mathcal{E}_2$ with a given Cartesian coordinate system. Let k be the x-axis and ℓ the y-axis of this system. Let O be the point [2, 1]. Extend $\mathcal{E}_2$ to $\mathcal{E}_2^*$, and let π be the central projection from k to ℓ with center O.

(a) Write an equation that describes what π does to an arbitrary point [x, 0] of k.
(b) What is $I\pi$, where I is the ideal point of k?
(c) What point of k is transformed by π into the ideal point of ℓ?

6. Let π and π' be central projections in $\mathcal{E}_2^*$.
   (a) Under what condition is the composite $\pi\pi'$ defined?
   (b) If $\pi\pi'$ *is* defined, is it a central projection? Why?

7. Let k and ℓ be distinct lines of $\mathcal{E}_2^*$, and let π be the central projection from k to ℓ with center O, π' the central projection from ℓ to k with center O', where $O' \neq O$. Then, $\pi\pi'$ is a function on the set of points of k (why?). Prove that $\pi\pi'$ fixes either one or two (no more and no less) points of k. Under what circumstance will $\pi\pi'$ fix only one point? (A point P is fixed by $\pi\pi'$ if and only if $P\pi\pi' = P$.)

1.3. Axioms of Incidence

The subject of projective geometry, which we now commence, is logically independent of its historical ties with Euclidean geometry, and we emphasize that the principal purpose of the preceding section was to provide motivation for the development that follows. Since it is impossible to construct an indefinitely receding chain of definitions or deductions, any mathematical system must ultimately rest upon certain primitive notions, which are accepted without definition, and a collection of axioms, which are assumed without proof. The primitive concepts of projective geometry are *point, line,* and *incidence;* no definitions are advanced for these, but in terms of them all other concepts will be defined. Also, certain properties and behaviors of point, line, and incidence are specified in the definition and axioms of a projective plane.

Definition 1.3.1. A *projective plane* is a set $\mathcal{P}$ of objects of two kinds—points and lines—together with a relation on $\mathcal{P}$ (that is, from $\mathcal{P}$ to $\mathcal{P}$) called *incidence,* which relates only lines to points and only points to lines. The incidence relation is symmetric, by which is meant that a line ℓ is related to a point P if and only if P is related to ℓ, in which case we say that ℓ is incident with P and P is incident with ℓ. Further, the points, lines, and incidence relation satisfy the *axioms of existence and incidence.*

> **Axiom 1.** There are four distinct points of $\mathcal{P}$ such that no three are incident with any one line of $\mathcal{P}$.
> **Axiom 2.** For any two distinct points of $\mathcal{P}$, there is one and only one line of $\mathcal{P}$ that is incident with both points.
> **Axiom 3.** For any two distinct lines of $\mathcal{P}$, there is one and only one point of $\mathcal{P}$ that is incident with both lines. ▮

Axiom 1 serves to rule out trivial and uninteresting possibilities, such as (a) a geometry in which all points are incident with a single line, and (b) a geometry with just three points and three lines (exercise 1). Axioms 2 and 3 are familiar, having been derived as the incidence properties 1.2.1 of $\mathcal{E}_2^*$, where, of course, incidence of a point and a line in $\mathcal{E}_2^*$ means that the line contains the point. In fact, since $\mathcal{E}_2^*$ satisfies Axioms 2 and 3, and since the vertices of any square in $\mathcal{E}_2$ are points of $\mathcal{E}_2^*$ that satisfy Axiom 1, it follows that $\mathcal{E}_2^*$ is a projective plane. We say that $\mathcal{E}_2^*$ is a *model* for Axioms 1–3; the existence of this model ensures that our subsequent discussion of projective planes will not be meaningless.

Although in $\mathcal{E}_2$ a line is usually regarded as a distinguished subset of the points, the definition of projective plane just given takes point and line as primitive notions on an equal footing. As we shall see, this viewpoint will prove particularly effective for the exploitation of the natural duality between point and line in a projective plane.

Notice the liberal use of the word "distinct" in Axioms 1–3. In this book, whenever the reader encounters a statement such as, "P and Q are points," he should give some thought to the possibility that P and Q may be the same point. In certain situations, the context will clarify the intent. Otherwise, the adjective "distinct" will be used for emphasis when it is surely meant that P and Q are different.

For the sake of variety and brevity of expression, it is customary to adopt certain usages of words, which will now be explained. The fact that a point P and a line ℓ are incident is frequently stated in one of these equivalent ways: P lies on ℓ, or, P is on ℓ, or, ℓ lies on P, or, ℓ is on P, or, ℓ is a line through P. If two lines are incident with a point, they are said to intersect, or meet, in that point. If two points are incident with a line, that line is said to join the points. If three or more points are incident with one line, they are collinear; if three or more lines are incident with one point, they are concurrent. The adjectives "triply noncollinear" will be used to describe a set of points in which no three are collinear; Axiom 1 can thus be rephrased, "There are four distinct, triply noncollinear points in $\mathcal{P}$." We also introduce two notations that will be used throughout the book. If P and Q are distinct points, the symbol $P \cup Q$ will represent the (unique by Axiom 2) line joining P and Q; if k and ℓ are distinct lines, the symbol $k \cap \ell$ will represent the (unique by Axiom 3) point of intersection of k and ℓ.

Although the axioms for a projective plane have been abstracted from very familiar notions, and although $\mathcal{E}_2^*$ is a rather easily understood model for these axioms, the reader may experience some awkwardness in his first encounter with projective planes in their full generality. At the beginning it may be difficult to resist the inclination to introduce extraneous reasons into arguments, yet this urge must be suppressed if precision is to be achieved. The valid weapons of argument are the axioms, previously proved theorems, and logic. The two theorems that follow illustrate how simple conclusions can be deduced from the axioms.

Theorem 1.3.2. Every line in a projective plane $\mathcal{P}$ is incident with at least three different points of $\mathcal{P}$.

Proof: Let ℓ be any line of $\mathcal{P}$. By Axiom 1, there exists in $\mathcal{P}$ a set $\mathcal{Q}$ of four distinct, triply noncollinear points. Then, at least two points of $\mathcal{Q}$ are not on ℓ. Let P be a point of $\mathcal{Q}$ that is not on ℓ, and let m, n, o be the lines joining P to the other three points of $\mathcal{Q}$ (Axiom 2). Since no three points of $\mathcal{Q}$ are collinear, m, n, o are distinct. Because m, n, o are on P, they are all different from ℓ, for ℓ is not on P. Let $X = \ell \cap m$, $Y = \ell \cap n$, and $Z = \ell \cap o$ (Axiom 3). The points X, Y, Z are on ℓ, and they are distinct, because $X \cup P\ (= m)$, $Y \cup P\ (= n)$, and $Z \cup P\ (= o)$ are distinct. Therefore, ℓ is incident with at least three different points of $\mathcal{P}$. ▮

Theorem 1.3.3. Let k and ℓ be any distinct lines in a projective plane $\mathcal{P}$. Suppose that P, Q are distinct points on k, both different from $k \cap \ell$, and that R, S are distinct points on ℓ, both different from $k \cap \ell$. Then, P, Q, R, S are triply noncollinear.

Proof: Imagine that P, Q, R *are* collinear. Since $k = P \cup Q$, and since k is the unique line on P and Q by Axiom 2, it follows that R is on k. Because R is also on ℓ, R must be $k \cap \ell$ by Axiom 3. But, by hypothesis, R is *not* $k \cap \ell$; therefore, P, Q, R cannot be collinear. Similar arguments show that P, Q, S are not collinear, P, R, S are not collinear, and Q, R, S are not collinear. ▮

The foregoing conclusions will be used often, sometimes without explicit reference to the theorems. Although considerable care has been exercised in the above proofs, not every detail has been supplied. The reader must become accustomed to filling in fine points in the proofs of theorems; his aim should be to satisfy himself that all statements made are correct. For instance, when it is asserted that $k = P \cup Q$, he should verify not only that k lies on P and Q, but also that $P \neq Q$, for otherwise the symbol $P \cup Q$ is meaningless.

If $\mathcal{S}$ is a nonempty set, a *figure* in $\mathcal{S}$ is defined to be any nonempty subset of $\mathcal{S}$. In our study of projective geometry, we shall frequently be concerned with triangles and complete quadrangles—special kinds of figures for which definitions are now presented.

Definition 1.3.4. In a projective plane:

(a) A *triangle* is a figure consisting of three noncollinear points together with the three lines joining the points in pairs. The points are the *vertices,* and the lines are the *sides* of the triangle (Figure 1.5).

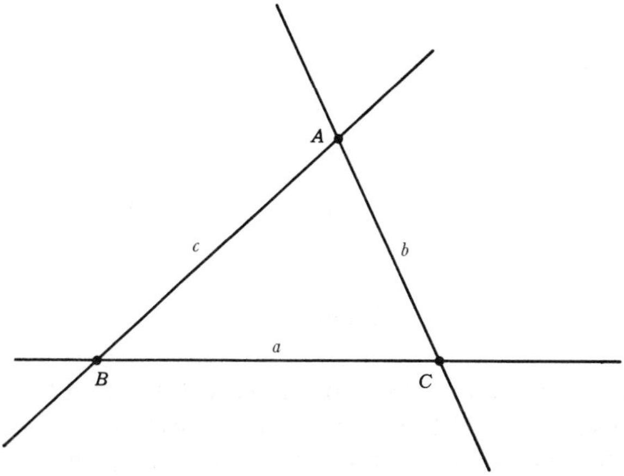

Figure 1.5

(b) A *complete quadrangle* (or briefly, *quadrangle*) is a figure consisting of four triply noncollinear points together with the six lines joining the points in pairs. The points are the *vertices,* and the lines are the *sides* of the quadrangle.

Two sides of a quadrangle that do not meet at any vertex are called *opposite* sides, and their point of intersection is a *diagonal point* of the quadrangle. (See Figure 1.6, in which the vertices are P, Q, R, S, and the diagonal points are D_1, D_2, D_3.) ▮

Observe that the only elements of a triangle are its vertices and sides; if a point, other than a vertex, lies on a side of the triangle, it is nevertheless not a part of the triangle, any more than is a line (other than a side) that happens to lie on a vertex. A similar remark applies to quadrangles. In particular, the diagonal points are not strictly parts of a quadrangle, though they will play a useful role in many of our discussions of quadrangles.

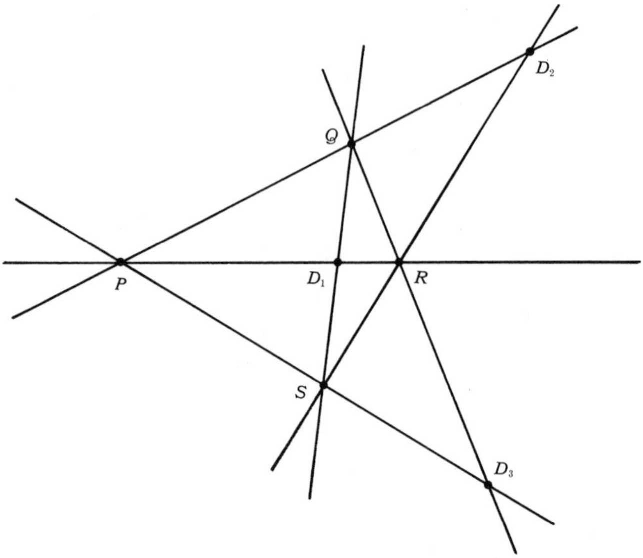

Figure 1.6

The four vertices of a quadrangle are distinct, for otherwise three of them (two coincident ones and one other) would be collinear. Axiom 2 then guarantees the existence and uniqueness of the line joining each pair of vertices. That there are six such lines is nothing more than the observation that there are six ways of choosing subsets of two from a set of four points. That these six sides are all different follows from the fact that no three vertices are collinear, for any two sides must be incident with at least three vertices all together, and coincidence of the sides would imply collinearity of those vertices.

Exercise 1.3.A

1. Prove that a triangle satisfies Axioms 2 and 3, but not Axiom 1.

2. Prove that in any projective plane there exist a line and a point not on the line.

3. Prove that in any projective plane there exists at least one complete quadrangle.

4. Prove that a complete quadrangle has exactly three distinct diagonal points.

5. (a) Which of the axioms for a projective plane is the one that implies that the geometry is plane rather than higher dimensional? (b) What is your opinion as to whether the diagonal points of a complete quadrangle can ever be collinear? Why?

Exercise 1.3.B

6. *Suppose* that, for the quadrangle of Figure 1.6, the points D_1, D_2, D_3 *are* collinear. Prove that the figure consisting of the quadrangle, the three diagonal points, and the line on these diagonal points satisfies Axioms 1, 2, and 3.

7. Prove that in any projective plane there are at least three distinct lines on every point.

8. Let k and ℓ be any lines of a projective plane $\mathcal{P}$. Prove that there is a point of $\mathcal{P}$ that is not incident with either line.

9. Suppose that $\mathcal{Q}$ is a quadrangle in a projective plane $\mathcal{P}$, and that ℓ is a line of $\mathcal{P}$ with not more than five points on it. Prove that ℓ is incident with at least one vertex or diagonal point of $\mathcal{Q}$.

10. In a projective plane four triply noncollinear points are necessarily distinct, as has been observed in the final paragraph of this section. Explain why the apparently superfluous word "distinct" is included in the statement of Axiom 1.

1.4. Models

In the beginning of an axiomatic study of a mathematical system it is instructive to examine models of the system, for models have an unexcelled power of clarifying concepts and of suggesting proper questions for investigation. By a model of a projective plane is meant a construction in which point, line, and incidence have explicit meanings in terms of familiar notions, and in which it is possible to verify that Axioms 1–3 are satisfied. It has been stated in the last section that $\mathcal{E}_2^*$ is one model of a projective plane. In this section four additional models are exhibited; the diversity of these models testifies to the generality of our axioms.

Model 1. Let $\mathcal{S}$ be a set containing 14 elements. Seven of these elements are labeled $P_0, P_1, \ldots, P_6$, and are the points of a plane $\mathcal{P}$ whose lines are the other seven elements of $\mathcal{S}$, named $\ell_0, \ell_1, \ldots, \ell_6$. The incidence relation on $\mathcal{P}$ is defined by Figure 1.7.

6	5	4	3	2	1	0
1	2	3	4	5	6	0
2	3	4	5	6	0	1
4	5	6	0	1	2	3

Figure 1.7

The number at the top of a column is the line subscript, while the numbers in the column below are the subscripts of the points that are incident with that line (and, of course, the line is incident with those points). For example, P_1 is incident with ℓ_2, but not with ℓ_4, while ℓ_3 is incident with P_5, but not with P_6. (See Figure 1.8, in which

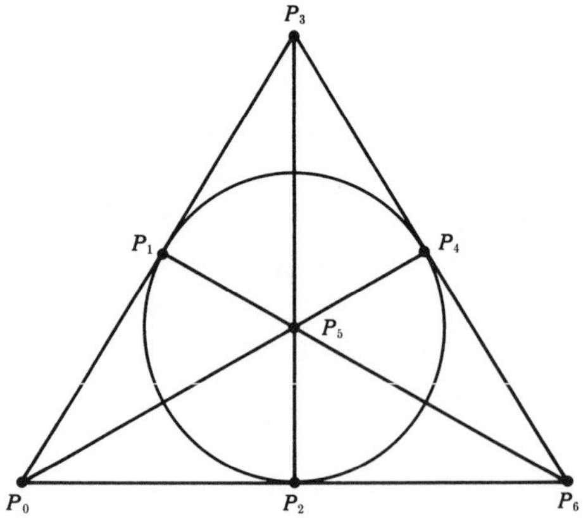

Figure 1.8

the circle through P_1, P_2, P_4 represents the line ℓ_6. Note that there is nothing wrong with this figure just because one of the lines is not "straight." Although in our other drawings points and lines will be represented in the usual way, the student should understand that any preconceived notion of their properties (such as "straightness" of a line) is inappropriate unless it conforms to the requirements of Axioms 1–3. For instance, the 14 elements of the set $\mathcal{S}$ of this model could be objects of any sort whatsoever, as long as we agree to call seven of them points, to call seven of them lines, and to define incidence by Figure 1.7. See exercise 11, which further illustrates the abstractness of the concept of projective plane.)

A scrutiny of Figure 1.7 reveals that each point of Model 1 is incident with three lines and each line is incident with three points; since, also, there are seven lines and seven points, this plane will be designated 7_3.

Theorem 1.4.1. The plane 7_3 is a projective plane.

Proof: Axioms 1–3 have to be verified.

(1) From the construction, P_1, P_3, P_4, and P_5 are distinct, and they are triply noncollinear, as is proved by verifying that no column of the incidence table above contains three of these points.

(2) and (3) To establish Axioms 2 and 3 for the plane 7_3 is merely a matter of checking that every one of the 21 possible pairs of points falls in exactly one column of Figure 1.7, and that every pair of columns of the table has exactly one point in common. The details are left to the reader. (See also exercise 8.) ▮

Model 2. Let $\mathcal{S}$ be a set with 26 elements; 13 of these are labeled $P_0, P_1, \ldots, P_{12}$, and are the points of a plane $\mathcal{P}$ whose lines are the other 13 elements of $\mathcal{S}$, named $\ell_0, \ell_1, \ldots, \ell_{12}$. The incidence relation on $\mathcal{P}$ is defined by Figure 1.9, which is read in the same way as the table (Figure 1.7) for the model 7_3.

12	11	10	9	8	7	6	5	4	3	2	1	0
1	2	3	4	5	6	7	8	9	10	11	12	0
2	3	4	5	6	7	8	9	10	11	12	0	1
4	5	6	7	8	9	10	11	12	0	1	2	3
10	11	12	0	1	2	3	4	5	6	7	8	9

Figure 1.9

In Model 2 there are 13 points, 13 lines, four points on each line, and four lines on each point. Therefore, this plane is designated 13_4.

Theorem 1.4.2. The plane 13_4 is a projective plane. (The proof is left for exercise 1a.) ▮

Model 3. Let $\mathcal{S}$ be a set with 42 elements; 21 of these are labeled $P_0, P_1, \ldots, P_{20}$, and are the points of a plane $\mathcal{P}$ whose lines are the other 21 elements of $\mathcal{S}$, named $\ell_0, \ell_1, \ldots, \ell_{20}$. The incidence relation on $\mathcal{P}$ is defined by the following table, which is read in the same way as the tables for the two previous models were read.

In Model 3 there are 21 points, 21 lines, five points on each line, and five lines on each point. Therefore, this plane is designated 21_5.

20	19	18	17	16	15	14	13	12	11	10	9	8	7	6	5	4	3	2	1	0
1	2	3	4	5	6	7	8	9	10	11	12	13	14	15	16	17	18	19	20	0
2	3	4	5	6	7	8	9	10	11	12	13	14	15	16	17	18	19	20	0	1
7	8	9	10	11	12	13	14	15	16	17	18	19	20	0	1	2	3	4	5	6
9	10	11	12	13	14	15	16	17	18	19	20	0	1	2	3	4	5	6	7	8
19	20	0	1	2	3	4	5	6	7	8	9	10	11	12	13	14	15	16	17	18

Figure 1.10

Theorem 1.4.3. The plane 21_5 is a projective plane. (The proof is left for exercise 1b.) ▮

Before inspecting Model 4, let us examine the structure of Models 1–3. Consider the incidence table for 13_4 (Figure 1.9). The set $\mathfrak{D} = \{1, 2, 4, 10\}$ is what is known as a *perfect difference set* modulo 13. By this is meant that every integer from 1 to 12, inclusive, can be obtained in one and only one way as the difference of two members of $\mathfrak{D}$, with the agreement that if the difference is negative, then 13 is to be added to it to bring the result into the range 1–12. (This is the meaning of the phrase "modulo 13.") For example, $11 = 2 - 4 + 13$, and there is no other way in which 11 can be obtained (modulo 13) as a difference of two elements of $\mathfrak{D}$.

To form the incidence table of 13_4, proceed as follows: To one line assign the points whose subscripts are the elements of $\mathfrak{D}$. Then, increase all subscripts by one, modulo 13; that is, if a total exceeds 12, reduce it by subtracting 13. Assign the points with these augmented subscripts to the next line. Continue until 13 lines have been made. The lines may be numbered in any fashion; but, for the most symmetric effect, number them backward, starting with 12. The result then is Figure 1.9. In this table the point P_i is on the line ℓ_j if and only if ℓ_i is on P_j, for all i and j.

The construction just described extends in an obvious way to give a finite projective plane with $n + 1$ points on each line whose incidence table has the symmetry property stated in the previous sentence, provided that a perfect difference set modulo $n^2 + n + 1$ can be found (exercises 9 and 10). No claim is made that a perfect difference set modulo $n^2 + n + 1$ exists for an arbitrary positive integer n. The only known examples with $n > 1$ occur when n is a power of a prime, and it is quite probable that there are none for other values of n.

The reader should not infer that perfect difference sets provide the only method of building finite projective planes. In fact, a great deal of thought has been devoted to the construction of these fascinating objects, and finite projective planes are closely related to many other important mathematical structures. The interested student will find a number of suitable references in the bibliography. We end this section with a presentation of the promised fourth model.

Model 4. The basis of this model is $\mathcal{E}_3$, Euclidean three-space. Choose a point O in $\mathcal{E}_3$. Construct a "plane" $\mathcal{P}$ as follows: The "points" of $\mathcal{P}$ are the lines of $\mathcal{E}_3$ that lie on O, and the "lines" of $\mathcal{P}$ are the planes of $\mathcal{E}_3$ that contain O. Incidence of a "point" X with a "line" ℓ in $\mathcal{P}$ has the meaning that the line X is in the plane ℓ in $\mathcal{E}_3$.

Proposition 1.4.4. The "plane" $\mathcal{P}$ of Model 4 is a projective plane.

Proof: (1) In $\mathcal{E}_3$ find four lines through O such that no three lie in the same plane. Such a set of lines surely exists, since there are infinitely many different planes containing O. (Furnish details.) These four lines become four distinct, triply noncollinear "points" of $\mathcal{P}$.

(2) Any two distinct lines through O in $\mathcal{E}_3$ determine exactly one plane containing O and the two lines. This statement translates into Axiom 2 for $\mathcal{P}$.

(3) Any two distinct planes on O in $\mathcal{E}_3$ intersect in exactly one line on O, for two planes of $\mathcal{E}_3$ that have a point in common have a line in common. Thus, Axiom 3 has been verified for $\mathcal{P}$. ▮

Exercise 1.4.A

1. (a) Prove that 13_4 is a projective plane.
(b) Prove that 21_5 is a projective plane.

2. (a) Prove that there does not exist a triply noncollinear set of five points in the plane 13_4.
(b) Exhibit a triply noncollinear set of five points in 21_5.

3. Prove that the set $\{1, 2, 7, 9, 19\}$ is a perfect difference set modulo 21. Can you find another perfect difference set modulo 21?

4. (a) Prove that $\{1, 2, 4, 9, 13, 19\}$ is a perfect difference set modulo 31.
(b) Use the difference set of part (a) to construct an incidence table for a projective plane with 31 points. (For uniformity, number the lines as suggested in the text.) Save this table for later work.

5. Suppose that there exists a perfect difference set modulo m. Prove that m is of the form $n^2 + n + 1$ for some integer n.

Exercise 1.4.B

6. (a) How many different quadrangles are there in the plane 7_3? (Two quadrangles are the same if and only if they have the same set of points for their vertices.)
(b) How many quadrangles are there in 13_4?
(c) How many quadrangles are there in 21_5?

7. Let $\mathcal{Q}$ be a quadrangle in 13_4, and let ℓ be a line of 13_4 that is not incident with any vertex of $\mathcal{Q}$. Prove that ℓ is incident with exactly two diagonal points of $\mathcal{Q}$.

8. Prove that to verify Axioms 2 and 3 for 7_3, 13_4, or 21_5, it suffices to demonstrate that both the following are true.
(a) Every pair of points is incident with at least one line.
(b) Every pair of lines has at least one point of intersection.

9. Let $\mathcal{D}$ be a perfect difference set modulo $n^2 + n + 1$, with $n > 1$. Prove that the method of construction outlined in this section can be used with $\mathcal{D}$ to produce a projective plane with $n^2 + n + 1$ points.

10. Continuing exercise 9, suppose that the lines are numbered backward (modulo $n^2 + n + 1$) as they are constructed. Prove that P_i lies on ℓ_j if and only if ℓ_i lies on P_j, for all i and j.

11. Thirteen ladies plan to give 13 parties and to share the duties as hostesses.
(a) Can you work out a scheme whereby each pair of ladies will be cohostesses for exactly one party and each pair of parties will have exactly one hostess in common?
(b) In your solution for part (a), how many hostesses does each party have?
(c) Can you further arrange it so that if the parties are held in the 13 different houses, each lady is one of the hostesses for the party given at her house?
(d) Can you find a similar scheme for four ladies who want to give four parties?

1.5. Affine and Projective Structures

In Section 1.2 the projective plane $\mathcal{E}_2^*$ was constructed by attaching ideal points and an ideal line to $\mathcal{E}_2$. To retrieve $\mathcal{E}_2$ it is clearly sufficient to remove from $\mathcal{E}_2^*$ the ideal line and all its ideal points. More generally, suppose that $\mathcal{P}$ is a projective plane and that ℓ is a line of $\mathcal{P}$. Let $\mathcal{A}$ be the set formed by deleting from $\mathcal{P}$ the line ℓ and all points incident with ℓ. Then, $\mathcal{A}$ is a set of points and lines and has an incidence relation that it inherits from $\mathcal{P}$. (That is, we agree that P and k in $\mathcal{A}$ are incident if and only if they were incident in $\mathcal{P}$.) Furthermore, it is easy to verify that $\mathcal{A}$ has the following incidence properties (exercise 1).

1.5.1. (a) There are four distinct, triply noncollinear points in $\mathcal{A}$.

(b) For any two distinct points of $\mathcal{A}$, there is one and only one line of $\mathcal{A}$ that is incident with both points.

(c) For any line k and any point P, not on k, in $\mathcal{A}$, there is exactly one line m of $\mathcal{A}$ that is incident with P and that does not intersect k. (The lines m and k are said to be parallel.)

Any set of points and lines that possesses a symmetric incidence relation between points on the one hand and lines on the other and that satisfies conditions 1.5.1 is called an ***affine plane***. Thus, the preceding paragraph can be rephrased as follows: If from any projective plane a line and the points on that line are removed, the resulting structure is an affine plane. (Observe that the definition of affine plane does not involve the concept of distance, and that $\mathcal{E}_2$ is a very special kind of affine plane.)

Conversely, if $\mathcal{A}$ is any affine plane, we can extend it to a projective plane $\mathcal{P}$, just as $\mathcal{E}_2$ was extended to $\mathcal{E}_2^*$, by the adjunction of ideal points and an ideal line subject to the following restrictions (exercise 6).

(1) Each line of $\mathcal{A}$ is incident with a single ideal point.

(2) Any two parallel lines of $\mathcal{A}$ are incident with the same ideal point.

(3) Any two distinct, intersecting lines of $\mathcal{A}$ are incident with different ideal points.

(4) The ideal line is incident with every ideal point, but with no other point.

Because of the possibility of extending an affine plane to a projective plane, or of obtaining an affine plane from a projective plane, we see that the subjects of affine and projective geometry are closely related. Two reasons for studying projective rather than affine geometry are the greater simplicity of the former, and the fact that it is easier to infer results of affine geometry from those of projective geometry than vice versa. Later (especially in Section 5.3) there will be opportunities for us to see how our general results for projective planes yield information about $\mathcal{E}_2$ and other affine planes.

There is another important advantage of the study of projective planes over that of affine planes. Consider again Models 1–3 of the last section. The special symmetry of the incidence tables for these models suggests the following experiment: Suppose that we construct a new incidence table for 13_4 by heading each column with the subscript of a point instead of a line, and then listing in the column the subscripts of the lines on that point. In a sense, we turn Figure 1.9 inside out. What do we discover? The new table is, except for possible (but inconsequential) rearrangements of the columns and the numbers in each column, exactly like Figure 1.9!

We have learned that in 13_4 (and, likewise, in 7_3 and 21_5), if the roles of point and line are exchanged, there results a structure identical to the original one. Although it is not true for every projective plane $\mathcal{P}$ that exchanging the roles of point and line will produce a structure just like $\mathcal{P}$, it *is* true—and it can be proved with very little difficulty (exercise 2)—that the result will always be a projective plane, called the ***dual*** of $\mathcal{P}$. We can understand why this is so by considering the nature of the definition of a projective plane (1.3.1). Suppose that in that definition the words "point" and "line" were everywhere interchanged. The sense of that part of the definition preceding the statement of the axioms would be entirely unaltered, Axioms 2 and 3 would be exchanged, and Axiom 1 would be converted into the statement of the following theorem for an arbitrary projective plane $\mathcal{P}$.

Theorem 1.5.2. There are four distinct lines of $\mathcal{P}$ such that no three are incident with any one point of $\mathcal{P}$.

Proof: Let P, Q, R, S be triply noncollinear points of $\mathcal{P}$; such a set of points exists by Axiom 1. Let $k = P \cup Q$, $\ell = Q \cup R$, $m = R \cup S$, and $n = S \cup P$. Then, k, ℓ, m, n are distinct lines, because they are four of the sides of the quadrangle $PQRS$. (See the discussion in the last paragraph of Section 1.3.) Furthermore, these lines are such that no three are concurrent. For, if k, ℓ, m, say, were concurrent, the point of intersection of the three would have to be $k \cap \ell = Q$, but would also have to be $\ell \cap m = R$. Since $Q \neq R$, it follows that k, ℓ, m are not concurrent. Similar arguments reveal that k, ℓ, n are not concurrent, k, m, n are not concurrent, and ℓ, m, n are not concurrent. ∎

Since Theorem 1.5.2 has been deduced from Axioms 1, 2, 3, it could be added, say as Axiom 0, to the original set of axioms without affecting the content of our geometry. Of course, the enlarged axiom system would be logically redundant, but it would also be *self-dual*, meaning that each axiom is converted into another axiom when the words "point" and "line" are interchanged throughout. This observation leads us to the formulation of the *principle of plane duality*, which asserts that from any theorem (that is, a statement that is deducible from the axioms) about the class of projective planes, one can derive a second theorem, called the *dual* of the first, by everywhere interchanging the words "point" and "line" in the first theorem. This interchange must be universal, extending to all those concepts in which point and line enter implicitly.

The principle of plane duality follows immediately from the self-duality of the set of statements consisting of Axioms 1–3 and Theorem 1.5.2 (Axiom 0). For, if a theorem can be proved from these statements (and, therefore, from Axioms 1–3 alone), the dual theorem can be proved from the dual statements (and, therefore, from Axioms 1–3) by dualizing all steps. The fact that definitions also enter the process of proof does not alter this conclusion, because, for any concept that has been defined in terms of the primitive notions, the dual concept (with an appropriately different name where necessary) can be defined by dualizing the definition of the first concept. This procedure is surely justifiable, since definitions are made merely as a matter of convenience, to shorten statements and to formalize thinking.

A note of caution needs to be inserted here. The principle of plane duality permits us to prove two theorems (one theorem and its dual) at the cost of constructing only one proof. However, the principle by itself does not constitute a proof of any theorem until the dual of that theorem has been proved. (Observe that the dual of the dual of a theorem is the original theorem.) Let us look at an example; consider these two statements.

(a) In a projective plane $\mathcal{P}$, if the diagonal points of every complete quadrangle are collinear, then the diagonal lines of every complete quadrilateral are concurrent.

(b) In a projective plane $\mathcal{P}$, if the diagonal lines of every complete quadrilateral are concurrent, then the diagonal points of every complete quadrangle are collinear.

Here, of course, *complete quadrilateral* is the concept dual to that of complete quadrangle (exercise 5). Therefore, statement (b) is the dual of statement (a), and it is a correct application of the principle of duality to say that if statement (a) is a valid theorem about projective planes, then so is statement (b). Now, (a) *is* a valid theorem (exercise 9); we thus obtain (b) as a theorem with no additional work.

Had statement (a) been written alone, it would have been tempting to err in the application of the principle of duality to it. For, one might reason, since the conclusion of this statement is the dual of the hypothesis, (a) itself is implied by the duality principle. However, such an argument would be fallacious, because the hypothesis of (a) has not been proved as a theorem (and, in fact, is not a true statement about all projective planes).

Exercise 1.5.A

1. Prove that any projective plane can be converted into an affine plane by removing one line and the points on that line from the projective plane.

2. Let $\mathcal{P}$ be a projective plane. The *dual plane*, $\mathcal{P}^\delta$, of $\mathcal{P}$ is defined as follows.

> The elements of the set $\mathcal{P}^\delta$ are the same as the elements of $\mathcal{P}$. A point of $\mathcal{P}$ is a *line* of $\mathcal{P}^\delta$, and a line of $\mathcal{P}$ is a *point* of $\mathcal{P}^\delta$. A point and line of $\mathcal{P}^\delta$ are *incident* in $\mathcal{P}^\delta$ if and only if the coinciding line and point of $\mathcal{P}$ are incident in $\mathcal{P}$.

Prove that the dual plane of $\mathcal{P}$ is a projective plane.

3. Show that the principle of duality does not hold in an affine plane.

4. (a) What concept is dual to that of "triangle?"
(b) Give the dual of the following statement: "In a projective plane, five triply noncollinear points determine exactly 10 lines joining them in pairs."

5. Define the concept that is dual to that of "complete quadrangle." (The figure obtained is called a *complete quadrilateral.*) Specify what the diagonal lines of a complete quadrilateral are.

Exercise 1.5.B

6. Prove that any affine plane can be extended to a projective plane by the adjunction of one ideal point for each class of parallel lines and one ideal line that is incident with all the ideal points. (The plane so constructed is called the projective extension of the affine plane.)

7. State the dual of Theorem 1.3.3 and prove it without using the principle of duality.

8. Show how the result of exercise 2 can be used to establish the principle of plane duality.

9. Let $\mathcal{P}$ be a projective plane. If the diagonal points of every complete quadrangle in $\mathcal{P}$ are collinear, prove that the diagonal lines of every complete quadrilateral in $\mathcal{P}$ are concurrent.

1.6. Elementary Correspondence

The set consisting of all the points on any line ℓ is the *pencil* of points on ℓ and will be denoted by $\mathcal{J}(\ell)$. (In most other books, this set is called a *range* of points.) Dually, the set of all lines on any point P is the *pencil* of lines on P and will be denoted by $\mathcal{J}(P)$. In Section 1.2 we studied a certain kind of correspondence, called a central projection, between two pencils of points. Our reason for extending $\mathcal{E}_2$ to $\mathcal{E}_2{}^*$ was to ensure that a central projection would be a function. We now consider the analogue of a central projection in an arbitrary projective plane.

Suppose that k and ℓ are lines of a projective plane $\mathcal{P}$ and that O is a point of $\mathcal{P}$ that is not on either k or ℓ. Define a function π from $\mathcal{J}(k)$ to $\mathcal{J}(\ell)$ as follows: For each point X on k, set $X\pi = (X \cup O) \cap \ell$. Since O is not on k, $X \neq O$; $X \cup O$ is thus a unique line on O. Because O is not on ℓ, $X \cup O \neq \ell$; $(X \cup O) \cap \ell$ is thus a unique point on ℓ. Therefore, π is indeed a function from $\mathcal{J}(k)$ to $\mathcal{J}(\ell)$. Figure 1.11 shows how the point X on k is "projected" by the line $X \cup O$ into the point $X\pi$ on ℓ.

The above construction can obviously be dualized, yielding a certain function from one pencil of lines to another. In the next definition a term is introduced to denote either a central projection or its dual.

Definition 1.6.1. Let $\mathcal{P}$ be a projective plane.

(a) Let k and ℓ be lines of $\mathcal{P}$, and O a point of $\mathcal{P}$ not on either k or ℓ. The function π from $\mathcal{J}(k)$ to $\mathcal{J}(\ell)$, defined by $X\pi = (X \cup O) \cap \ell$ for each point X on k, is the *perspectivity* from k to ℓ with *center* O.

(b) Let K and L be points of $\mathcal{P}$, and o a line of $\mathcal{P}$ not on either K or L. The function π' from $\mathcal{J}(K)$ to $\mathcal{J}(L)$, defined by $x\pi' = (x \cap o) \cup L$ for each line x on K, is the *perspectivity* from K to L with *axis* o. ∎

Let us investigate the properties of the perspectivity π from k to ℓ with center O. (These properties have their counterparts, of course, for a perspectivity whose domain and codomain are pencils of lines. See exercise 2.) Since we shall allow the domain and codomain of a perspectivity to be the same pencil—a permissiveness that will simplify later discussions—we can distinguish two cases.

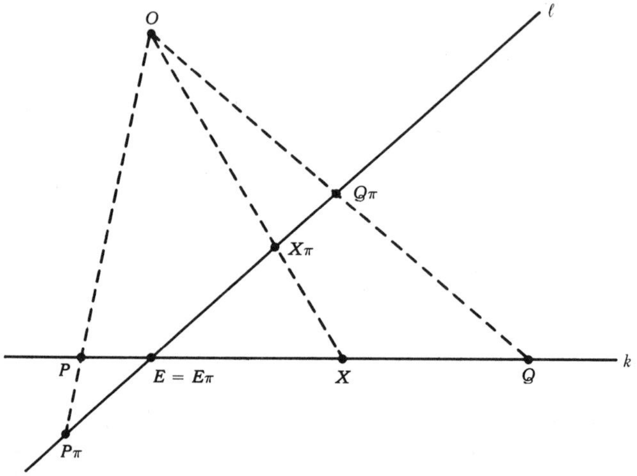

Figure 1.11

Case 1: $k \neq \ell$. Let $E = k \cap \ell$. Apply π to get $E\pi = (E \cup O) \cap \ell$. Since E is the unique point on both $E \cup O$ and ℓ, it follows that $E\pi = E$. That is, π fixes the point of intersection of k and ℓ. (Refer to Figure 1.11.) If X is any point on k other than E, $X\pi \neq X$, and $X\pi \cup X$ is a line on O (why?). Therefore, the center O is uniquely determined as the point of intersection of all lines of the form $X\pi \cup X$, where X is a point on k different from E.

Case 2: $k = \ell$. If X is any point on k, $X\pi = (X \cup O) \cap \ell = (X \cup O) \cap k = X$, so that π fixes every point on k in this case.

The process by which a point X on k is transformed by π into $X\pi$ can be dissected into two steps: first the "projection" of X from O by the line $X \cup O$, then the "section" of $X \cup O$ by ℓ. From this point of view π is a composite of two simpler functions, one of which we now construct. This function, from a pencil of points $\mathcal{G}(k)$ to a pencil of lines $\mathcal{G}(O)$, relates to each point of $\mathcal{G}(k)$ the line of $\mathcal{G}(O)$ that is incident with that point. Specifically, let k and O be a nonincident line and point, and define a function δ from $\mathcal{G}(k)$ to $\mathcal{G}(O)$ as follows: For each point X on k, set $X\delta = X \cup O$. (See Figure 1.12.)

Since O is not on k, $X \neq O$; hence $X \cup O$ is a unique line on O. Therefore, δ is indeed a function.

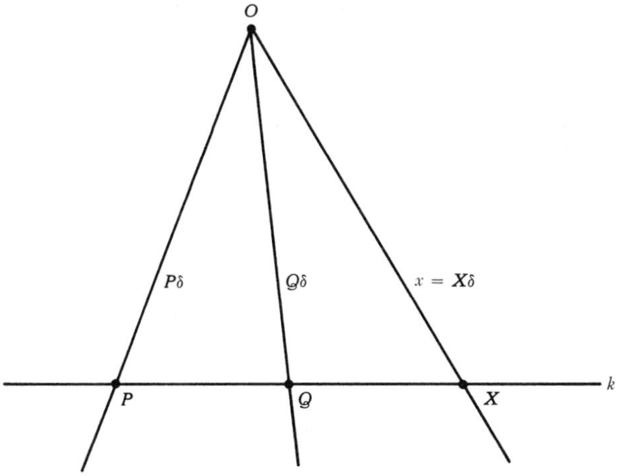

Figure 1.12

Definition 1.6.2. Let $\mathcal{P}$ be a projective plane.

(a) Let k and O be a nonincident line and point in $\mathcal{P}$. The function δ from $\mathcal{I}(k)$ to $\mathcal{I}(O)$, defined by $X\delta = X \cup O$ for each point X on k, is the *elementary correspondence* from k to O, and we write $\delta = k \circ O$.

(b) Let K and o be a nonincident point and line in $\mathcal{P}$. The function δ' from $\mathcal{I}(K)$ to $\mathcal{I}(o)$, defined by $x\delta' = x \cap o$ for each line x on K, is the *elementary correspondence* from K to o, and we write $\delta' = K \circ o$. ∎

Suppose that $\delta = k \circ O$ and $\delta' = O \circ \ell$; then, $\delta\delta'$ is defined as a function from $\mathcal{I}(k)$ to $\mathcal{I}(\ell)$. If X is any point on k, $X\delta\delta' = (X \cup O)\delta' = (X \cup O) \cap \ell$. Therefore, $\delta\delta'$ is the perspectivity from k to ℓ with center O. We write $\delta\delta' = k \circ O \circ \ell$, omitting one occurrence of the common O. (Note that the symbol $k \circ O \circ \ell$ has meaning if and only if O is not on either k or ℓ.) Dually, $K \circ o \circ L$ is the perspectivity from K to L with axis o. Thus, any perspectivity can be expressed as a composite of two elementary correspondences. (See also exercise 7.)

Composition of elementary correspondences can be extended to any number of factors as long as the codomain of each factor (except the last) is the domain of the one following it in the composite. For example, if $\delta_1 = k \circ O$, $\delta_2 = O \circ \ell$, and $\delta_3 = \ell \circ P$, the composite $\delta_1\delta_2\delta_3$ is defined, and we write $\delta_1\delta_2\delta_3 = k \circ O \circ \ell \circ P$.

Definition 1.6.3. A *projectivity* is any (meaningful) composite of elementary correspondences. ▮

If a projectivity π is the composite of the elementary correspondences $\delta_1, \delta_2, \ldots, \delta_n$, in that order, the General Associative Law (Exercise 1.1.6) allows us to write $\pi = \delta_1\delta_2 \cdots \delta_n$ without ambiguity, since all possible associations of the factors yield the same function. If π has domain $\mathcal{I}(k)$ and codomain $\mathcal{I}(P)$, for example, then, of course, π is a function from $\mathcal{I}(k)$ to $\mathcal{I}(P)$. Nevertheless, for simplicity and because it is customary, we shall say that π is a projectivity from k to P; similar remarks apply to the cases that arise when the domain of π is a pencil of lines or the codomain of π is a pencil of points.

Consider again the elementary correspondence $\delta = k \circ O$ (Figure 1.12). Suppose that x is any line on O, and let $X = x \cap k$. Then, $X\delta = X \cup O = x$. Hence, every line of $\mathcal{I}(O)$ is in the range of δ, and we say that δ is a mapping *onto* $\mathcal{I}(O)$. Next, suppose that P and Q are distinct points on k. Then, $P\delta = P \cup O$ and $Q\delta = Q \cup O$, and these are distinct lines on O (why?). Therefore, $P\delta \neq Q\delta$ whenever $P \neq Q$, and we say that δ is a *one-to-one* mapping from $I(k)$ to $\mathcal{I}(O)$. These two properties of an elementary correspondence are characteristic of many of the functions used in geometry, for in comparing two figures by transforming the first into the second, it is essential that the second figure be completely covered by the (image of) the first and that there be no collapsing of the first figure.

Definition 1.6.4. A *bijection* ϕ is a function that satisfies the conditions:

(a) ϕ is *onto*. That is, the range of ϕ is all of the codomain. Equivalently, for any W in the codomain, there is an X in the domain such that $X\phi = W$.

(b) ϕ is *one-to-one*. That is, ϕ maps any two different elements of its domain into two different elements of its codomain. Equivalently, whenever $X\phi = Y\phi$, then $X = Y$. ▮

Elementary correspondences are bijections, and many more examples will occur as our work progresses. (Refer also to Examples 1.1.3 and 1.1.4 and exercises 10 and 11.) It will often be necessary to compose bijections. The next theorem gives the condition under which the result will again be a bijection.

Theorem 1.6.5. (Composition of Bijections) If ϕ and ψ are bijections, and if the domain of ψ is the same as the codomain of ϕ, then $\phi\psi$ is a bijection.

Proof: Let $\mathcal{S}_1$ be the domain of ϕ, $\mathcal{S}_2$ the codomain of ϕ and domain of ψ, and $\mathcal{S}_3$ the codomain of ψ. It must be shown that $\phi\psi$ is (a) onto and (b) one-to-one.

(a) Let Z be any element of $\mathcal{S}_3$. Because ψ is onto, there is a W in $\mathcal{S}_2$ such that $Z = W\psi$. Since ϕ is onto, with codomain $\mathcal{S}_2$, there is an X in $\mathcal{S}_1$ such that $W = X\phi$. Then, $Z = W\psi = (X\phi)\psi = X(\phi\psi)$, proving that every element of $\mathcal{S}_3$ is in the range of $\phi\psi$.

(b) Suppose that $X(\phi\psi) = Y(\phi\psi)$. Then, $(X\phi)\psi = (Y\phi)\psi$. Since ψ is one-to-one, it follows that $X\phi = Y\phi$, which in turn implies that $X = Y$, because ϕ is also one-to-one. ▮

In particular, a perspectivity is a bijection, and (by induction) every projectivity is a bijection, since a projectivity is a composite of elementary correspondences whose domains and codomains are related in the required way. If ϕ is a bijection whose domain and codomain are the same set $\mathcal{S}$, then ϕ is called a bijection *on* $\mathcal{S}$. On any nonempty set there is at least one very simple (but very important) bijection.

Theorem 1.6.6. (Identity Function) Let $\mathcal{S}$ be any nonempty set. The function ι (the *identity*) on $\mathcal{S}$, defined by $X\iota = X$ for each X in $\mathcal{S}$, is a bijection. If α is any function on $\mathcal{S}$, then $\iota\alpha = \alpha\iota = \alpha$. Moreover, if $\mathcal{S}_1$ is any other nonempty set, then $\iota\beta = \beta$ for every function β from $\mathcal{S}$ to $\mathcal{S}_1$, and $\gamma\iota = \gamma$ for every function γ from $\mathcal{S}_1$ to $\mathcal{S}$.

Proof: It is immediate that ι is indeed a bijection on $\mathcal{S}$. For any function α on $\mathcal{S}$, $X(\iota\alpha) = (X\iota)\alpha = X\alpha$, and $X(\alpha\iota) = (X\alpha)\iota = X\alpha$ for every X in $\mathcal{S}$; since $\iota\alpha$ and $\alpha\iota$ are both functions on $\mathcal{S}$, the definition of equality of functions (1.1.6) says that $\iota\alpha = \alpha\iota = \alpha$. Similar arguments show that $\iota\beta = \beta$ for every function β from $\mathcal{S}$ to $\mathcal{S}_1$, and that $\gamma\iota = \gamma$ for every function γ from $\mathcal{S}_1$ to $\mathcal{S}$. ▮

It is easy to see (exercise 3a) that the function ι of the above theorem is the *unique* function on $\mathcal{S}$ with the property that $\iota\alpha = \alpha\iota = \alpha$ for every function α on $\mathcal{S}$. We have previously observed that the perspectivity $k \circ O \circ k$ fixes each point on k; hence it is the identity on $\mathcal{G}(k)$. Dually, the perspectivity $K \circ o \circ K$ is the identity function on $\mathcal{G}(K)$. Thus, the identity function on a pencil of points or a pencil of lines in a projective plane can be realized as a perspectivity. Notice that $k \circ O \circ k$ is the composite of the elementary correspondences $k \circ O$ and $O \circ k$, so that $O \circ k$ inverts the action of $k \circ O$. The next theorem shows that, quite generally, every bijection posesses an *inverse*—a function that reverses its effect.

Theorem 1.6.7. (Inverse of a Bijection) Let $\mathcal{S}_1$ and $\mathcal{S}_2$ be nonempty sets (not necessarily different), and let ι_1 and ι_2 be the respective identity functions on $\mathcal{S}_1$ and $\mathcal{S}_2$. If ϕ is a bijection from $\mathcal{S}_1$ to $\mathcal{S}_2$, there exists a bijection ϕ^{-1} (the *inverse* of ϕ), from $\mathcal{S}_2$ to $\mathcal{S}_1$, with the properties that $\phi\phi^{-1} = \iota_1$ and $\phi^{-1}\phi = \iota_2$.

Proof: The function ϕ^{-1} is defined by the equation $W\phi^{-1} = X$, where X is the element of $\mathcal{S}_1$ such that $X\phi = W$, with W an arbitrary element of $\mathcal{S}_2$. Since ϕ is onto, at least one such X exists for any W in $\mathcal{S}_2$. Because ϕ is one-to-one, there is only one such X for each W, since $X_1\phi = X_2\phi = W$ implies that $X_1 = X_2$. Therefore, ϕ^{-1} *is* a function from $\mathcal{S}_2$ to $\mathcal{S}_1$. It is easy to check that $\phi\phi^{-1} = \iota_1$ and that $\phi^{-1}\phi = \iota_2$, and it remains to be proved that ϕ^{-1} is a bijection.

If X is any element of $\mathcal{S}_1$, let $W = X\phi$; then, $W\phi^{-1} = (X\phi)\phi^{-1} = X\iota_1 = X$. Therefore, ϕ^{-1} is onto. Suppose that $W_1\phi^{-1} = W_2\phi^{-1}$; then, $(W_1\phi^{-1})\phi = (W_2\phi^{-1})\phi$, implying that $W_1\iota_2 = W_2\iota_2$, or $W_1 = W_2$. Therefore, ϕ^{-1} is one-to-one and is a bijection. ∎

If ϕ is a bijection, ϕ^{-1} is the *unique* function with the property that $\phi\phi^{-1}$ and $\phi^{-1}\phi$ are the respective identity functions on the domain and codomain of ϕ (exercise 3b). In particular, since $k \circ O \circ k$ is the identity on $\mathcal{I}(k)$ and $O \circ k \circ O$ is the identity on $\mathcal{I}(O)$, we see that $(k \circ O)^{-1} = O \circ k$ (and dually). From the uniqueness of the inverse it also follows that $(\phi^{-1})^{-1} = \phi$ for any bijection ϕ (exercise 3c).

If ϕ and ψ are bijections such that the codomain of ϕ is the domain of ψ, then the bijection $\phi\psi$ has the inverse $\psi^{-1}\phi^{-1}$ (exercise 5a). This result extends by induction to any bijection that is a composite of other bijections (exercise 5b). For instance, if $\pi = \delta_1\delta_2 \cdots \delta_n$, where each δ_i is an elementary correspondence, then $\pi^{-1} = \delta_n^{-1} \cdots \delta_2^{-1}\delta_1^{-1}$. Since each δ_i^{-1} is also an elementary correspondence (as noted in the preceding paragraph), the inverse of a projectivity is a projectivity. In particular, if π is the perspectivity $k \circ O \circ \ell$, then $\pi^{-1} = \ell \circ O \circ k$, which is also a perspectivity.

Exercise 1.6.A

1. Let $\delta = K \circ o$.
   (a) Draw a figure showing how δ transforms a line on K into a point on o.
   (b) Prove that δ is a bijection.

2. Let $\pi = K \circ o \circ L$.
(a) Draw a figure showing how π transforms a line on K into a line on L.
(b) If $K \neq L$, prove that $(K \cup L)\pi = K \cup L$.
(c) If $K \neq L$, prove that π uniquely determines its axis o.

3. (a) Prove that the identity function ι on $\mathcal{S}$ is the only function with the property that $\iota\alpha = \alpha\iota = \alpha$ for every function α on $\mathcal{S}$.
(b) Let ϕ be a bijection. Prove that ϕ^{-1} is the only function such that $\phi\phi^{-1}$ and $\phi^{-1}\phi$ are the respective identity functions on the domain and codomain of ϕ.
(c) From part (b) deduce that $(\phi^{-1})^{-1} = \phi$.

4. Suppose that α and β are functions with the same codomain $\mathcal{S}$ and that ϕ is a bijection with domain $\mathcal{S}$. If $\alpha\phi = \beta\phi$, prove that $\alpha = \beta$.

5. (a) Let ϕ be a bijection from $\mathcal{S}_1$ to $\mathcal{S}_2$, ψ a bijection from $\mathcal{S}_2$ to $\mathcal{S}_3$. Prove that $(\phi\psi)^{-1} = \psi^{-1}\phi^{-1}$. (The uniqueness of the inverse, guaranteed by exercise 3b, is needed here. Why?)
(b) Use the result of part (a) and mathematical induction to prove that if $\theta = \phi_1\phi_2 \cdots \phi_n$, where each ϕ_i is a bijection and the codomain of ϕ_i is the domain of ϕ_{i+1} for $i = 1, 2, \ldots, n - 1$, then $\theta^{-1} = \phi_n^{-1} \ldots \phi_2^{-1}\phi_1^{-1}$.

6. Let $\mathcal{R}$ be the set of all real numbers.
(a) Give an example of a function on $\mathcal{R}$ that is one-to-one but not onto.
(b) Give an example of a function on $\mathcal{R}$ that is onto but not one-to-one.

Exercise 1.6.B

7. (a) In 7_3, is the projectivity $\ell_0 \circ P_4 \circ \ell_1 \circ P_3 \circ \ell_3$ a perspectivity? (Be careful!)
(b) In 7_3, is the projectivity $\ell_0 \circ P_4 \circ \ell_1 \circ P_3 \circ \ell_2$ a perspectivity? Why?

8. Let α be a function from $\mathcal{S}_1$ to $\mathcal{S}_2$.
(a) If a function β, from $\mathcal{S}_2$ to $\mathcal{S}_1$, exists such that $\beta\alpha = \iota_2$, the identity on $\mathcal{S}_2$, prove that α is onto.
(b) If a function γ, from $\mathcal{S}_2$ to $\mathcal{S}_1$, exists such that $\alpha\gamma = \iota_1$, the identity on $\mathcal{S}_1$, prove that α is one-to-one.

9. (a) State and prove the converse of exercise 8a.
(b) State and prove the converse of exercise 8b.

10. Show that a translation of $\mathcal{E}_2$ (defined in Example 1.1.4) is a bijection. (By exercise 8, it is enough to show that a translation has an inverse.)

11. Show that an isometry of $\mathcal{E}_2$ is a bijection. (See Exercises 1.1.8 and 1.1.10.)

12. Suppose that α is a function from $\mathcal{S}_1$ to $\mathcal{S}_2$ that is one-to-one but not onto. If $\mathcal{S}_1$ has more than one element, prove that there are at least two different functions, β_1 and β_2, such that $\alpha\beta_1 = \alpha\beta_2 = \iota_1$, the identity on $\mathcal{S}_1$.

1.7. Projectivities

When we say that two functions are the same, we mean that they are equal (in the sense of Definition 1.1.6). Likewise, when we say that two projectivities are the same, we mean that they are equal (as functions). For example, the projectivities $\pi_1 = \ell \circ O \circ k$ and $\pi_2 = \ell \circ O \circ m \circ O \circ k$ are the same, because $O \circ m \circ O$ is the identity on $\mathcal{G}(O)$. Thus, π_2 is a perspectivity, though the given representation of it is a composite of four elementary correspondences. (See also exercise 9 and Exercise 1.6.7.)

The ability to build a projectivity that suitably transforms a few elements of a given pencil will be essential for our later work. Since projectivities are very special kinds of bijections, we should not expect to have unlimited freedom in their construction. In this section we explore some of the possibilities. The first result is an existence and uniqueness theorem for perspectivities.

Theorem 1.7.1. (Construction of Perspectivities) Let ℓ and ℓ' be any distinct lines in a projective plane. Let P, Q be any distinct points, other than $\ell \cap \ell'$, on ℓ, and let P', Q' be any distinct points, other than $\ell \cap \ell'$, on ℓ'. Then, there is a unique perspectivity π, from ℓ to ℓ', that sends P into P' and Q into Q'.

Proof: Let $O = (P \cup P') \cap (Q \cup Q')$; then, O is uniquely determined and does not lie on either ℓ or ℓ' (why?). From the discussion in the last section of the properties of perspectivities, we know that if the required perspectivity exists, its center must be O; therefore, there cannot be two different perspectivities that do the job. Let $\pi = \ell \circ O \circ \ell'$. Then, $P\pi = (P \cup O) \cap \ell' = (P \cup P') \cap \ell' = P'$ (since $P \cup O = P \cup P'$). Similarly, $Q\pi = Q'$. Thus, π is the unique perspectivity fulfilling the requirements. (See Figure 1.13.) ∎

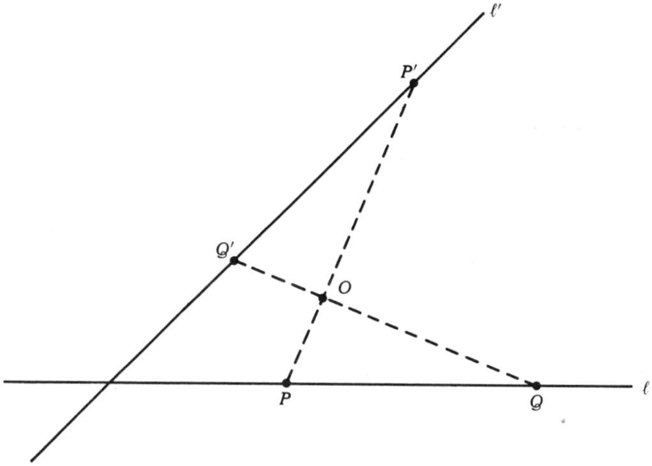

Figure 1.13

According to the above theorem, a perspectivity permits nearly complete freedom in the movement of two points. When two perspectivities are composed, with the second fixing the image of a point that the first has transformed in a suitable fashion, the result can be to map three collinear points in a prescribed manner. This idea is incorporated in the next theorem.

Theorem 1.7.2. (First Existence Theorem for Projectivities) In a projective plane, let ℓ and ℓ' be any lines. Let P, Q, R be any distinct points on ℓ, and let P', Q', R' be any distinct points on ℓ'. Then:

(a) If $\ell \neq \ell'$, a projectivity π, from ℓ to ℓ', can be constructed as a composite of two perspectivities such that $P\pi = P'$, $Q\pi = Q'$, and $R\pi = R'$.

(b) If $\ell = \ell'$, a projectivity π', from ℓ to ℓ, can be constructed as a composite of three perspectivities such that $P\pi' = P'$, $Q\pi' = Q'$, and $R\pi' = R'$.

Proof: (a) In this case at least one of Q', R' is different from $\ell \cap \ell'$. Without loss of generality (by exchanging the labels of Q, R, and the labels of Q', R', if necessary), we may suppose that $R' \neq \ell \cap \ell'$. Then, also, $R' \neq R$. Let O be a point on $R \cup R'$ that is different from both R and R', and let k be a line on R' that is different from both ℓ' and $R \cup R'$. Let $\pi_1 = \ell \circ O \circ k$; then, $R\pi_1 = R'$. By Theorem

1.7.1, there is a perspectivity π_2, from k to ℓ', that sends $P\pi_1$ into P' and $Q\pi_1$ into Q'; since $R' = k \cap \ell'$, π_2 fixes R'. (The center of π_2 is $O' = (P\pi_1 \cup P') \cap (Q\pi_1 \cup Q')$. See Figure 1.14.) The projectivity $\pi = \pi_1\pi_2$ is a composite of two perspectivities, and it maps P into P', Q into Q', and R into R'.

(b) Let m be any line different from ℓ, and let M be any point not on either ℓ or m. Define $\pi_1 = \ell \circ M \circ m$. Since π_1 is a bijection, $P\pi_1$, $Q\pi_1$, $R\pi_1$ are distinct points on m. By part (a), a projectivity π, from m to ℓ, can be constructed as a composite of two perspectivities such that $(P\pi_1)\pi = P'$, $(Q\pi_1)\pi = Q'$, and $(R\pi_1)\pi = R'$. Then, the projectivity $\pi' = \pi_1\pi$, from ℓ to ℓ, is a composite of three perspectivities, and it maps P into P', Q into Q', and R into R'. ∎

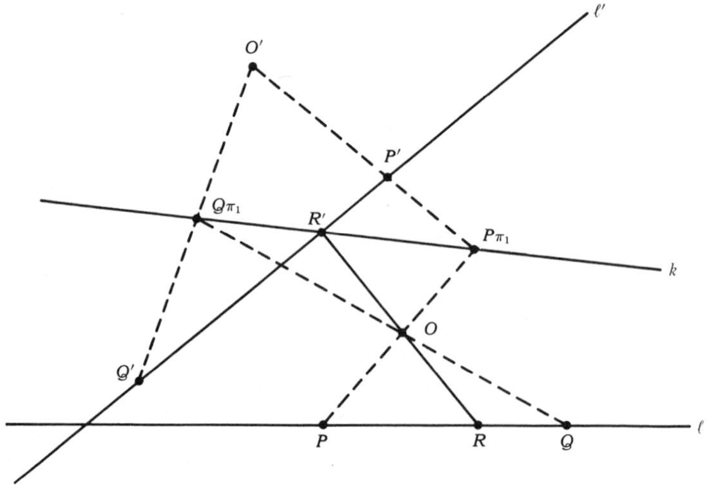

Figure 1.14

In the proof of case (a) of the preceding theorem, a very simple and obvious idea was employed—to have π_1 transform R correctly at once and then to use π_2 to move $P\pi_1$ and $Q\pi_1$ as required while holding $R\pi_1$ fixed. In the next theorem, no such obvious idea appears, and, indeed, the conclusion (at least in the case that $Q \neq Q'$) seems fortuitous rather than self-evident.

Theorem 1.7.3. (Second Existence Theorem for Projectivities) Let ℓ be a line in a projective plane, and let P, P', Q, Q' be points on ℓ such that P, P', Q are distinct and P, P', Q' are distinct. Then, there is a projectivity on ℓ (that is, from ℓ to ℓ) that exchanges P and P' and also exchanges Q and Q'.

Proof: If ℓ has only three points on it (as is the case in 7_3), then $Q = Q'$. In general, the theorem admits two cases—when $Q = Q'$ and when $Q \neq Q'$. However, the proof is the same for both cases. (Observe that the case in which $Q = Q'$ can also be handled by the preceding theorem.)

Choose a point B not on ℓ, and a point C, different from both B and P, on the line $B \cup P$. Let $D = (C \cup Q') \cap (B \cup Q)$, $O = (C \cup Q') \cap (B \cup P')$, and $E = (P \cup O) \cap (B \cup Q)$. (See Figure 1.15, which is drawn for the case that $Q \neq Q'$.)

Define $\pi_1 = \ell \circ B \circ (C \cup Q')$, $\pi_2 = (C \cup Q') \circ P \circ (B \cup Q)$, and $\pi_3 = (B \cup Q) \circ O \circ \ell$. Let $\pi = \pi_1\pi_2\pi_3$. Then, $P\pi = P\pi_1\pi_2\pi_3 = C\pi_2\pi_3 = B\pi_3 = P'$, and $P'\pi = P'\pi_1\pi_2\pi_3 = O\pi_2\pi_3 = E\pi_3 = P$. Also, $Q\pi = Q\pi_1\pi_2\pi_3 = D\pi_2\pi_3 = D\pi_3 = Q'$, and $Q'\pi = Q'\pi_1\pi_2\pi_3 = Q'\pi_2\pi_3 = Q\pi_3 = Q$. Thus, the projectivity π, on ℓ, meets the requirements. ▮

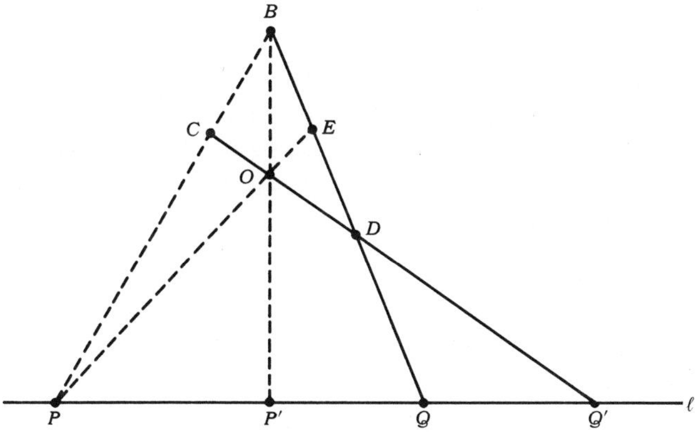

Figure 1.15

After B, C, D, O, E, π_1, π_2, π_3 have been constructed in the proof of the last theorem, Figure 1.15 shows that π $(= \pi_1\pi_2\pi_3)$ gives the desired mapping of P, P', Q, and Q'. However, if the proof is valid, it must be possible to verify that π fulfills the conditions without reference to a figure. Thus, $P\pi_1 = (P \cup B) \cap (C \cup Q') = C$, because C is on $P \cup B$ by the construction. Then, $C\pi_2 = (C \cup P) \cap (B \cup Q) = B$, because $C \cup P = B \cup P$, also from the construction, and $(B \cup P) \cap (B \cup Q)$ is clearly B. Next, $B\pi_3 = (B \cup O) \cap \ell = P'$, because, from the construction, O is on $B \cup P'$; hence P' is on $B \cup O$ as well as on ℓ. Thus, $P\pi = P\pi_1\pi_2\pi_3 = C\pi_2\pi_3 = B\pi_3 = P'$. By similar reasoning we see that P', Q, and Q' are transformed as stated.

Since Figure 1.15 implies no incidences that were not given or constructed, the use of this diagram to draw the same conclusions obtained by more laborious reasoning in the last paragraph is justified. When used correctly, a drawing is a valuable tool because it is a simple and accessible record of known incidences and because it often suggests what needs to be done. In many of the proofs in this book, drawings will be used to permit us to get results whose demonstrations would otherwise exact a great expenditure of words.

The student is encouraged to make drawings for most of the theorems and exercises. Two words of caution need to be given concerning drawings.

(1) Only those incidences that are given or that have been legitimately constructed, using axioms and previously proved theorems, should be exhibited in a drawing.

(2) A drawing alone is insufficient reason for inferring that a certain point and line are *not* incident, or that two points (or two lines) are different.

The projectivity on ℓ of Theorem 1.7.3 was constructed as a composite of three perspectivities. Of special interest are those projectivities on a line (or on a point) that can be expressed as composites of *two* perspectivities.

Definition 1.7.4. A Π_2 on a line ℓ is a projectivity on ℓ that can be represented as a composite of two perspectivities. Dually, a Π_2 on a point L is a projectivity on L that can be represented as a composite of two perspectivities. ▮

If π is a Π_2 on the line ℓ in a projective plane, then $\pi = \ell \circ M \circ k \circ N \circ \ell$ for some choice of a line k and points M and N. If $k = \ell$, or if $M = N$, then $\pi = \iota$, the identity function on $\mathcal{I}(\ell)$ (why?). Suppose that $k \neq \ell$ and $M \neq N$, and set $\pi_1 = \ell \circ M \circ k$ and $\pi_2 = k \circ N \circ \ell$, so that $\pi = \pi_1\pi_2$. If E is the point $\ell \cap k$, then $E\pi_1 = E$ and $E\pi_2 = E$. Thus, $E\pi = E\pi_1\pi_2 = E\pi_2 = E$, or E is a fixed point of π. Also, let $O = (M \cup N) \cap \ell$. Then, $O\pi_1 = (O \cup M) \cap k = O'$, where O' is on k and is collinear with O, M, and N. Hence, $O'\pi_2 = (O' \cup N) \cap \ell = (M \cup N) \cap \ell = O$. Therefore, $O\pi = O\pi_1\pi_2 = O'\pi_2 = O$, and O is also a fixed point of π. (See Figure 1.16.) These fixed points of π receive special names in the next definition.

Definition 1.7.5. If $\pi = \ell \circ M \circ k \circ N \circ \ell$, where $k \neq \ell$ and $M \neq N$, then the point $E = \ell \cap k$ is the *axial invariant point* of π, and the point $O = (M \cup N) \cap \ell$ is the *central invariant point* of π. ▌

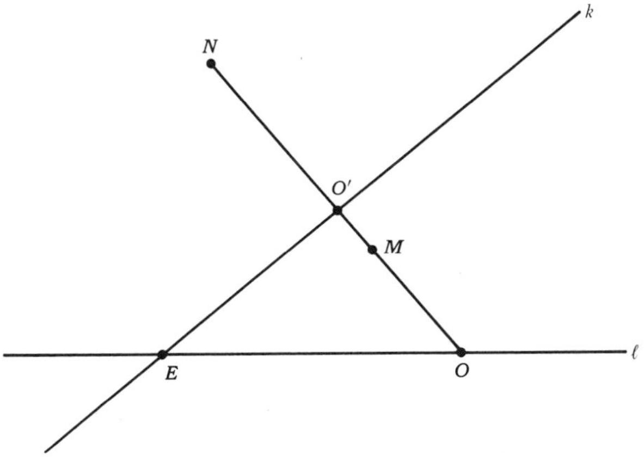

Figure 1.16

Since it is possible for E, M, N to be collinear, we see that the axial and central invariant points of the Π_2 of the above definition need not be different. It will be useful to agree that the identity projectivity on ℓ (which is a Π_2 via the expressions $\iota = \ell \circ M \circ \ell \circ N \circ \ell$ and $\iota = \ell \circ M \circ k \circ M \circ \ell$) has axial and central invariant points, too, and that these may be taken, at our convenience, as any two (not necessarily different) points on ℓ. The next theorem completes our knowledge of the fixed points of a Π_2 on a line.

Theorem 1.7.6. (Fixed Points of a Π_2) If $\pi = \ell \circ M \circ k \circ N \circ \ell$, where $k \neq \ell$ and $M \neq N$, then π has no fixed points other than its axial and central invariant points.

Proof: Let $E = \ell \cap k$, $O = (M \cup N) \cap \ell$, $\pi_1 = \ell \circ M \circ k$, and $\pi_2 = k \circ N \circ \ell$. Suppose that P is a fixed point of π and that $P \neq E$. Since $P\pi = P$, it is true that $(P\pi_1)\pi_2 = P$; hence P, $P\pi_1$, and N are collinear. Also, P, $P\pi_1$, and M are collinear. Now $P \neq P\pi_1$ (because, by assumption, $P \neq E$); so, the last two sentences imply that both M and N are on $P\pi_1 \cup P$. Therefore, $P\pi_1 \cup P = M \cup N$. Since $P = (P\pi_1 \cup P) \cap \ell$, it follows that $P = (M \cup N) \cap \ell = O$, and π has no fixed points other than E and O. ▌

Corollary: If π is a Π_2 on a line that has a fixed point in addition to its axial and central invariant points, then $\pi = \iota$, the identity projectivity on the line.

Proof: If $\pi = \ell \circ M \circ k \circ N \circ \ell$, then either $k = \ell$ or $M = N$, for otherwise, by the theorem, π would fix no points other than its axial and central invariant points. If $k = \ell$, or if $M = N$, then $\pi = \iota$. ▮

Exercise 1.7.A

1. In the plane 13_4, let π be the perspectivity from ℓ_8 to ℓ_4 that sends P_6 into P_{12} and P_8 into P_9. Find the center of π and compute $P_1\pi$.

2. Let ℓ be a line in a projective plane $\mathcal{P}$, and let P, Q, R be distinct points on ℓ. Let L be a point in $\mathcal{P}$, and let p, q, r be distinct lines on L. Prove that a projectivity π, from ℓ to L, can be constructed as a composite of five elementary correspondences such that $P\pi = p$, $Q\pi = q$, and $R\pi = r$.

3. Let ℓ be a line of 13_4, and let the points on ℓ be labeled A, B, C, D. Prove that there is a projectivity π, on ℓ, such that $A\pi = B$, $B\pi = C$, $C\pi = D$, and $D\pi = A$. Prove also that π is not a Π_2 on ℓ.

4. Let ℓ be a line of 21_5, and let P and Q be distinct points on ℓ. Suppose that π is a Π_2 on ℓ that exchanges P and Q. How many points on ℓ are fixed by π? Why?

5. In 21_5, let π be the Π_2 on the line ℓ_0 defined by $\ell_0 \circ P_2 \circ \ell_7 \circ P_3 \circ \ell_0$. Name the axial and central invariant points of π and compute $P_6\pi$.

6. Prove that in the plane 13_4 any projectivity between two distinct lines can be realized as a composite of two perspectivities.

Exercise 1.7.B

7. In the plane 13_4, construct a projectivity from ℓ_7 to ℓ_{10} that sends P_6 into P_{12}, P_7 into P_6, and P_9 into P_3. (Use Figure 1.9.) Is this projectivity a perspectivity? Why?

8. Let k and ℓ be distinct lines of 13_4, and let $E = k \cap \ell$. Prove that if π is a projectivity from k to ℓ that fixes the point E, then π is a perspectivity.

9. In 7_3, is the projectivity $\ell_0 \circ P_4 \circ \ell_1 \circ P_3 \circ \ell_3 \circ P_2 \circ \ell_0$ a Π_2? (Be careful!)

10. Given a line ℓ of a projective plane, together with points E, O, P,

P' on ℓ, with P, P' different from both E and O, show how to construct a Π_2 on ℓ with axial invariant point E, central invariant point O, sending P into P'.

11. Let ℓ be a line of a projective plane, and let M, P, P', Q, Q' be points on ℓ such that M, P, Q are distinct and M, P', Q' are also distinct.

(a) Show how to construct a Π_2 on ℓ with axial invariant point M, sending P into P' and Q into Q'.

(b) Show how to construct a Π_2 on ℓ with central invariant point M, sending P into P' and Q into Q'.

1.8. Cardinal Number

The natural idea of the number of elements in a set seems simple enough until one tries to give it a precise definition. Fortunately, for our purposes an intuitive understanding of cardinal number is sufficient, provided that we have an exact method of comparing cardinal numbers. The concept of bijection furnishes the perfect tool for such comparisons.

Definition 1.8.1. The set $\mathcal{S}_2$ has the *same cardinal number* as the set $\mathcal{S}_1$ (written $\#\mathcal{S}_2 = \#\mathcal{S}_1$) if and only if both sets are empty *or* both are nonempty and there exists a bijection from $\mathcal{S}_1$ to $\mathcal{S}_2$. ▮

In the discussion of Models 1–3 in Section 1.4, the term "finite" was used in the expectation that its meaning is well understood. To align our intuition with the above definition, we can say that by a *finite set* we mean either the empty set, whose cardinal number is defined to be 0, or a set $\mathcal{S}$ having the same cardinal number as the set $\{1, 2, \cdots, n\}$ for some positive integer n, in which case $\mathcal{S}$ has cardinal number n. If a set is not empty and does not have cardinal number n for any positive integer n, it is said to be *infinite*.

Another way of saying that $\mathcal{S}_2$ has the same cardinal number as $\mathcal{S}_1$ is to say that $\mathcal{S}_2$ is *equipotent* with $\mathcal{S}_1$. A relation called *equipotence* can be defined on any set $\mathcal{C}$ of sets by pairing with the set $\mathcal{S}$ in $\mathcal{C}$ every set $\mathcal{S}'$ in $\mathcal{C}$ such that $\#\mathcal{S}' = \#\mathcal{S}$. Equipotence has the following properties.

(a) If $\mathcal{S}$ is any set, $\#\mathcal{S} = \#\mathcal{S}$. This is clear if $\mathcal{S}$ is empty, and, if $\mathcal{S}$ is nonempty, the identity function ι on $\mathcal{S}$ is a bijection from $\mathcal{S}$ to $\mathcal{S}$ that exhibits the equipotence of $\mathcal{S}$ with itself.

(b) If $\#\mathcal{S}_2 = \#\mathcal{S}_1$, then $\#\mathcal{S}_1 = \#\mathcal{S}_2$. Again, this is clear if both sets are empty. If both are nonempty, and if ϕ is a bijection from $\mathcal{S}_1$ to $\mathcal{S}_2$, then ϕ^{-1} is a bijection from $\mathcal{S}_2$ to $\mathcal{S}_1$, by the theorem Inverse of a Bijection (1.6.7).

(c) If $\#\mathcal{S}_2 = \#\mathcal{S}_1$ and $\#\mathcal{S}_3 = \#\mathcal{S}_2$, then $\#\mathcal{S}_3 = \#\mathcal{S}_1$. For, if $\mathcal{S}_1$ and $\mathcal{S}_2$ are both empty, then so is $\mathcal{S}_3$; hence $\#\mathcal{S}_3 = \#\mathcal{S}_1$. Otherwise, there is a bijection ϕ, from $\mathcal{S}_1$ to $\mathcal{S}_2$, and a bijection ψ, from $\mathcal{S}_2$ to $\mathcal{S}_3$. Then, $\phi\psi$ is a bijection from $\mathcal{S}_1$ to $\mathcal{S}_3$, by the theorem Composition of Bijections (1.6.5).

Relations that have the properties (a), (b), (c) above are of such fundamental importance in mathematics that it is worthwhile for us to make the following definition.

Definition 1.8.2. A relation $\sim$ on a set $\mathcal{S}$ is an *equivalence relation* if and only if it is all of the following:

(a) Reflexive; that is, $X \sim X$ for every X in $\mathcal{S}$.
(b) Symmetric; that is, whenever $Y \sim X$, then $X \sim Y$.
(c) Transitive; that is, whenever $Y \sim X$ and $Z \sim Y$, then $Z \sim X$. ▮

We have already seen that equipotence is an equivalence relation on any set whose elements are themselves sets. Ordinary equality (that is, identity) and equality of functions are further examples of equivalence relations on any set and on any set of functions, respectively. A less obvious example occurs in the next section, and in later chapters several important equivalence relations will appear. We now apply the idea of equipotence to projective planes.

Theorem 1.8.3. In a projective plane, $\#\mathcal{I}(P) = \#\mathcal{I}(Q) = \#\mathcal{I}(k) = \#\mathcal{I}(\ell)$ for any points P and Q and any lines k and ℓ.

Proof: The proof is made in three steps.

(1) If R is a point and m a line not on R, then $\#\mathcal{I}(R) = \#\mathcal{I}(m)$, for the elementary correspondence $m \circ R$ is a bijection from $\mathcal{I}(m)$ to $\mathcal{I}(R)$.

(2) If k and ℓ are any lines, then $\#\mathcal{I}(\ell) = \#\mathcal{I}(k)$. To see this, let O be any point not on either k or ℓ. Then, the perspectivity $k \circ O \circ \ell$ is a bijection from $\mathcal{I}(k)$ to $\mathcal{I}(\ell)$. Dually, if P and Q are any points, then $\#\mathcal{I}(Q) = \#\mathcal{I}(P)$.

(3) If the point R is on the line m, then, still, $\#\mathcal{I}(R) = \#\mathcal{I}(m)$. For proof, let S be a point not on m; then, $\#\mathcal{I}(S) = \#\mathcal{I}(R)$ by (2), and $\#\mathcal{I}(S) = \#\mathcal{I}(m)$ by (1). Therefore, since equipotence is an equivalence relation, $\#\mathcal{I}(R) = \#\mathcal{I}(m)$.

When (1), (2), (3) and the fact that equipotence is an equivalence relation are combined, the conclusion of the theorem is obtained. ▮

Thus, in a projective plane the cardinal number of lines on any point is the same as the cardinal number of lines on any other point, and this is also the same as the cardinal number of points on any line. This property of a projective plane has especially interesting consequences for finite projective planes—those projective planes containing only finitely many points. Since any subset of a finite set is finite, each line of a finite projective plane lies on only a finite number of points. The precise relation between the number of points on a line of a finite projective plane and the total number of points in the plane is the content of the next theorem.

Theorem 1.8.4. (Cardinality of a Finite Plane) If a line ℓ in a projective plane $\mathcal{P}$ is incident with exactly $n + 1$ points, then (1) every line in $\mathcal{P}$ is incident with exactly $n + 1$ points, (2) every point in $\mathcal{P}$ is incident with exactly $n + 1$ lines, and (3) $\mathcal{P}$ has exactly $n^2 + n + 1$ points and $n^2 + n + 1$ lines.

Proof: Statements (1) and (2) follow immediately from the previous theorem. To prove (3), let P be any point of $\mathcal{P}$. If Q is any other point of $\mathcal{P}$, then Q lies on a unique line through P, namely $P \cup Q$. Therefore, all points of $\mathcal{P}$ lie on lines through P. There are $n + 1$ of these lines, and each of them is incident with just n points in addition to P. All these $n(n + 1)$ points are different, because no two of the lines being considered intersect in a point other than P. When P is counted, the total is $n(n + 1) + 1 = n^2 + n + 1$ points. The corresponding statement for lines is obtained by dualizing all steps. ▮

When a projective plane has $n + 1$ points on each line, it is said to be of *order n*. For example, the planes 7_3, 13_4, 21_5 have orders two, three, and four, respectively. It might seem more reasonable to say that a plane with $n + 1$ points on each line has order $n + 1$, or even $n^2 + n + 1$ in view of the last theorem. However, the terminology given here is standard, and there are several good reasons for it. For one thing, when a line and the points on it are removed from a projective plane $\mathcal{P}$ with $n + 1$ points on each line, there results (Section 1.5) an affine plane $\mathcal{A}$ with n points on each of its lines. It is natural to say that $\mathcal{A}$ has order n, and it is desirable to give $\mathcal{P}$ the same order as $\mathcal{A}$.

The theorem Cardinality of a Finite Plane shows that it is impossible to have a finite projective plane with, for example, 28 points, or with any number of points not of the form $n^2 + n + 1$. It does not say that for every $n > 1$ there exists a finite projective plane with $n^2 + n + 1$ points. In fact, in every known example of a finite projective plane, the order n is of the form p^k, where p is a prime and k is a positive integer. Whether projective planes of other orders exist is not known. It is known that there is no projective plane of order six, for instance, and the Bruck-Ryser theorem [25, pp. 25–26] rules out a large class of integers as possible orders for finite projective planes.

If a projective plane has $n^2 + n + 1$ points all together, its order must be n. (If its order is m, then it has $m^2 + m + 1$ points; hence $m^2 + m + 1 = n^2 + n + 1$. From this equality it follows that $m = n$, since m and n are both positive.) Thus, any projective plane with seven points has three points on each line, three lines on each point, and seven lines in all. Such a plane will be called a *7-point plane*, as well as a plane of order two. Similar remarks apply to 13- and 21-point planes, which have orders three and four, respectively. This section concludes with a theorem concerning the diagonal points of quadrangles in 7-, 13-, and 21-point planes.

Theorem 1.8.5. In any 7-point plane, or in any 21-point plane, the diagonal points of every complete quadrangle are collinear. In any 13-point plane, the diagonal points of every complete quadrangle are noncollinear.

Proof: (1) Let $\mathcal{Q}$ be any quadrangle in a 7-point plane $\mathcal{P}$. $\mathcal{Q}$ has six sides. If the diagonal points of $\mathcal{Q}$ were *not* collinear, they would determine, in pairs, three lines (not sides of $\mathcal{Q}$), for a total of at least nine lines in $\mathcal{P}$, which is not possible.

(2) Let $\mathcal{Q}$ be any quadrangle in a 13-point plane $\mathcal{P}$, and let us count the lines of $\mathcal{P}$ that are incident with the vertices and diagonal points of $\mathcal{Q}$. First, $\mathcal{Q}$ has six sides, three of which lie on each vertex. Therefore, on each vertex of $\mathcal{Q}$ lies another line of $\mathcal{P}$, and this line is on no other vertex or diagonal point (why?). Thus, a total of 10 lines lie on the vertices of $\mathcal{Q}$, and each diagonal point of $\mathcal{Q}$ is incident with just two of these lines. *If* the diagonal points were collinear, one line of $\mathcal{P}$ would lie on all three diagonal points, and there would still be one more line on each diagonal point, for a total of 14 lines in $\mathcal{P}$. This impossibility proves that the diagonal points of $\mathcal{Q}$ are not collinear.

(3) Let $\mathcal{Q}$ be any quadrangle in a 21-point plane $\mathcal{P}$. Again we count the lines of $\mathcal{P}$ incident with the vertices and diagonal points of $\mathcal{Q}$. There are six sides of $\mathcal{Q}$ and two more lines on each vertex of $\mathcal{Q}$, for a

total of 14 lines. So far, two lines on each diagonal point have been counted. *Suppose* that the diagonal points of $\mathcal{Q}$ are not collinear. Then, they determine, in pairs, three more lines, two of which lie on each diagonal point. There is one more line on each diagonal point, for a total of 20 lines on the vertices and diagonal points of $\mathcal{Q}$. Since $\mathcal{P}$ has 21 lines, there must be a line that is not incident with any vertex or diagonal point of $\mathcal{Q}$. This line intersects the sides of $\mathcal{Q}$ in six distinct points, since all intersections of pairs of sides of $\mathcal{Q}$ occur at the vertices and diagonal points. Because no line of a 21-point plane is incident with six distinct points, the supposition that $\mathcal{Q}$ has noncollinear diagonal points was false. ∎

Exercise 1.8.A

1. Prove that the cardinal number of the set of real numbers between 0 and 1, inclusive, is the same as the cardinal number of the set of real numbers between 0 and 2, inclusive.

2. Let a relation $\sim$ be defined on the set of all integers as follows: $m \sim n$ if and only if $m - n$ is an integral multiple of 12. Prove that $\sim$ is an equivalence relation.

3. Let a relation $\sim$ be defined on the set of lines of $\mathcal{E}_2$ as follows: $k \sim \ell$ if and only if $k = \ell$ or k is parallel to ℓ. Prove that $\sim$ is an equivalence relation.

4. Suppose that α is a function from $\mathcal{S}_1$ to $\mathcal{S}_2$ and that $\sim$ is an equivalence relation on $\mathcal{S}_2$. Let a relation $*$ be defined on $\mathcal{S}_1$ as follows: $Y * X$ in $\mathcal{S}_1$ if and only if $Y\alpha \sim X\alpha$ in $\mathcal{S}_2$. Prove that $*$ is an equivalence relation.

5. (a) What is the order of a projective plane with 133 points in all?
(b) Prove that the total number of points in a finite projective plane is never even.

6. Choose any four triply noncollinear points of 21_5 and calculate the diagonal points of the quadrangle that has these points for its vertices. Verify that the diagonal points are collinear.

7. Let $\mathcal{Q}$ be a quadrangle in a 21-point plane $\mathcal{P}$. Prove that every point of $\mathcal{P}$ is either on one of the sides of $\mathcal{Q}$ or on the line joining the diagonal points.

Exercise 1.8.B

8. By a *subplane* $\mathcal{P}'$ of a projective plane $\mathcal{P}$ is meant a collection of points and lines of $\mathcal{P}$ that together satisfy Axioms 1–3, incidence in $\mathcal{P}'$ being interpreted as incidence in $\mathcal{P}$.

(a) Prove that a 13-point plane has no 7-point subplane.
(b) Prove that a 21-point plane has 7-point subplanes.
(c) Prove that a 21-point plane has no 13-point subplane.

9. 31-point planes have been shown to exist in Exercise 1.4.4. Let $\mathcal{Q}$ be a quadrangle in a 31-point plane. Prove that there are lines of the plane that are not incident with any vertex or diagonal point of $\mathcal{Q}$.

10. State and prove the analogue of Theorem 1.8.4 for affine planes.

11. Prove that no finite set is equipotent with any proper subset of itself.

12. (a) Let $\mathcal{S}$ be any infinite set. Prove that $\mathcal{S}$ contains a subset that is equipotent with the set of all positive integers.
(b) Prove that any infinite set is equipotent with some proper subset of itself. (In view of exercise 11, this property characterizes infinite sets.)

13. (a) Let $\mathcal{S}$ be any nonempty set, and let $\sim$ be an equivalence relation on $\mathcal{S}$. If X is in $\mathcal{S}$, the *equivalence class* (relative to $\sim$) of X is defined to be the subset of elements of $\mathcal{S}$ that are related to X by $\sim$. If X and Y are any elements of $\mathcal{S}$, prove that their equivalence classes are identical if $Y \sim X$ and are disjoint (that is, have no element in common) if Y is not related to X by $\sim$.
(b) Let $\mathcal{S}$ be any nonempty set, and suppose that $\mathcal{S}$ is partitioned into mutually disjoint subsets. (That is, any two distinct subsets of the partition are disjoint, and every element of $\mathcal{S}$ belongs to some subset.) Let a relation $\sim$ be defined on $\mathcal{S}$ as follows: $Y \sim X$ if and only if Y and X belong to the same subset of the partition. Prove that $\sim$ is an equivalence relation.

Chapter 2

TRANSFORMATIONS OF PROJECTIVE PLANES

2.1. Isomorphy

In any 7-point plane, there are seven lines, three points on every line and three lines on every point, and the diagonal points of every complete quadrangle are collinear. Are all 7-point planes just alike? The answer to this question depends upon the meaning that we are to assign to the word "alike" in comparing projective planes. The existence of at least one 7-point plane has been established by the construction of 7_3. Suppose that $\mathcal{P}$ is any 7-point plane, and let us attempt to compare $\mathcal{P}$ with 7_3. In order to facilitate the comparison, we draw up an incidence table for $\mathcal{P}$. This task is not as difficult as it may sound, for Axioms 1–3 give us a good deal of information about $\mathcal{P}$. We shall make some arbitrary decisions about the names of points and lines in $\mathcal{P}$, but, having made these decisions, we shall find that our incidence table takes unequivocal form under the restrictions imposed by the axioms.

By Axiom 1 there are four triply noncollinear points in $\mathcal{P}$; suppose that A, B, C, D are such points. Set $a = A \cup B$, $b = A \cup C$, $c = A \cup D$, $d = B \cup C$, $e = B \cup D$, and $f = C \cup D$. Thus, we have selected names for four points of $\mathcal{P}$ and the sides of the quadrangle whose vertices are those points. This information appears in the first three rows (including the row containing the names of the lines) and six columns of Figure 2.1. By Axiom 3, a and f intersect, and their point of intersection cannot be A, B, C, or D (why?); set $E = a \cap f$. Similarly, let $F = b \cap e$ and $G = c \cap d$. Since no point lies on four lines, E, F, G are distinct. We have named all the points of $\mathcal{P}$ and all but one of the lines, and the incidences among these points and lines are displayed in the first six columns of Figure 2.1. Let g be the name of the seventh line of $\mathcal{P}$. Since A is on a, b, c, it is not on g; similarly, none of B, C, D is on g. Therefore, the three points on g must be E, F, and G, and Figure 2.1 is completed.

a	b	c	d	e	f	g
A	A	A	B	B	C	E
B	C	D	C	D	D	F
E	F	G	G	F	E	G

Figure 2.1

The pertinent fact about our construction of Figure 2.1 is that, except for the arbitrariness of our names for the points and lines, the resulting configuration was compelled by Axioms 1–3. Consequently, we surmise that, except for name changes, Figure 2.1 is like the incidence table for 7_3 (Figure 1.7). To prove the correctness of our conjecture, we define a function ϕ from 7_3 to the plane $\mathcal{P}$ as follows: $P_0\phi = G$, $P_1\phi = E$, $P_2\phi = A$, $P_3\phi = F$, $P_4\phi = B$, $P_5\phi = C$, $P_6\phi = D$, and $\ell_6\phi = a$, $\ell_5\phi = b$, $\ell_4\phi = e$, $\ell_3\phi = d$, $\ell_2\phi = f$, $\ell_1\phi = c$, $\ell_0\phi = g$. If in Figure 1.7 the symbol of each element of 7_3 is replaced by the symbol of the corresponding element (under ϕ) of $\mathcal{P}$, the result is Figure 2.1, except for some rearrangements of the columns and of the points in each column—rearrangements that do not affect incidences.

We have reached the conclusion that any 7-point plane is essentially identical to 7_3, the only differences arising from the choices of names for the elements. Our investigation also suggests the method by which we shall decide whether two projective planes are alike. The function ϕ constructed above is a bijection from 7_3 to $\mathcal{P}$ that transforms points into points, lines into lines, and an incident point and line into an incident point and line. Since all projective concepts are defined in terms of point, line, and incidence, it appears that the next definition provides the desired criterion for the abstract identity of two projective planes.

Definition 2.1.1. The projective plane $\mathcal{P}_2$ is *isomorphic* to the projective plane $\mathcal{P}_1$, written $\mathcal{P}_2 \cong \mathcal{P}_1$, if and only if there exists a function θ from $\mathcal{P}_1$ to $\mathcal{P}_2$ with the properties:

(a) θ is a bijection.
(b) If P is a point of $\mathcal{P}_1$, then $P\theta$ is a point of $\mathcal{P}_2$.
(c) If ℓ is a line of $\mathcal{P}_1$, then $\ell\theta$ is a line of $\mathcal{P}_2$.
(d) If P and ℓ are an incident point and line in $\mathcal{P}_1$, then $P\theta$ and $\ell\theta$ are incident in $\mathcal{P}_2$.

A function θ satisfying all the above conditions is an *isomorphism* of $\mathcal{P}_1$ onto $\mathcal{P}_2$. ▮

In addition to restriction (d) of the above definition, we should also expect an isomorphism to transform a nonincident point and line into a nonincident point and line. This extra condition has not been included in Definition 2.1.1 for the reason that it would be redundant, as we now prove. Suppose that θ is an isomorphism of $\mathcal{P}_1$ onto $\mathcal{P}_2$, and let P and ℓ be any nonincident point and line of $\mathcal{P}_1$. Let Q be any point on ℓ, and set $m = P \cup Q$. Because Q is on both ℓ and m, and θ is an isomorphism, $Q\theta$ is on both $\ell\theta$ and $m\theta$. The lines $\ell\theta$ and $m\theta$ are distinct (why?); so, $\ell\theta \cap m\theta = Q\theta$. Since P is on m, $P\theta$ is on $m\theta$; because $P\theta \neq Q\theta$ (why?), $P\theta$ cannot also be on $\ell\theta$. Therefore, $P\theta$ and $\ell\theta$ are nonincident in $\mathcal{P}_2$.

A relation $\cong$, called *isomorphy,* can be defined on the set of projective planes as follows: $\mathcal{P}_2$ is related to $\mathcal{P}_1$ by $\cong$ if and only if $\mathcal{P}_2$ is isomorphic to $\mathcal{P}_1$. Since the identity function is an obvious isomorphism of any given projective plane onto itself, $\cong$ is a reflexive relation. If θ is an isomorphism of $\mathcal{P}_1$ onto $\mathcal{P}_2$, then θ^{-1} is an isomorphism of $\mathcal{P}_2$ onto $\mathcal{P}_1$ (exercise 1a); therefore, $\cong$ is a symmetric relation. If θ_1 is an isomorphism of $\mathcal{P}_1$ onto $\mathcal{P}_2$, and if θ_2 is an isomorphism of $\mathcal{P}_2$ onto $\mathcal{P}_3$, then $\theta_1\theta_2$ is an isomorphism of $\mathcal{P}_1$ onto $\mathcal{P}_3$ (exercise 1b); therefore, $\cong$ is a transitive relation. Isomorphy is thus an equivalence relation on the set of projective planes. As a consequence, we obtain the following theorem.

Theorem 2.1.2. Any two 7-point planes are isomorphic.

Proof: Let $\mathcal{P}_1$ and $\mathcal{P}_2$ be 7-point planes. By the argument at the beginning of this section, $\mathcal{P}_1 \cong 7_3$. Likewise, $\mathcal{P}_2 \cong 7_3$. Since $\cong$ is an equivalence relation, $\mathcal{P}_2 \cong \mathcal{P}_1$. ▮

The ease with which we were able to prove that Axioms 1–3 completely determine the simple structure of a 7-point plane is somewhat misleading, and it should not be inferred that two projective planes are necessarily isomorphic just because they have the same cardinal number of points, even if that cardinal number is finite. For instance, there are at least four different (nonisomorphic) projective planes of order nine [28]. The 13- and 21-point planes are unique (to within isomorphisms—see Section 2.3), as are the projective planes of orders five, seven, and eight. (See [14] and [28].) Thus, the small order planes are unique, but at least some larger orders permit a variety of structures.

An isomorphism between projective planes can be visualized as a renaming of the points and lines of one plane in order to exhibit the equivalence of the two planes—just as we viewed the function ϕ constructed earlier in this section. Another way of thinking of an isomorphism is as a structure-preserving movement of one plane onto the other. This latter view—analogous to the conception of translations and rotations of $\mathcal{E}_2$ advocated in Section 1.1—is especially useful when we consider isomorphisms of a projective plane onto itself. These self-isomorphisms of a projective plane will play a decisive part in our study and receive a special name in the next definition.

Definition 2.1.3. A *collineation* of a projective plane $\mathcal{P}$ is an isomorphism of $\mathcal{P}$ onto $\mathcal{P}$. ▌

In working with isomorphisms (and, especially, collineations) of projective planes, we shall have frequent need of the characteristic property of these transformations expressed by the following equations.

2.1.4. (a) $(P \cup Q)\theta = P\theta \cup Q\theta$.
(b) $(k \cap \ell)\theta = k\theta \cap \ell\theta$.

(Observe how parentheses are used to indicate the element to which a function is applied. Thus, $(P \cup Q)\theta$ means the line that is the image under θ of $P \cup Q$, while $P \cup Q\theta$ would mean the line joining P to $Q\theta$. Similarly, $P\theta \cup Q\theta$ is the line joining $P\theta$ to $Q\theta$.) To establish the validity of Equations 2.1.4, let θ be an isomorphism of the projective plane $\mathcal{P}_1$ onto the (not necessarily different) plane $\mathcal{P}_2$. If P and Q are distinct points of $\mathcal{P}_1$, then $P\theta$ and $Q\theta$ are distinct points of $\mathcal{P}_2$, and they lie on the line $(P \cup Q)\theta$, for θ preserves incidence. Therefore, $(P \cup Q)\theta = P\theta \cup Q\theta$, proving 2.1.4a. Since *isomorphism* is a self-dual term (proof?), and since Equation 2.1.4a is true for any isomorphism, 2.1.4b follows by the principle of duality.

Suppose that τ is a collineation of the projective plane $\mathcal{P}$. If P is a point of $\mathcal{P}$, it may happen that $P\tau = P$, in which case P is said to be a *fixed* (or *invariant*) point of τ. If P and Q are distinct fixed points of τ, then $P \cup Q$ is a fixed line of τ, for $(P \cup Q)\,\tau = P\tau \cup Q\tau = P \cup Q$

(using 2.1.4a). Dually, if k and ℓ are distinct fixed lines of τ, then $k \cap \ell$ is a fixed point of τ. Just because P is a fixed point of τ, we would not expect all the lines on P to be fixed lines of τ. Dually, a line may be a fixed line of a collineation without all the points on that line being fixed points of the collineation. (See exercise 8.)

This section ends with an example of a class of nontrivial collineations of a 7-point plane.

Example 2.1.5. (Elations of a 7-Point Plane) Suppose that $\mathcal{P}$ is a 7-point plane. Let ℓ be any line of $\mathcal{P}$, O any point on ℓ, and P and Q points of $\mathcal{P}$ such that O, P, Q are collinear and neither P nor Q is on ℓ. Then, there is a collineation ϵ of $\mathcal{P}$ that fixes every line on O, fixes every point on ℓ, and sends P into Q. (In Section 2.4, ϵ will be named an *elation*.)

Proof: If $P = Q$, take ϵ to be the identity collineation. For the rest of the proof, assume that $P \neq Q$. Let us construct an incidence table for $\mathcal{P}$. First, set $a = P \cup Q$. Lines a and ℓ lie on O, and there is a third line b on O. Let R and S be the points on b other than O. By Theorem 1.3.3, P, Q, R, S are triply noncollinear. Let $c = P \cup R$, $d = P \cup S$, $e = Q \cup R$, and $f = Q \cup S$. We have thus named all the lines of $\mathcal{P}$ and five of the points. (See Figure 2.2.) Let $T = c \cap f$ and $U = d \cap e$; then, T and U are also on ℓ (why?).

a	b	c	d	e	f	l
P	R	P	P	Q	Q	O
Q	S	R	S	R	S	T
O	O	T	U	U	T	U

Figure 2.2

Define a function ϵ on $\mathcal{P}$ as follows: $P\epsilon = Q$, $Q\epsilon = P$, $R\epsilon = S$, $S\epsilon = R$, $T\epsilon = T$, $U\epsilon = U$, $O\epsilon = O$; $a\epsilon = a$, $b\epsilon = b$, $c\epsilon = f$, $d\epsilon = e$, $e\epsilon = d$, $f\epsilon = c$, $\ell\epsilon = \ell$. Then, ϵ is a bijection that maps points into points and lines into lines. To prove that ϵ satisfies condition (d) of Definition 2.1.1 is a matter of checking that ϵ preserves each of 21 incidences. Since this is the case, ϵ is an isomorphism of $\mathcal{P}$ onto $\mathcal{P}$. From the definition of ϵ, this collineation fixes every line on O, fixes every point on ℓ, and maps P into Q. ∎

2. Transformations of Projective Planes

Exercise 2.1.A

1. (a) Prove that if θ is an isomorphism from $\mathcal{P}_1$ to $\mathcal{P}_2$, then θ^{-1} is an isomorphism from $\mathcal{P}_2$ to $\mathcal{P}_1$. (Note that the converse of (d) of Definition 2.1.1, (the contrapositive of which is) proved immediately following that definition, is needed here.)
(b) Prove that if θ_1 is an isomorphism from $\mathcal{P}_1$ to $\mathcal{P}_2$, and θ_2 is an isomorphism from $\mathcal{P}_2$ to $\mathcal{P}_3$, then $\theta_1\theta_2$ is an isomorphism from $\mathcal{P}_1$ to $\mathcal{P}_3$.

2. Prove that every 7-point plane is isomorphic to its dual plane. (The dual plane is defined in Exercise 1.5.2.)

3. If $\mathcal{P}_2 \cong \mathcal{P}_1$, prove that $\#\mathcal{I}(\ell_2) = \#\mathcal{I}(\ell_1)$, where ℓ_2 and ℓ_1 are any lines of $\mathcal{P}_2$ and $\mathcal{P}_1$, respectively.

4. Suppose that τ is a collineation of a projective plane $\mathcal{P}$, and that τ fixes every point of $\mathcal{P}$. Prove that τ is the identity.

5. Criticize the following:
Theorem: If a collineation of a projective plane $\mathcal{P}$ has a fixed point, then it has a fixed line.
Proof: The dual of the statement, "a collineation has a fixed point," is the statement, "a collineation has a fixed line," since "collineation" is a self-dual term. Therefore, the theorem follows from the principle of duality.

Exercise 2.1.B

6. Construct a collineation of 7_3 that sends P_2 into P_4, P_4 into P_2, P_5 into P_6, and P_6 into P_5.

7. Prove that if a collineation fixes every point on each of two distinct lines, it is the identity.

8. (a) Construct a collineation of 7_3 with exactly one fixed point.
(b) How many fixed lines has the collineation that you constructed for part (a)?
(c) Do the fixed lines of your collineation have any fixed points on them?

9. Suppose that $\mathcal{P}_2 \cong \mathcal{P}_1$, and that the diagonal points of every complete quadrangle in $\mathcal{P}_1$ are collinear. Prove that the diagonal points of every complete quadrangle in $\mathcal{P}_2$ are collinear.

10. Define the concept of isomorphy for affine planes.

2.2 Extension of Point Functions

Suppose that θ is an isomorphism of the projective plane $\mathcal{P}_1$ onto the projective plane $\mathcal{P}_2$. If ℓ is any line of $\mathcal{P}_1$, we can find distinct points P and Q on ℓ; since $\ell = P \cup Q$, $\ell\theta = P\theta \cup Q\theta$ by Equation 2.1.4a. Thus, we can determine how θ transforms lines if we know how it transforms points (and conversely, by duality). A more fruitful formulation of this observation is the following: If α is a suitably conditioned function from the set of points of $\mathcal{P}_1$ to the set of points of $\mathcal{P}_2$, there is an isomorphism θ of $\mathcal{P}_1$ onto $\mathcal{P}_2$ such that $P\theta = P\alpha$ for each point P of $\mathcal{P}_1$. This second formulation can be made the basis of a simpler criterion for isomorphy of two projective planes than that furnished by Definition 2.1.1, provided that we can ascertain the suitable conditions on α. Our investigation is aided by use of the concepts of restriction and extension of a function, presented in the next definition.

Definition 2.2.1. The function α is a *restriction* of the function β, and β is an *extension* of α, if (and only if) the domain and codomain of α are subsets of the domain and codomain, respectively, of β, and $X\alpha = X\beta$ for every X in the domain of α. ▌

The problem under study can now be phrased as follows: If α is a function from the points of $\mathcal{P}_1$ to the points of $\mathcal{P}_2$, what conditions on α ensure that it has an extension to an isomorphism of $\mathcal{P}_1$ onto $\mathcal{P}_2$? We tackle this question by first discovering some conditions on α that are *necessary* for the existence of the desired extension.

Suppose that we start with a function α from the points of $\mathcal{P}_1$ to the points of $\mathcal{P}_2$ and attempt to extend it to an isomorphism θ. Since the required θ is to be one-to-one and is to map the points of $\mathcal{P}_1$ *onto* the points of $\mathcal{P}_2$, we see that α must be a *bijection*.

We define θ on the points of $\mathcal{P}_1$ by setting $P\theta = P\alpha$ for each point P of $\mathcal{P}_1$. There remains the problem of defining θ on the lines of $\mathcal{P}_1$. Suppose that ℓ is a line of $\mathcal{P}_1$, and let P and Q be distinct points on ℓ. Then, $\ell = P \cup Q$, and, if θ is to be an isomorphism, it is necessary that $\ell\theta = P\theta \cup Q\theta = P\alpha \cup Q\alpha$. Why not simply define $\ell\theta$ to be $P\alpha \cup Q\alpha$? In fact, that is what we must do, but there is a difficulty—there are other possible choices of two points on ℓ, and it is not obvious that another choice would yield the same value for $\ell\theta$. The question raised here is whether θ is *well-defined* on the lines of $\mathcal{P}_1$ by the prescription $\ell\theta = P\alpha \cup Q\alpha$, where P, Q are distinct points on ℓ. (In general, when one attempts to define a function by giving, for the calculation of its values, a rule that involves choices, that function is said to be well-defined if its values are independent of those choices. Because a function is required to have a unique value for each element of its domain, the existence of the function hinges on whether it has been well-defined by such a rule. The question of whether a function is well-defined has not arisen before, because whenever we have constructed a function previously, we have given an unequivocal rule for the calculation of each of its values.)

Clearly, what is needed to ensure that θ is well-defined on the lines of $\mathcal{P}_1$ is the following condition on α: Whenever $P \cup Q = P' \cup Q'$, then $P\alpha \cup Q\alpha = P'\alpha \cup Q'\alpha$. The condition just stated is somewhat awkward. Fortunately, the following simpler form is equivalent (exercise 8): Whenever P, Q, R are collinear points of $\mathcal{P}_1$, then $P\alpha$, $Q\alpha$, $R\alpha$ are collinear in $\mathcal{P}_2$. Suppose, then, that we impose the following conditions on α.

(a) α is a bijection from the points of $\mathcal{P}_1$ to the points of $\mathcal{P}_2$.

(b) Whenever P, Q, R are collinear in $\mathcal{P}_1$, then $P\alpha$, $Q\alpha$, $R\alpha$ are collinear in $\mathcal{P}_2$.

These conditions, which we have seen to be necessary, are also sufficient to guarantee that α can be extended to an isomorphism of $\mathcal{P}_1$ onto $\mathcal{P}_2$ (exercise 10). For later work, a somewhat stronger version of the indicated result is quite useful, and we prove that version in the next theorem.

Theorem 2.2.2. (Extension Theorem) Let $\mathcal{P}_1$ and $\mathcal{P}_2$ be projective planes, ℓ_1 a line of $\mathcal{P}_1$, and ℓ_2 a line of $\mathcal{P}_2$. For $i = 1, 2$, let $\mathcal{S}_i$ be the set of all points of $\mathcal{P}_i$ except the points on ℓ_i. Suppose that α is a function from $\mathcal{S}_1$ to $\mathcal{S}_2$ that satisfies the following conditions.

(a) α is a bijection.

(b) Whenever P, Q, R are collinear points of $\mathcal{S}_1$, then $P\alpha$, $Q\alpha$, $R\alpha$ are collinear points of $\mathcal{S}_2$.

Then, α has a unique extension to an isomorphism of $\mathcal{P}_1$ onto $\mathcal{P}_2$.

Proof: The proof is made in seven steps.

Step 1: To construct a function β from the lines of $\mathcal{P}_1$ to the lines of $\mathcal{P}_2$. First, define $\ell_1\beta = \ell_2$. Next, if ℓ is any line of $\mathcal{P}_1$ other than ℓ_1, choose distinct points P and Q of $\mathcal{S}_1$ that lie on ℓ, and set $\ell\beta = P\alpha \cup Q\alpha$. Since ℓ has at least three points on it, all but one of which are in $\mathcal{S}_1$, it is possible to choose P, Q in at least one way. If the choice can be made in more than one way—as it can in any plane with more than seven points—we must show that any such choice leads to the same determination of $\ell\beta$. That is, we must prove that β is well-defined.

Accordingly, suppose that $\ell = P \cup Q$, and, also, $\ell = P' \cup Q'$, with P, Q, P', Q' all in $\mathcal{S}_1$. Then, P, Q, P' are collinear; hence $P\alpha$, $Q\alpha$, $P'\alpha$ are collinear by hypothesis (b). Therefore, $P'\alpha$ is on $P\alpha \cup Q\alpha$. Similarly, $Q'\alpha$ is on $P\alpha \cup Q\alpha$. Since $P'\alpha$ and $Q'\alpha$ are distinct (α is one-to-one), it follows that $P\alpha \cup Q\alpha = P'\alpha \cup Q'\alpha$. Thus, β is well-defined.

Step 2: To prove that P, Q, R are collinear in $\mathcal{S}_1$ whenever $P\alpha$, $Q\alpha$, $R\alpha$ are collinear in $\mathcal{S}_2$. If either $\mathcal{P}_1$ or $\mathcal{P}_2$ is a 7-point plane, then so is the other, and the result is obvious (exercise 3). For the rest of Step 2, we assume that $\mathcal{P}_1$ is not a 7-point plane, and, proceeding by indirect argument, that P, Q, R are noncollinear points of $\mathcal{S}_1$ whose images under α are collinear in $\mathcal{S}_2$. Then, there is a point S on $P \cup Q$ that is different from both P and Q and is not on ℓ_1. By hypothesis (b), $P\alpha$, $Q\alpha$, $S\alpha$ are collinear, so that $S\alpha$ is on the line $P\alpha \cup Q\alpha$, which is the same as the line $Q\alpha \cup R\alpha$ because of our assumption that $P\alpha$, $Q\alpha$, $R\alpha$ are collinear.

Let X be any point of $\mathcal{S}_1$. If X is on any side of triangle PQR, it follows from (b) and our assumption that $P\alpha$, $Q\alpha$, $R\alpha$ are collinear that $X\alpha$ is on $Q\alpha \cup R\alpha$. If X is not on any side of the triangle PQR (as in Figure 2.3), construct $Y = (X \cup P) \cap (Q \cup R)$ and $Z =$

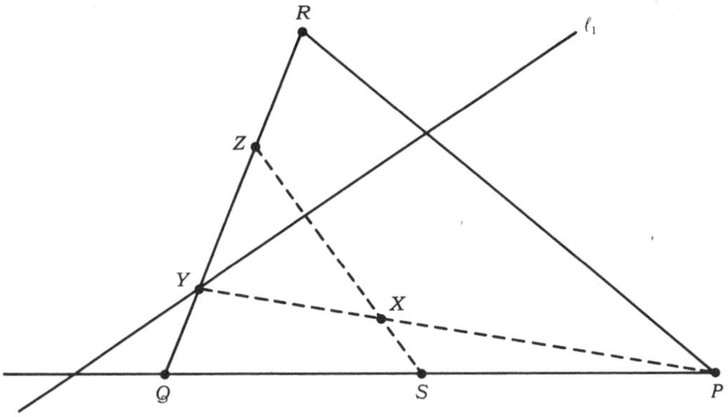

Figure 2.3

$(X \cup S) \cap (Q \cup R)$. Then, Y and Z are different points on $Q \cup R$, and not both of them are on ℓ_1. Thus, at least one, say Z, is in $\mathcal{S}_1$. Since Z is on $Q \cup R$, $Z\alpha$ is on $Q\alpha \cup R\alpha$, by (b). Because X is on $S \cup Z$, $X\alpha$ is on $S\alpha \cup Z\alpha$, which is the same as $Q\alpha \cup R\alpha$. Hence, the assumption that $P\alpha$, $Q\alpha$, $R\alpha$ are collinear has led to the conclusion that $X\alpha$

is on $Q\alpha \cup R\alpha$ for every X in $\mathcal{S}_1$, contrary to the hypothesis that α maps *onto* $\mathcal{S}_2$. This contradiction establishes Step 2.

Step 3: To prove that β is a bijection. First, we show that β is *onto* the lines of $\mathcal{P}_2$. Let k' be any line of $\mathcal{P}_2$. If $k' = \ell_2$, then $k' = \ell_1\beta$. If $k' \neq \ell_2$, there are points P' and Q' on k', with $P' \neq Q'$ and with both P' and Q' in $\mathcal{S}_2$. Since α is onto $\mathcal{S}_2$, $P' = P\alpha$ and $Q' = Q\alpha$ for certain (distinct) points P, Q in $\mathcal{S}_1$. Let $k = P \cup Q$ (in $\mathcal{P}_1$). Then, $k\beta = k'$ by Step 1, proving that β is onto.

To prove that β is one-to-one, let k and m be lines of $\mathcal{P}_1$ such that $k\beta = m\beta$. If $k\beta = \ell_2$, then $k = \ell_1$, for no other line of $\mathcal{P}_1$ is mapped on ℓ_2 by β. Hence, if $k\beta = m\beta = \ell_2$, then $k = m = \ell_1$. We have still to consider the case that $k\beta = m\beta$, and both k and m are different from ℓ_1. In this case, $k = P \cup Q$ and $m = R \cup S$ for some points P, Q, R, S in $\mathcal{S}_1$. By Step 1, $k\beta = P\alpha \cup Q\alpha$ and $m\beta = R\alpha \cup S\alpha$. Since $k\beta = m\beta$, $P\alpha$, $Q\alpha$, $R\alpha$ are collinear; hence, by Step 2, P, Q, R are collinear. Similarly, P, Q, S are collinear, so that $P \cup Q = R \cup S$, or $k = m$. Therefore, β is one-to-one.

Step 4: To prove that if k, m, ℓ_1 are concurrent in $\mathcal{P}_1$, then $k\beta$, $m\beta$, ℓ_2 are concurrent in $\mathcal{P}_2$. Suppose that $k\beta$, $m\beta$, ℓ_2 are not concurrent. Then, necessarily, $k\beta \neq m\beta$, and $k\beta \cap m\beta = P'$ is not on ℓ_2. Thus, $P' = P\alpha$ for some P in $\mathcal{S}_1$. Let Q' in $\mathcal{S}_2$ be such that $k\beta = Q' \cup P'$, and let R' in $\mathcal{S}_2$ be such that $m\beta = R' \cup P'$. Then, $Q' = Q\alpha$ and $R' = R\alpha$ for some Q, R in $\mathcal{S}_1$, both different from P. Let $n = Q \cup P$ and $o = R \cup P$. By Step 1, $n\beta = Q\alpha \cup P\alpha = Q' \cup P' = k\beta$, from which $n = k$ by Step 3. Similarly, $o = m$. Therefore, $k \cap m = n \cap o = P$, which is not on ℓ_1; so, k, m, ℓ_1 are not concurrent. Step 4 follows by contraposition.

Step 5: To extend α to a bijection α^* from the points of $\mathcal{P}_1$ to the points of $\mathcal{P}_2$. If P is in $\mathcal{S}_1$, set $P\alpha^* = P\alpha$. If Q is on ℓ_1, let k be any line, other than ℓ_1, on Q; then, $Q = k \cap \ell_1$. Set $Q\alpha^* = k\beta \cap \ell_2$. It must be shown that α^* is well-defined for each Q on ℓ_1, since there is more than one choice for the line k. If m is any other line on Q, different from ℓ_1, then k, m, ℓ_1 are concurrent (at Q), so that, by Step 4, $k\beta$, $m\beta$, ℓ_2 are concurrent. Hence, $k\beta \cap \ell_2 = m\beta \cap \ell_2$, and the value of $Q\alpha^*$ is independent of the choice of k. Therefore, α^* is well-defined, and it is an extension of α.

To prove that α^* is a bijection, we first show that it is onto the points of $\mathcal{P}_2$. If P' is any point of $\mathcal{S}_2$, then $P' = P\alpha = P\alpha^*$ for some P in $\mathcal{S}_1$. If Q' is any point on ℓ_2, let k' be a line of $\mathcal{P}_2$, other than ℓ_2, on Q'.

Then, $k' = k\beta$ for some line k, other than ℓ_1, in $\mathcal{P}_1$, by Step 3. Set $Q = k \cap \ell_1$; then, $Q\alpha^* = k\beta \cap \ell_2 = k' \cap \ell_2 = Q'$. Thus, α^* is onto the points of $\mathcal{P}_2$.

Finally, to show that α^* is one–to–one, suppose that $P\alpha^* = Q\alpha^*$. If P, Q are in $\mathcal{S}_1$, then $P\alpha^* = P\alpha = Q\alpha^* = Q\alpha$; hence $P = Q$, for α is one-to-one. If either of P, Q is on ℓ_1, then so is the other (why?), and $P\alpha^* = Q\alpha^*$ is on ℓ_2. Let R be a point of $\mathcal{S}_1$, and set $k = R \cup P$, $m = R \cup Q$. Then, $P = k \cap \ell_1$ and $Q = m \cap \ell_1$, so that $P\alpha^* = k\beta \cap \ell_2$ and $Q\alpha^* = m\beta \cap \ell_2$. Since $P\alpha^* = Q\alpha^*$, $k\beta$ and $m\beta$ both lie on $R\alpha$ and $P\alpha^*$; hence $k\beta = m\beta$. By Step 3, $k = m$, and, therefore, $P = Q$. Thus, α^* is one-to-one.

Step 6: To extend α^* and β to an isomorphism θ of $\mathcal{P}_1$ onto $\mathcal{P}_2$. For P in $\mathcal{P}_1$, define $P\theta = P\alpha^*$; for k in $\mathcal{P}_1$, define $k\theta = k\beta$. Then, θ is a bijection from $\mathcal{P}_1$ to $\mathcal{P}_2$, by Steps 3 and 5, and θ maps points into points and lines into lines. It remains to be proved that θ preserves incidence. Suppose that P and k are incident in $\mathcal{P}_1$. There are three possibilities.

(1) P is in $\mathcal{S}_1$. Then, $k \neq \ell_1$. Let Q be a point of $\mathcal{S}_1$, other than P, on k, so that $k = P \cup Q$. Then, $k\theta = k\beta = P\alpha \cup Q\alpha = P\theta \cup Q\theta$, so that $P\theta$ is on $k\theta$.

(2) P is on ℓ_1, but $k \neq \ell_1$. In this case, $P\theta = P\alpha^* = k\beta \cap \ell_2 = k\theta \cap \ell_2$; hence $P\theta$ is on $k\theta$.

(3) P is on ℓ_1, and $k = \ell_1$. Then, $P\theta = P\alpha^*$ is on ℓ_2, and $k\theta = \ell_1\theta = \ell_1\beta = \ell_2$, so that $P\theta$ and $k\theta$ are incident.

Thus, θ is an isomorphism of $\mathcal{P}_1$ onto $\mathcal{P}_2$. Since θ is an extension of α^*, it is also an extension of α (exercise 1).

Step 7: To prove that θ is the unique extension of α to an isomorphism of $\mathcal{P}_1$ onto $\mathcal{P}_2$. Suppose that θ' is an isomorphism of $\mathcal{P}_1$ onto $\mathcal{P}_2$, and that θ' is also an extension of α. Then, $\sigma = \theta'\theta^{-1}$ is a collineation of $\mathcal{P}_1$ (why?). For any point P in $\mathcal{S}_1$, $P\sigma = P\theta'\theta^{-1} = P\alpha\theta^{-1} = P\alpha\alpha^{-1} = P$, because θ^{-1} is an extension of α^{-1} (exercise 2). If k is any line of $\mathcal{P}_1$ other than ℓ_1, let $k = P \cup Q$ with P, Q in $\mathcal{S}_1$. Then, $k\sigma = (P \cup Q)\sigma = P\sigma \cup Q\sigma = P \cup Q = k$. Thus, σ fixes every line of $\mathcal{P}_1$ with the possible exception of ℓ_1. But, $\ell_1\sigma$ cannot be any line other than ℓ_1; for if $\ell_1\sigma = k$, with $k \neq \ell_1$, then, since $k = k\sigma$, we would have $\ell_1\sigma = k\sigma$, contradicting the fact that σ is one-to-one. Therefore, $\ell_1\sigma = \ell_1$, and σ fixes every line of $\mathcal{P}_1$. Finally, if P is any point of $\mathcal{P}_1$, let k and m be distinct lines on P, so that $P = k \cap m$. Then, $P\sigma = (k \cap m)\sigma = k\sigma \cap m\sigma = k \cap m = P$. Hence, σ fixes every point and every line of $\mathcal{P}_1$, or $\sigma = \iota$, the identity collineation. It follows that $\theta'\theta^{-1} = \iota$, or $\theta' = \theta$, establishing the uniqueness of θ. ∎

Exercise 2.2.A

1. Let α, β, γ be functions such that β is an extension of α, and γ is an extension of β. Prove that γ is an extension of α.

2. Suppose that the bijection θ is an extension of the bijection α. Prove that θ^{-1} is an extension of α^{-1}.

3. Prove that if either $\mathcal{P}_1$ or $\mathcal{P}_2$ in the hypotheses of the Extension Theorem is a 7-point plane, then so is the other. Also, show that if $\mathcal{P}_1$ and $\mathcal{P}_2$ are 7-point planes, then Step 2 in the proof of the Extension Theorem is immediate.

4. Let $\mathcal{S}$ be a set with n elements, and $\mathcal{S}'$ a nonempty subset of $\mathcal{S}$ with m elements. Suppose that ϕ is a bijection on $\mathcal{S}'$. In how many ways can ϕ be extended to a bijection on $\mathcal{S}$?

5. Suppose that σ is a collineation of the projective plane $\mathcal{P}$, and that σ fixes every point of $\mathcal{P}$ except possibly the points on a certain line ℓ. Prove that σ is the identity collineation.

6. Let $\{A, B, C, D\}$ and $\{A', B', C', D'\}$ be any (not necessarily different) sets of four triply noncollinear points in a 7-point plane $\mathcal{P}$. Prove that there is one and only one collineation of $\mathcal{P}$ that sends A into A', B into B', C into C', and D into D'.

Exercise 2.2.B

7. (a) Use exercise 6 to calculate the total number of collineations of a 7-point plane.
(b) Use exercise 6 and Example 2.1.5 to calculate the total number of elations of a 7-point plane.

8. Let α be a bijection from the points of a projective plane $\mathcal{P}_1$ to the points of a projective plane $\mathcal{P}_2$. Prove that the following conditions on α are equivalent.
(a) Whenever $P \cup Q = P' \cup Q'$ in $\mathcal{P}_1$, then $P\alpha \cup Q\alpha = P'\alpha \cup Q'\alpha$.
(b) Whenever P, Q, R are collinear in $\mathcal{P}_1$, then $P\alpha$, $Q\alpha$, $R\alpha$ are collinear.

9. Suppose that α is a bijection from the points of $\mathcal{P}_1$ to the points of

$\mathcal{P}_2$ such that whenever P, Q, R are collinear points of $\mathcal{P}_1$, then $P\alpha$, $Q\alpha$, $R\alpha$ are collinear. Prove that if P, Q, R are noncollinear points of $\mathcal{P}_1$, then $P\alpha$, $Q\alpha$, $R\alpha$ are noncollinear.

10. Prove the following extension theorem: Let α be a bijection from the points of $\mathcal{P}_1$ to the points of $\mathcal{P}_2$, and suppose that whenever P, Q, R are collinear points of $\mathcal{P}_1$, then $P\alpha$, $Q\alpha$, $R\alpha$ are collinear. Then, α has a unique extension to an isomorphism of $\mathcal{P}_1$ onto $\mathcal{P}_2$. (Use the result of exercise 9.)

11. Prove that if two affine planes are isomorphic (Exercise 2.1.10), their projective extensions (Exercise 1.5.6) are isomorphic. (Thus, the projective extension of an affine plane is essentially unique.)

2.3. Applications of the Extension Theorem

As a first application of the Extension Theorem (2.2.2), we prove the uniqueness (to within isomorphisms) of the 21-point plane. A similar (but easier) argument suffices to establish the uniqueness of the 13-point plane (exercise 6).

Theorem 2.3.1. Any two 21-point planes are isomorphic.

Proof: In view of the fact that isomorphy is an equivalence relation, it is enough to prove that an arbitrary 21-point plane $\mathcal{P}$ is isomorphic to the plane 21_5. Let A, B, C, D be triply noncollinear points of $\mathcal{P}$, and set $X = (A \cup B) \cap (C \cup D)$, $Y = (A \cup C) \cap (B \cup D)$, $Z = (A \cup D) \cap (B \cup C)$. By Theorem 1.8.5, X, Y, Z are collinear. Let ℓ_1 be the line on which they lie, and let V, W be the other points on ℓ_1. We aim to define a function α from the 16 points of $\mathcal{P}$ that are not on ℓ_1 to 16 points of 21_5, such that α satisfies the hypotheses of the Extension Theorem. First it is necessary to see how these 16 points of $\mathcal{P}$ and the 20 lines of $\mathcal{P}$ different from ℓ_1 are related. We know that each of the 20 lines has four of the 16 points on it, and that each of the 16 points is on five of the 20 lines (why?). Let us construct an incidence table for the points of $\mathcal{P}$ not on ℓ_1 and the lines of $\mathcal{P}$ other than ℓ_1. This table will have 20 columns, with 16 different points appearing. Four points will be in each column, and each point will lie in five columns.

The first six columns are determined by the sides of $\mathcal{Q}$, the quadrangle $ABCD$. Consider the lines, other than ℓ_1, lying on V. One line connects V to each vertex of $\mathcal{Q}$, and each such line intersects the three sides of $\mathcal{Q}$ that do not pass through that vertex (on which the line in question lies) in distinct points. Let the points on $A \cup V$ be named

E, F, G in such a way that E is on $B \cup C$, F is on $B \cup D$, and G is on $C \cup D$. Continuing in this manner for the lines on V, we obtain the first 10 columns of Figure 2.4, in which all 16 required points appear.

A	A	A	B	B	C	A	B	C	D	A	B	C	D	H	S	O	R	O	R
B	C	D	C	D	D	E	H	O	R	T	S	R	O	P	I	I	P	S	H
O	H	I	E	F	G	F	I	P	S	Q	P	I	H	T	E	T	E	F	Q
R	S	P	T	Q	J	G	J	Q	T	J	G	F	E	F	Q	G	J	J	G

Figure 2.4

The next four columns can be quickly filled in by using the lines, other than ℓ_1, on W. For instance, $A \cup W$ intersects $B \cup C$, $B \cup D$, $C \cup D$ in three distinct points, not vertices of $\mathcal{Q}$ and not points in which $A \cup V$ intersects these sides of $\mathcal{Q}$; the only such points are T, Q, J, respectively. Similarly, columns 12–14 of Figure 2.4 can be found.

Now look at the lines, besides $A \cup B$, $C \cup D$, and ℓ_1, on the point X. There are two of these lines, and each of them must intersect the other four sides of $\mathcal{Q}$ (besides $A \cup B$ and $C \cup D$) in distinct points (why?). A glance at the first six columns of Figure 2.4 shows that one of these lines must lie on H and the other on S, and that the line on H must lie on exactly one point of each of the pairs $\{I, P\}$, $\{E, T\}$, $\{F, Q\}$, whereas the line on S lies on the other point of each pair. Since H and I are already together in the eighth column, P must be on the line on H. Similar reasoning permits the completion of columns 15 and 16. Consideration of the lines on Y and Z yields columns 17–20, and the table is finished.

We are ready to define α. Let $A\alpha = P_0$, $B\alpha = P_1$, $C\alpha = P_2$, $D\alpha = P_3$, $E\alpha = P_7$, $F\alpha = P_{17}$, $G\alpha = P_{20}$, $H\alpha = P_{12}$, $I\alpha = P_4$, $J\alpha = P_{10}$, $O\alpha = P_6$, $P\alpha = P_{11}$, $Q\alpha = P_{13}$, $R\alpha = P_{18}$, $S\alpha = P_{15}$, and $T\alpha = P_{19}$, where the values of α are points of 21_5. By means of the incidence table for 21_5 (Figure 1.10), it is readily verified that α satisfies the hypotheses of the Extension Theorem. (To check the condition (b) of that theorem, it is sufficient to show that α takes the points of any column of Figure 2.4 into collinear points of 21_5.) Therefore, α can be extended to an isomorphism of $\mathcal{P}$ onto 21_5; hence $\mathcal{P} \cong 21_5$. ∎

The next application of the Extension Theorem is to the proof that Model 4 (Section 1.4) and $\mathcal{E}_2^*$ are isomorphic.

Proposition 2.3.2. Model 4 and $\mathcal{E}_2^*$ are isomorphic.

Proof: Let O be a point of $\mathcal{E}_3$, and let $\mathcal{P}$ be a plane of $\mathcal{E}_3$ not containing O; we identify $\mathcal{P}$ with $\mathcal{E}_2$, which is justified by the fact that each plane of $\mathcal{E}_3$ is a Euclidean plane. Let $\mathcal{S}$ be the set of all lines on O that are not parallel to $\mathcal{P}$. Define a function α from the lines in $\mathcal{S}$ to the points of $\mathcal{P}$ as follows: For each line k in $\mathcal{S}$, $k\alpha$ is the point in which k intersects $\mathcal{P}$. The function α is clearly a bijection from $\mathcal{S}$ to $\mathcal{P}$. Furthermore, if k, ℓ, m are coplanar lines of $\mathcal{S}$, then $k\alpha$, $\ell\alpha$, $m\alpha$ are collinear points of $\mathcal{P}$.

The "points" of Model 4 consist of the lines of $\mathcal{S}$ and the lines of $\mathcal{E}_3$ that lie on O and are parallel to $\mathcal{P}$. Thus, all the "points" that are not in $\mathcal{S}$ lie on the "line" of Model 4 determined by the plane of $\mathcal{E}_3$ that lies on O and is parallel to $\mathcal{P}$. Also, the points of $\mathcal{P}$ (which is $\mathcal{E}_2$ by our identification) comprise all the points of $\mathcal{E}_2^*$ except the ideal points, which lie on the ideal line. Therefore, the function α defined in the preceding paragraph satisfies the hypotheses of the Extension Theorem; hence it has an extension to an isomorphism of Model 4 onto $\mathcal{E}_2^*$. ∎

Before giving our third application of the Extension Theorem, we consider a certain class of bijections on $\mathcal{E}_2$.

Example 2.3.3. (Central Dilatations of $\mathcal{E}_2$) A *central dilatation* of $\mathcal{E}_2$ is a function δ on (the set of points) of $\mathcal{E}_2$ with the property that there is a point H in $\mathcal{E}_2$ and a real number r, different from zero, such that, for every point X in $\mathcal{E}_2$, the points H, X, and $X\delta$ are collinear, and the *directed* distance from H to $X\delta$ is r times the directed distance from H to X. The point H is a *center* for δ, and the number r is the *ratio* of δ.

From the above definition it is apparent that a central dilatation is completely determined by the specification of its center and ratio, or, equivalently, by the specification of its center and the image of one other given point. The ratio of a central dilatation may be either negative or positive, corresponding, respectively, to the two cases where H is between X and $X\delta$ and where it is not. Figure 2.5 depicts the action of a central dilatation δ, with negative ratio, upon several points of $\mathcal{E}_2$.

Assume that a Cartesian coordinate system exists in $\mathcal{E}_2$ and that a central dilatation δ has center $H = [h, k]$ and ratio r. Writing $[x, y]\delta = [x', y']$, we obtain the equations: $x' - h = r(x - h)$ and

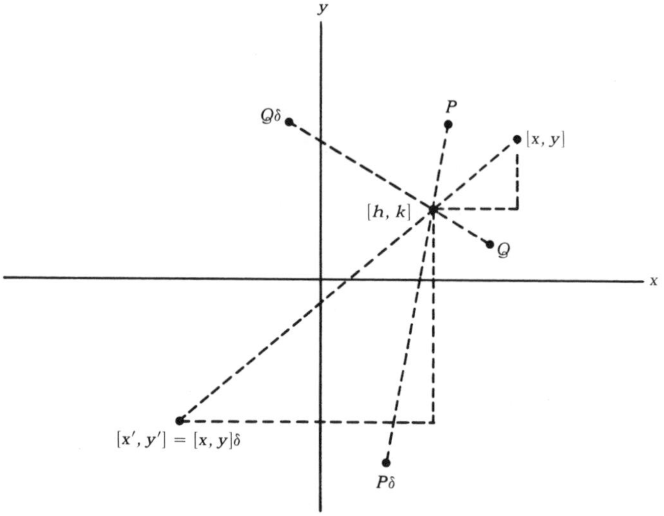

Figure 2.5

$y' - k = r(y - k)$. (Refer to Figure 2.5.) Solving these equations for $[x', y']$ yields

$$[x, y]\delta = [x', y'] = [rx + (1 - r)h, ry + (1 - r)k].$$

In Example 1.1.4 (Translations of $\mathcal{E}_2$) the operation of adding two number pairs was introduced as a device to give a simple and highly visual form for the equation of a translation (1.1.5). Similarly, we can define the operation of multiplying a number pair by a number as follows: $r[x, y] = [rx, ry]$. When the two operations of adding number pairs and multiplying number pairs by numbers are applied to the above equation for a central dilatation, there results the following useful expression.

2.3.4. $[x, y]\delta = r[x, y] + (1 - r)[h, k]$.

If δ is a central dilatation, with center H and ratio r, let δ' be the central dilatation with center H and ratio r^{-1} $(= 1/r)$. Then, it is easy to see (exercise 4) that $\delta\delta' = \delta'\delta = \iota$, the identity function on $\mathcal{E}_2$. In view of Exercise 1.6.8, we have thus proved that a central dilatation is a bijection on $\mathcal{E}_2$ and, furthermore, that the inverse of a central dilatation is a central dilatation with the same center (and reciprocal ratio). ∎

In addition to being a bijection on $\mathcal{E}_2$, a central dilatation transforms collinear points of $\mathcal{E}_2$ into collinear points (exercise 10b). Thus, if we take $\mathcal{P}_2 = \mathcal{P}_1 = \mathcal{E}_2^*$, $\mathcal{S}_2$ and $\mathcal{S}_1$ to be the set of points of $\mathcal{E}_2$, and ℓ_2 and ℓ_1 to be the ideal line of $\mathcal{E}_2^*$, we see that a central dilatation δ is a function that satisfies the hypotheses of the Extension Theorem, and therefore δ has a unique extension to a collineation η of $\mathcal{E}_2^*$. Suppose that H (in $\mathcal{E}_2$) is a center for δ, and let k be any line of $\mathcal{E}_2^*$ on H. Let X be any point of $\mathcal{E}_2$, other than H, on k. Then, $k = H \cup X$, so that $k\eta = (H \cup X)\eta = H\eta \cup X\eta = H\delta \cup X\delta$, because η is an extension of δ. Since δ fixes H (exercise 5a), $H\delta \cup X\delta = H \cup X\delta$, and $H \cup X\delta = H \cup X = k$, because H, X, $X\delta$ are collinear by the definition of a central dilatation. Therefore, $k\eta = k$, and we have proved the second part of the next proposition. (The first part is proved by a similar argument (exercise 11).)

Proposition 2.3.5. Let τ be any translation of $\mathcal{E}_2$, say the translation by $[e, f]$. Let δ be any central dilatation of $\mathcal{E}_2$, and suppose that H is a center for δ. Then:

(a) τ has a unique extension to a collineation ϵ of $\mathcal{E}_2^*$, and ϵ fixes every line on the ideal point I determined as follows: If $[e, f] \neq [0, 0]$, I is the ideal point on the line joining $[0, 0]$ to $[e, f]$. If $[e, f] = [0, 0]$, I can be any ideal point, for $\epsilon = \iota$ (the identity) in this case.

(b) δ has a unique extension to a collineation η of $\mathcal{E}_2^*$, and η fixes every line on H. ∎

In closing this section, we remark on the intimate relation between the translations and central dilatations of $\mathcal{E}_2$ and the arithmetic operations of the real number system. The equation $[x, y]\tau = [x, y] + [e, f]$ clearly exhibits the connection between translations and addition. To make the connection between central dilatations and multiplication just as obvious, consider the central dilatation δ, with center $[0, 0]$ and ratio r, whose equation (by 2.3.4) is $[x, y]\delta = r[x, y] = [rx, ry]$. In our study of translations and central dilatations, we have used our knowledge of the real number system to aid us in deriving properties of these transformations. This process can be reversed, and properties of the number system can be derived from a knowledge of the translations and central dilatations of $\mathcal{E}_2$. In Section 3.7, the reverse procedure will be employed to construct number systems of a very general nature by making use of certain collineations of projective planes—collineations that are analogous to those obtained by the extension of translations and central dilatations of $\mathcal{E}_2$ to collineations of $\mathcal{E}_2^*$.

Exercise 2.3.A

1. (a) Name the points of 21_5 that are not in the range of the function α constructed in the proof of Theorem 2.3.1, and show that these points are collinear.
(b) Let θ be the isomorphism that is the extension of the function α constructed in the proof of Theorem 2.3.1. Name the points of 21_5 that are the respective images, under θ, of V, W, X, Y, Z.
(c) Prove that any 21-point plane is isomorphic to its dual plane (defined in Exercise 1.5.2).

2. (a) Let δ be the central dilatation of $\mathcal{E}_2$ with center $[0, 1]$ that maps $[2, 1]$ into $[-1, 1]$. Write an equation for δ.
(b) Let β be the function on $\mathcal{E}_2$ defined by the equation $[x, y]\beta = [-2x + 3, -2y - 6]$. Show that β is a central dilatation, and find its center and ratio.

3. Let δ_1 and δ_2 be central dilatations with the same center H and with ratios r_1 and r_2, respectively.
(a) Prove that $\delta_1\delta_2$ is the central dilatation with center H and ratio r_2r_1.
(b) Prove that $\delta_1\delta_2 = \delta_2\delta_1$.

4. Let δ be a central dilatation, with center H and ratio r. Let δ' be the central dilatation with center H and ratio r^{-1} $(= 1/r)$. Prove that $\delta\delta' = \delta'\delta = \iota$, the identity function on $\mathcal{E}_2$. (Use exercise 3.)

5. Let δ be a central dilatation with center H.
(a) Prove that $H\delta = H$.
(b) If $\delta \neq \iota$, the identity function, prove that H is the unique fixed point of δ.

Exercise 2.3.B

6. Prove that any two 13-point planes are isomorphic.

7. Discuss the implicit use of an affine isomorphism between Euclidean planes in the "identification" of $\mathcal{P}$ with $\mathcal{E}_2$ in the proof of Proposition 2.3.2.

8. (a) Let δ_1 be the central dilatation with center $[0, 0]$ and ratio $1/2$, and let δ_2 be the central dilatation with center $[1, -3]$ and ratio 3. Write an equation for $\delta_1\delta_2$, show that it is a central dilatation, and find its center and ratio.
(b) Let δ be the central dilatation of $\mathcal{E}_2$ with center $[0, 0]$ and

ratio 2, and let τ be the translation by $[1, 0]$. Write an equation for $\delta\tau$, show that it is a central dilatation, and find its center and ratio.

9. (a) Let δ be a central dilatation of $\mathcal{E}_2$ with ratio r. If P and Q are any points of $\mathcal{E}_2$, prove that the distance between $P\delta$ and $Q\delta$ is $|r|$ times the distance between P and Q.
(b) Let $\mathcal{C}$ be a circle in $\mathcal{E}_2$, and let δ be a central dilatation. Denote by $\mathcal{C}\delta$ the set of all points that are images under δ of points of $\mathcal{C}$. Prove that $\mathcal{C}\delta$ is a circle with center at $O\delta$, where O is the center of $\mathcal{C}$. How does the radius of $\mathcal{C}\delta$ compare with the radius of $\mathcal{C}$?

10. Let the line ℓ of $\mathcal{E}_2$ have the equation $ax + by + c = 0$.
(a) Let τ be the translation by $[e, f]$. Prove that the point $[x_1, y_1]$ lies on ℓ if and only if the point $[x_1, y_1]\tau$ lies on the line with equation $ax + by + (c - ae - bf) = 0$.
(b) Let δ be the central dilatation with center $[h, k]$ and ratio r. Prove that the point $[x_1, y_1]$ lies on ℓ if and only if $[x_1, y_1]\delta$ lies on the line with equation $ax + by + \{cr - (1 - r)(ah + bk)\} = 0$. Deduce that a central dilatation maps collinear points into collinear points.

11. Prove part (a) of Proposition 2.3.5. (Use Exercise 1.6.10 and exercise 10a.)

2.4. Central Collineations

The close connection between the translations and central dilatations of $\mathcal{E}_2$ on the one hand and both the geometry of $\mathcal{E}_2$ and arithmetic of the real numbers on the other hand suggests that we ought to study, in an arbitrary projective plane, the collineations that are analogous to those obtained in the last section by extending translations and central dilatations. Each of the collineations so obtained has the characteristic property that it fixes every line on a certain point (Proposition 2.3.5), and we can use this property to define the class of collineations that we want to investigate.

Definition 2.4.1. A *central collineation* of a projective plane $\mathcal{P}$ is a collineation of $\mathcal{P}$ that has a pencil of invariant lines. A point carrying a pencil of invariant lines of a central collineation is a *center* of the collineation. ∎

In particular, the identity collineation of $\mathcal{P}$ is a central collineation whose center may be taken as any point of $\mathcal{P}$. We wish to show that the identity is the only central collineation of a projective plane $\mathcal{P}$ that has more than one center. Accordingly, suppose that μ is a central collineation of $\mathcal{P}$ with two different centers, H and K. Let P be any point of $\mathcal{P}$ that is not on $\ell = H \cup K$. Then, the lines $k = H \cup P$ and $m = K \cup P$ are distinct and are fixed by μ, since they lie on H and K, respectively. Therefore, $P = k \cap m$ is a fixed point of μ. Because μ fixes every point not on ℓ, $\mu = \iota$ by Exercise 2.2.5 (or by Step 7 of the proof of the Extension Theorem (2.2.2)). The contrapositive of what has just been proved is that if a central collineation of $\mathcal{P}$ is not the identity, then its center is unique.

The concept dual to "central collineation" is "collineation that has a pencil of invariant points," which may also be called *axial collineation*. A line that carries a pencil of invariant points of an axial collineation is an *axis* of the collineation. The next theorem shows that "central collineation" and "axial collineation" are not different notions.

Theorem 2.4.2. (Axis of a Central Collineation) A central collineation is an axial collineation. Dually, an axial collineation is a central collineation, so that "central collineation" is a self-dual concept.

Proof: Let μ be an arbitrary central collineation. It is only necessary to prove that μ has a pencil of invariant points, for the rest of the theorem will then follow from the principle of duality. If $\mu = \iota$, the conclusion is obvious. Otherwise, let H be the unique center of μ. There are two possibilities.

Case 1: μ has a fixed line ℓ that is not on H. Let P be any point on ℓ. Then, P is the point of intersection of the fixed lines (under μ) $H \cup P$ and ℓ. Therefore, P is fixed by μ, and ℓ is an axis of the collineation.

Case 2: μ has no fixed line that is not on H. Let k be any line not on H; then, $k\mu \neq k$. Set $A = k \cap k\mu$ and $\ell = H \cup A$. Since $\ell \neq k$, $A = \ell \cap k$; hence $A\mu = \ell\mu \cap k\mu = \ell \cap k\mu = A$. Thus, A is a fixed point of μ. If B is a fixed point of μ different from A, then $B \cup A$ is a fixed line of μ; hence it lies on H by assumption. Therefore, $B \cup A = H \cup A = \ell$, implying that every fixed point of μ is on ℓ.

Suppose that P is any point on ℓ other than H. Let m be a line on P but not on H, and let $P' = m \cap m\mu$. Then, since $m \neq H \cup P'$, it follows that $P' = m \cap (H \cup P')$. Therefore, $P'\mu = m\mu \cap (H \cup P') = P'$, proving that P' is on ℓ, by the last sentence of the preceding paragraph. Thus, $P' = \ell \cap m = P$, so that P is fixed by μ. We have proved that μ fixes every point on ℓ other than H, and, of course, $H\mu = H$, for the center of any central collineation is a fixed point of that collineation (why?). Hence, ℓ is an axis for μ. ▮

Any line of the projective plane $\mathcal{P}$ serves as an axis for the identity collineation of $\mathcal{P}$. If μ is a central collineation different from the identity, its axis is unique, as is seen by dualizing the argument for the uniqueness of its center. Furthermore, in this case the unique axis and center of μ may be incident or not, and it is worthwhile to distinguish the two possibilities.

Definition 2.4.3. An *elation* is a central collineation whose center is on its axis. A *homology* is a central collineation whose center is not on its axis. The identity collineation will be considered to be both an elation and a homology. ▮

If μ is a central collineation with center H, and if P is a point of the plane different from H, then $P\mu$ is collinear with H and P. This is true because P is on the fixed line $H \cup P$; hence $P\mu$ is on $(H \cup P)\mu = H \cup P$. Dually, if ℓ is an axis of μ, and if k is any line different from ℓ, then ℓ, k, and $k\mu$ are concurrent.

If μ is a central collineation with center H and axis ℓ, then μ^{-1} is a collineation, and it fixes all lines on H and all points on ℓ (why?). Thus, the inverse of a central collineation μ is central with the same center and axis as μ. When two central collineations are composed, the resulting collineation is not ordinarily central. (See exercise 6.) An exception occurs when the two central collineations have a common axis (or, dually, a common center), as the next theorem shows.

Theorem 2.4.4. (Coaxial Collineations) Let μ_1 and μ_2 be central collineations, both different from ι, with common axis ℓ and centers H and K, respectively. Then, $\mu_1\mu_2$ is a central collineation with axis ℓ. Furthermore, if $H = K$, $\mu_1\mu_2$ has H as a center; if $H \neq K$, the center of $\mu_1\mu_2$ is on the line $H \cup K$ and is different from both H and K.

Proof: Let $\mu_3 = \mu_1\mu_2$. Clearly, μ_3 fixes every point on ℓ and is therefore axial, hence central, with axis ℓ. If $H = K$, μ_3 fixes every line on H, so that H is a center of μ_3. For the rest, it is assumed that $H \neq K$.

If the center of μ_3 were H, then $\mu_2 = \mu_1^{-1}\mu_3$ would have center H, by what has been proved. Similarly, if the center of μ_3 were K, then $\mu_1 = \mu_3\mu_2^{-1}$ would have center K. Since H is not a center of μ_2 and K is not a center of μ_1, it follows that L, the center of μ_3, is different from H and K. It remains to be proved that L is on $H \cup K$.

Let $k = H \cup L$ and $m = K \cup L$. Then, $k\mu_2 = k\mu_1^{-1}\mu_3 = k\mu_3 = k$ (why?). Therefore, either k is on K, or else k is an axis for μ_2 (because, if k is not on K, and if P is any point on k, then $P = k \cap (K \cup P)$; thus $P\mu_2 = k\mu_2 \cap (K \cup P)\mu_2 = k \cap (K \cup P) = P$). Hence, either k is on K, or else $k = \ell$, since the axis of μ_2 is unique. Similarly, $m\mu_1 = m\mu_3\mu_2^{-1} = m\mu_2^{-1} = m$, so that either m is on H, or else $m = \ell$. If both $k = \ell$ and $m = \ell$, then H, K, L are all on ℓ. If $k \neq \ell$, then k is on K, and H, K, L are all on k; similarly, if $m \neq \ell$, then H, K, L are all on m. Thus, in every case L is on $H \cup K$. ∎

The restriction in the preceding theorem that μ_1 and μ_2 be different from ι was made merely to simplify the statement of the theorem. Obviously, if either μ_1 or μ_2 is ι, we have complete information about $\mu_1\mu_2$. The next theorem establishes a simple, but most important, uniqueness criterion by showing that a central collineation is determined by a rather small set of data.

Theorem 2.4.5. (Uniqueness Theorem for Central Collineations) Let ℓ be a line in a projective plane $\mathcal{P}$, and let H be a point of $\mathcal{P}$. Let P, P' be points, both different from H and neither one on ℓ, such that H, P, P' are collinear. Suppose that μ is a central collineation with axis ℓ, center H, and mapping P into P'. Then μ is unique.

Proof: Suppose that μ' is also a central collineation with axis ℓ, center H, sending P into P'. Then, $\mu'\mu^{-1}$ is a central collineation with axis ℓ, center H, sending P into P. If k is any line on P, k is incident with two different fixed points of $\mu'\mu^{-1}$, namely P and $k \cap \ell$. Therefore, k is a fixed line of $\mu'\mu^{-1}$, proving that P is another center for $\mu'\mu^{-1}$. It follows that $\mu'\mu^{-1} = \iota$; hence $\mu' = \mu$, and μ is unique. ∎

It should be emphasized that the above theorem proves merely the uniqueness, not the existence, of the central collineation μ corresponding to the data of the hypothesis. Whether a projective plane possesses such a collineation cannot be decided in general from Axioms 1–3 alone, and in Section 3.1 a fourth axiom will be introduced to ensure the existence of the collineation μ. It will be helpful to have a name for the kind of set occurring in the hypothesis of Theorem 2.4.5.

Definition 2.4.6. A *determining set* is a figure in a projective plane consisting of a line ℓ, a point H, and points P, P', such that H, P, P' are collinear, and P, P' are both different from H and not on ℓ. ∎

For a determining set we use the notation $\mathfrak{D} = \{\ell, H, P, P'\}$; if there exists a central collineation μ with axis ℓ, center H, sending P into P', then $\mathfrak{D}$ is said to be a determining set *for* μ. Thus, the Uniqueness Theorem for Central Collineations can be rephrased, "The set $\mathfrak{D} = \{\ell, H, P, P'\}$ is a determining set for at most one central collineation." There are two immediate consequences of this theorem that are worth emphasizing.

(1) If μ is a central collineation different from the identity, then μ fixes no point except its center and the points on its axis (exercise 1); dually, μ fixes no line except its axis and the lines on its center.

(2) If μ is a central collineation with determining set $\mathfrak{D} = \{\ell, H, P, P'\}$, then it must be possible, given any point Q of the plane, to construct $Q\mu$ from ℓ, H, P, P', and Q. The method of doing this will be developed in the next section. (See Theorem 2.5.1, the discussion following that theorem, and Figure 2.6.)

This section closes with an important theorem concerning commuting central collineations.

Theorem 2.4.7. (First Commuting Theorem) Let μ_1 and μ_2 be central collineations with distinct centers, H_1 and H_2, respectively, and with axes ℓ_1 and ℓ_2, respectively. Suppose that H_1 lies on ℓ_2 and that H_2 lies on ℓ_1. Then, $\mu_1\mu_2 = \mu_2\mu_1$.

Proof: Set $\mu = \mu_1\mu_2\mu_1^{-1}\mu_2^{-1}$, and let k be any line on H_1. Then, $k\mu_1 = k$; hence $k\mu_1\mu_2 = k\mu_2$. Since k is on H_1, $k\mu_2$ is on $H_1\mu_2$, which is H_1 because H_1 is on ℓ_2 and thus is fixed by μ_2. Therefore, $k\mu_2\mu_1^{-1} = k\mu_2$, so that $k\mu_2\mu_1^{-1}\mu_2^{-1} = k\mu_2\mu_2^{-1} = k$. It follows that $k\mu = k$, and that H_1 is a center for μ. A similar argument shows that H_2 is also a center for μ. Thus, $\mu = \iota$, because it has two different centers. Therefore, $\mu_1\mu_2\mu_1^{-1}\mu_2^{-1} = \iota$; hence $\mu_1\mu_2\mu_1^{-1} = \mu_2$, and $\mu_1\mu_2 = \mu_2\mu_1$. ∎

Exercise 2.4.A

1. Let μ be a central collineation different from the identity. Prove that the only fixed points of μ are its center and the points on its axis. Also, prove a dual result for the fixed lines of μ.

2. What homologies does a 7-point plane possess?

3. Let μ and ν be central collineations with common axis ℓ, and suppose that $P\mu = P\nu$ and $Q\mu = Q\nu$ for distinct points, P and Q, not on ℓ. Prove that $\mu = \nu$.

4. (a) Let ϵ be a central collineation of $\mathcal{E}_2^*$ that is obtained by extending a translation τ of $\mathcal{E}_2$. What is the axis of ϵ?

(b) Let η be a central collineation of $\mathcal{E}_2^*$ that is obtained by extending a central dilatation δ of $\mathcal{E}_2$. What is the axis of η?

5. Distinguish three cases of the First Commuting Theorem (2.4.7), according to whether the collineations involved are elations or homologies.

Exercise 2.4.B

6. Construct two central collineations of 7_3 whose composite is not a central collineation.

7. Refer to the incidence table of 13_4 (Figure 1.9). Construct the homology of 13_4 with axis ℓ_0, center P_{10}, sending P_6 into P_{11}. Verify that the function you have constructed really is a collineation.

8. Let σ be a collineation of a projective plane with the property that there is a point H of the plane such that every line on H is incident with two distinct fixed points of σ. Prove that σ is a homology.

9. Interpret the theorem Coaxial Collineations (2.4.4) and the Uniqueness Theorem for Central Collineations (2.4.5) for translations and central dilatations of $\mathcal{E}_2$. Consider all cases.

10. A *dilatation* ϕ of $\mathcal{E}_2$ is defined to be a bijection on (the set of points of) $\mathcal{E}_2$ that has the further property that if k is any line of $\mathcal{E}_2$, then the points of k are transformed by ϕ into points of a line k' that is either parallel to k or is k itself.

(a) Prove that a dilatation ϕ of $\mathcal{E}_2$ has a unique extension to a central collineation μ of $\mathcal{E}_2^*$, and that the ideal line of $\mathcal{E}_2^*$ is an axis for μ.

(b) Using the results of Proposition 2.3.5, the Uniqueness Theorem for Central Collineations, and part (a), deduce that every dilatation of $\mathcal{E}_2$ is either a translation or a central dilatation.

2.5. Projectivities and Collineations

A collineation σ of a projective plane $\mathcal{P}$ is a bijection whose domain consists of all the points and lines of $\mathcal{P}$. We shall often be concerned with the effect of σ on the points of a certain pencil (or the lines of a certain pencil). If k is a line of $\mathcal{P}$, the points on k are transformed by σ into points on $k\sigma$. Any discussion of the action of σ upon the points on k is expedited by considering, instead of σ itself, the function with domain $\mathcal{I}(k)$ and codomain $\mathcal{I}(k\sigma)$ obtained by restricting σ. For brevity, this restricted function will be called the "restriction of σ to $\mathcal{I}(k)$," with the codomain being understood to be $\mathcal{I}(k\sigma)$ without explicit mention. Moreover, this restricted function will still be designated by σ, with the context clarifying when a restriction is implied and what the domain of that restriction is.

If σ is a collineation and k a line, the restriction of σ to $\mathcal{I}(k)$ is a bijection from $\mathcal{I}(k)$ to $\mathcal{I}(k\sigma)$. The first theorem of this section shows that when σ is a central collineation, its restriction to $\mathcal{I}(k)$ (for any line k) is a projectivity.

Theorem 2.5.1. (Projectivities Induced by Central Collineations) Let μ be a central collineation of a projective plane $\mathcal{P}$, and suppose that μ has center H and axis ℓ. Let k be any line of $\mathcal{P}$. Then:

(a) If k is an axis for μ, the restriction of μ to $\mathcal{I}(k)$ is the identity function, which is a projectivity on k.

(b) If k is a noninvariant line under μ, the restriction of μ to $\mathcal{I}(k)$ is the perspectivity $k \circ H \circ k\mu$.

(c) If k is an invariant line, but not the axis, of μ, the restriction of μ to $\mathcal{I}(k)$ is a Π_2 on k with central invariant point H and axial invariant point $k \cap \ell$. An explicit expression for this Π_2 is $k \circ O \circ \ell \circ O\mu \circ k$, where O is any point not on either k or ℓ.

Proof: (a) Since μ fixes every point on k in this case, the restriction of μ to $\mathcal{I}(k)$ is the identity function on $\mathcal{I}(k)$. That the identity on $\mathcal{I}(k)$ is a projectivity follows from the expression $\iota = k \circ O \circ k$, where O may be taken as any point not on k.

(b) Let P be any point on k. Then, $P \neq H$, and $P\mu$ is on $P \cup H$. Since $P\mu$ is also on $k\mu$, we see that $P\mu = (P \cup H) \cap k\mu = P\pi$, where π is the perspectivity $k \circ H \circ k\mu$.

(c) In this case, k is a line on H. Let O be a point not on either k or ℓ, and construct the perspectivities $\pi_1 = k \circ O \circ \ell$ and $\pi_2 = \ell \circ O\mu \circ k$. The projectivity $\pi = \pi_1\pi_2$ is a Π_2 on k with central invariant point H (why?) and axial invariant point $k \cap \ell$, and we want to show that $Q\pi = Q\mu$ for every point Q on k. (Refer to Figure 2.6, which illustrates the situation for a homology.)

Let Q be any point on k, and construct $S = (Q \cup O) \cap \ell$. Then, $Q = (S \cup O) \cap k$, so that $Q\mu = (S \cup O\mu) \cap k$. Also, $Q\pi_1 = (Q \cup O) \cap \ell = S$, and $S\pi_2 = (S \cup O\mu) \cap k = Q\mu$. Therefore, $Q\pi = Q\pi_1\pi_2 = S\pi_2 = Q\mu$. ∎

Because of the choice of names for the invariant points of a Π_2, it is easy to remember the result in part (c) of the above theorem; the

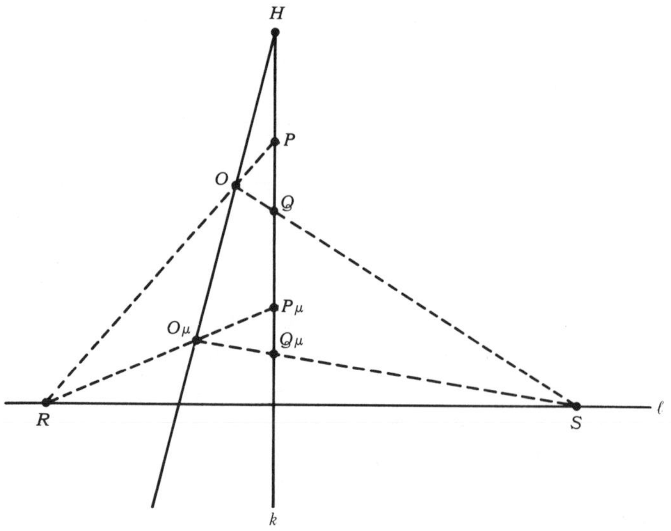

Figure 2.6

Π_2 on k has for its central invariant point the center of μ and for its axial invariant point the point of intersection of k with the axis of μ. The theorem just proved also provides a method of constructing the image of any point under a central collineation μ. By the Uniqueness Theorem for Central Collineations (2.4.5), μ is completely specified by the determining set $\{\ell, H, P, P\mu\}$ (Figure 2.6). If O is a noninvariant point under μ, not on $P \cup H$, then $O\mu$ can be found as the image of O under the perspectivity $(R \cup P) \circ H \circ (R \cup P\mu)$, where $R = (O \cup P) \cap \ell$. If Q is a noninvariant point *on* $P \cup H$, then $Q\mu$ can be found as the image of Q under the projectivity $k \circ O \circ \ell \circ O\mu \circ k$, where O is any noninvariant point not on $P \cup H$, and $O\mu$ is constructed as in the previous sentence. (Refer to Figure 2.6 and see also exercise 1.)

The student is urged to learn well the constructions of the preceding paragraph. Observe that in the construction of $Q\mu$ from Q, P, and $P\mu$, the only guarantee that the same $Q\mu$ would be found if a different intermediate point O were used is the assumption that the central collineation μ exists in the first place. Thus, the construction does not prove the existence of μ, for the uniqueness of $Q\mu$ is essential in order that μ be a well-defined function.

When μ is a central collineation, the previous theorem states that the restriction of μ to $\mathcal{S}(k)$, where k is any line, is a projectivity. Dually, the restriction of μ to $\mathcal{S}(P)$, where P is any point, is also a projectivity. We say that μ induces a projectivity from any pencil to its image. The remarks just made suggest the following definition of a class of collineations that includes the central collineations.

Definition 2.5.2. A collineation σ is *projective* for the pencil $\mathcal{S}(k)$ (respectively, $\mathcal{S}(P)$) if and only if the restriction of σ to $\mathcal{S}(k)$ (respectively, $\mathcal{S}(P)$) is a projectivity from k (respectively, P) to $k\sigma$ (respectively, $P\sigma$). A *projective collineation* is a collineation that is projective for every pencil. ▮

Projective collineations are of special significance for our geometry because of the way in which they relate the two basic kinds of transformations in a projective plane—projectivities and collineations. It is fortunate that a much simpler criterion than that of the above definition can be established for deciding whether a given collineation is projective (Theorem 2.5.4). To find this simpler criterion, we investigate the action of collineations upon projectivities.

Suppose first that π is the perspectivity $k \circ O \circ \ell$ and that ρ is a collineation. Since ρ transforms k, O, ℓ into $k\rho$, $O\rho$, $\ell\rho$, respectively, we say that ρ transforms π into the perspectivity $\pi' = k\rho \circ O\rho \circ \ell\rho$, and we want to express π' in terms of π and ρ. The rather natural guess that $\pi' = \pi\rho$ is seen to be incorrect by noticing that π' has domain $\mathcal{S}(k\rho)$, whereas $\pi\rho$ has domain $\mathcal{S}(k)$.

To obtain the correct expression for π', let P be any point on k. Then, $P\rho$ is on $k\rho$, and $(P\rho)\pi' = (P\rho \cup O\rho) \cap \ell\rho = [(P \cup O) \cap \ell]\rho = (P\pi)\rho$. Thus, $\rho\pi' = \pi\rho$, where the ρ on the left side of this equation is the restriction of the collineation to $\mathcal{S}(k)$, and the ρ on the right side is the restriction of the collineation to $\mathcal{S}(\ell)$. Since the inverse of the restriction of ρ to $\mathcal{S}(k)$ is the restriction of ρ^{-1} to $\mathcal{S}(k\rho)$ (exercise 3a), the equation $\rho\pi' = \pi\rho$ can be solved for π' to yield $\pi' = \rho^{-1}\pi\rho$. We say that π' is the *conjugate* (or *transform*) of π by ρ.

The extension of the above result to the effect of a collineation ρ upon an arbitrary projectivity is most easily obtained by deriving the effect of ρ upon an elementary correspondence, then deducing the general theorem by composition of elementary correspondences.

Theorem 2.5.3. (Conjugate of an Elementary Correspondence)

(a) If ρ is a collineation, and if $\delta_1 = k \circ O$, then $k\rho \circ O\rho = \rho^{-1}\delta_1\rho$.

(b) If ρ is a collineation, and if $\delta_2 = K \circ o$, then $K\rho \circ o\rho = \rho^{-1}\delta_2\rho$.

Proof: (a) Let P be any point on $k\rho$. Then, $P\rho^{-1}$ is on k. Thus,

$(P\rho^{-1})\delta_1 = P\rho^{-1} \cup O$, and $(P\rho^{-1}\delta_1)\rho = P \cup O\rho = P\delta_1'$, where $\delta_1' = k\rho \circ O\rho$. Therefore, $k\rho \circ O\rho = \delta_1' = \rho^{-1}\delta_1\rho$.

(b) This part is proved by dualizing the argument in part (a). ▮

Corollary: If π is a projectivity, and if ρ is a collineation, then $\pi' = \rho^{-1}\pi\rho$ is a projectivity, with domain and codomain the respective images under ρ of the domain and codomain of π. Furthermore, π' is expressible with the same number of elementary factors as π. In particular, if π is a perspectivity, then so is π', while if π is a Π_2 on a line k, then π' is a Π_2 on $k\rho$.

Proof: Express π with elementary correspondences: $\pi = \delta_1\delta_2 \cdots \delta_n$. Then, $\pi' = \rho^{-1}\pi\rho = \rho^{-1}\delta_1\delta_2 \cdots \delta_n\rho = (\rho^{-1}\delta_1\rho)(\rho^{-1}\delta_2\rho) \cdots (\rho^{-1}\delta_n\rho)$, and the result follows from the theorem. (The insertion of the extra factors of ρ and ρ^{-1} into the expression $\rho^{-1}\delta_1\delta_2 \cdots \delta_n\rho$ is justified by careful attention to the exact meaning of each inserted factor. Suppose that the codomain of δ_1 and the domain of δ_2 are $\mathcal{I}(O)$. (An identical argument holds if these sets are a pencil of points.) Then, in the expression $\rho^{-1}\delta_1\rho$, ρ denotes the function from $\mathcal{I}(O)$ to $\mathcal{I}(O\rho)$ obtained by restricting the collineation ρ, and in the expression $\rho^{-1}\delta_2\rho$, ρ^{-1} denotes the function from $\mathcal{I}(O\rho)$ to $\mathcal{I}(O)$ obtained by restricting the collineation ρ^{-1}. Thus, the ρ^{-1} in $\rho^{-1}\delta_2\rho$ is the inverse of the ρ in $\rho^{-1}\delta_1\rho$, so that $\rho^{-1}\delta_1\delta_2\rho = (\rho^{-1}\delta_1\rho)(\rho^{-1}\delta_2\rho)$, and this result can be extended by induction to any composite of elementary correspondences.) ▮

The discussion of the conjugate of a projectivity by a collineation can be summarized by saying that $\rho^{-1}\pi\rho$ is essentially like π, except that it is applied after the domain and codomain of π have been moved by ρ. Armed with our knowledge of the transform of a projectivity by a collineation, we return to the problem of determining whether a given collineation is projective.

Theorem 2.5.4. (Criterion for Projective Collineations) If a collineation σ is projective for a single pencil of points, then it is a projective collineation.

Proof: Let $\mathcal{I}(k)$ be a pencil for which σ is projective, and let ℓ be any line of the plane. Let O be a point not on either k or ℓ, and construct the perspectivity $\pi = \ell \circ O \circ k$. Then, $\pi^{-1} = k \circ O \circ \ell$; hence $\sigma^{-1}\pi^{-1}\sigma = k\sigma \circ O\sigma \circ \ell\sigma$. Thus, the composite of π, the restriction of σ to $\mathcal{I}(k)$, and $\sigma^{-1}\pi^{-1}\sigma$, in that order, is a projectivity π_1 from ℓ to $\ell\sigma$. Furthermore, if P is any point on ℓ, then $P\pi_1 = P\pi\sigma(\sigma^{-1}\pi^{-1}\sigma) = P\sigma$, so that σ is projective for the pencil $\mathcal{I}(\ell)$.

Next, let Q be any point of the plane, and choose a line m not on Q. From the above, the restriction of σ to $\mathcal{I}(m)$ is a projectivity. Define $\delta = Q \circ m$. Then, $\delta^{-1} = m \circ Q$; hence $\sigma^{-1}\delta^{-1}\sigma = m\sigma \circ Q\sigma$. Thus, the composite of δ, the restriction of σ to $\mathcal{I}(m)$, and $\sigma^{-1}\delta^{-1}\sigma$, in that order, is a projectivity π_2 from Q to $Q\sigma$. Furthermore, if n is any line on Q, then $n\pi_2 = n\delta\sigma(\sigma^{-1}\delta^{-1}\sigma) = n\sigma$, so that σ is projective for the pencil $\mathcal{I}(Q)$. ▮

If σ and τ are projective collineations and ℓ is a line, the restriction of σ to $\mathcal{I}(\ell)$ composed with the restriction of τ to $\mathcal{I}(\ell\sigma)$, in that order, is a projectivity from ℓ to $\ell\sigma\tau$, and it is induced by $\sigma\tau$. Hence, a composite of two projective collineations induces a projectivity from each line to its image and is therefore a projective collineation; this result obviously extends by induction to a composite of any number of projective collineations. Similar reasoning shows that the inverse of a projective collineation is a projective collineation.

Exercise 2.5.A

1. Let ϵ be an elation with determining set $\{\ell, H, P, P\epsilon\}$. Draw a figure similar to Figure 2.6 and give a detailed analysis of the constructions of the images of noninvariant points on $H \cup P$ and not on $H \cup P$.

2. (a) Prove that every collineation of a 7-point plane is projective.
(b) Prove that every collineation of a 13-point plane is projective.

3. (a) Let ρ be a collineation and k a line of a projective plane. Prove that the inverse of the restriction of ρ to $\mathcal{I}(k)$ is the restriction of ρ^{-1} to $\mathcal{I}(k\rho)$.
(b) In the proof of the theorem Criterion for Projective Collineations (2.5.4), a projectivity π_1 was defined by the expression $\pi\sigma(\sigma^{-1}\pi^{-1}\sigma)$. Give a precise explanation of the meaning of each σ and σ^{-1} in this expression.

4. Prove that a composite of a projective collineation and a nonprojective collineation is a nonprojective collineation.

5. Let π be a projectivity on a line ℓ, and suppose that $P\pi = P$ for a certain point P on ℓ. Let ρ be a collineation. Prove that $P\rho$ is a fixed point of the projectivity $\rho^{-1}\pi\rho$ on $\ell\rho$.

6. Refer to the incidence table of 21_5 (Figure 1.10). Construct the elation of 21_5 with axis ℓ_0, center P_0, sending P_5 into P_7. Verify that the function you have constructed is indeed a collineation.

Exercise 2.5.B

7. Let π be a Π_2 on the line ℓ with central invariant point O and axial invariant point E. If ρ is a collineation, prove that $\rho^{-1}\pi\rho$ has central invariant point $O\rho$ and axial invariant point $E\rho$.

8. Suppose that η is a homology with center H, axis ℓ, and that X and Y are distinct noninvariant points of η. Set $k = H \cup X$, $m = H \cup Y$, $M = k \cap \ell$, and $N = m \cap \ell$. Prove that there is a projectivity π from k to m that sends H, X, $X\eta$, M, into H, Y, $Y\eta$, N, respectively.

9. Let a relation $\sim$, called *conjugacy*, be defined on the set of projectivities in a projective plane $\mathcal{P}$ as follows: $\pi_2 \sim \pi_1$ if and only if there is a collineation ρ of $\mathcal{P}$ such that $\pi_2 = \rho^{-1}\pi_1\rho$. Prove that $\sim$ is an equivalence relation.

10. (a) Let $\mathcal{P}$ be a projective plane in which the diagonal points of every complete quadrangle are collinear. Prove that if ϵ is an elation of $\mathcal{P}$, then either $\epsilon = \iota$ or $\epsilon\epsilon = \iota$.

(b) Suppose that ϵ is an elation of a projective plane $\mathcal{P}$, and that $\epsilon\epsilon = \iota$, but $\epsilon \neq \iota$. Prove that there exists a quadrangle in $\mathcal{P}$ whose diagonal points are collinear.

11. Refer to the incidence table for a 31-point plane that you constructed (and saved) in Exercise 1.4.4. Construct the homology of this plane with axis ℓ_2, center P_2, sending P_4 into P_9. Verify that your construction is a collineation, and save it.

2.6. Groups

Suppose that $\mathcal{S}$ is a nonempty set. A *binary operation* (or *operation*, for short) on $\mathcal{S}$ is a function whose domain is the set of ordered pairs of elements of $\mathcal{S}$ and whose codomain is $\mathcal{S}$. In less formal language, a binary operation on $\mathcal{S}$ is a rule that permits any two elements of $\mathcal{S}$ to be combined in a specified order to yield a (unique) third element of $\mathcal{S}$. Here are some examples of familiar operations.

Example 2.6.1. (a) Addition $(+)$ is an operation on the set of positive integers. If m and n are positive integers, then $m + n$ is a positive integer uniquely determined by m, n, and the operation $+$.

(b) Multiplication $(\cdot)$ is an operation on the set of real numbers. If x and y are real numbers, then $x \cdot y$ is a real number uniquely determined by x, y, and the operation $\cdot$.

(c) Let $\mathcal{S}$ be a nonempty set, and let $\mathcal{G}(\mathcal{S})$ denote the set of all bijections on $\mathcal{S}$. Composition of functions is an operation on $\mathcal{G}(\mathcal{S})$. If ϕ, ψ are any elements of $\mathcal{G}(\mathcal{S})$, then, by the theorem Composition of Bijections (1.6.5), $\phi\psi$ is an element of $\mathcal{G}(\mathcal{S})$, uniquely determined by ϕ, ψ, and the operation of composition. ∎

Although an operation is a special kind of function, we shall not employ the usual function notation for it, because the commonly occurring operations are more naturally denoted by such symbols as $+$, $\cdot$, or simply by juxtaposition of the two elements being combined. When discussing operations in general, we shall use the symbol $\cdot$, and $X \cdot Y$ will indicate the result of applying the operation $\cdot$ to the elements X, Y, in that order.

In Example 2.6.1 (a), the integers m and n can be added in either of the orders $m + n$ and $n + m$ without affecting the result. In general, if $\cdot$ is an operation on $\mathcal{S}$, and if $X \cdot Y = Y \cdot X$ for any elements X, Y in $\mathcal{S}$, we say that $\cdot$ is a *commutative* operation. While the operations of Examples 2.6.1 (a) and (b) are commutative, that of Example 2.6.1 (c) ordinarily is not (exercise 1). For noncommutative operations, one must be careful to observe the correct order of combining the elements.

Suppose that $\cdot$ is a binary operation on $\mathcal{S}$, and let X, Y, Z be any elements of $\mathcal{S}$. We can form $X \cdot Y$, then combine this element of $\mathcal{S}$ with Z to get $(X \cdot Y) \cdot Z$. Also, we can combine X with $Y \cdot Z$ to get $X \cdot (Y \cdot Z)$. If $(X \cdot Y) \cdot Z = X \cdot (Y \cdot Z)$ for all choices of X, Y, Z, then $\cdot$ is said to be an *associative* operation. All the operations in Example 2.6.1 are associative.

The operation of Example 2.6.1 (c) has two additional properties that are worthy of notice.

(1) There is an identity element for the operation. The identity function ι on $\mathcal{S}$ is such that $\phi\iota = \iota\phi = \phi$ for every element ϕ in $\mathcal{G}(\mathcal{S})$, by the Identity Function theorem (1.6.6).

(2) Each element of $\mathcal{G}(\mathcal{S})$ has an inverse with respect to the operation. If ϕ is a bijection on $\mathcal{S}$, there is a function ϕ^{-1} in $\mathcal{G}(\mathcal{S})$ such that $\phi\phi^{-1} = \phi^{-1}\phi = \iota$, by the theorem Inverse of a Bijection (1.6.7).

The set $\mathcal{G}(\mathcal{S})$, together with the operation of composition, is an example of the important concept of a group, presented in the next definition.

Definition 2.6.2. A *group* is a set $\mathcal{G}$, together with a binary operation $\cdot$ on $\mathcal{G}$, for which the following postulates hold.

(a) If G, H belong to $\mathcal{G}$, then $G \cdot H$ is in $\mathcal{G}$ (*closure* under the operation). (In view of our definition of operation, this postulate is redundant. It is included for emphasis.)
(b) $(G \cdot H) \cdot K = G \cdot (H \cdot K)$ for any elements G, H, K, of $\mathcal{G}$ (*associativity* of the operation).
(c) There is an element I in $\mathcal{G}$ such that $I \cdot G = G \cdot I = G$ for any G in $\mathcal{G}$ (existence of *identity*).
(d) If G is any element of $\mathcal{G}$, there is an element G^{-1} in $\mathcal{G}$ such that $G \cdot G^{-1} = G^{-1} \cdot G = I$ (existence of *inverses*). ▮

It is worth remarking that in a group the identity element is unique, and that the inverse of each element is also unique (exercise 2). If $\mathcal{S}$ is any nonempty set, we have already seen that $\mathcal{G}(\mathcal{S})$ is a group under the operation of composition of functions. Here are some further examples of groups.

Example 2.6.3. (a) The set of all real numbers is a group under the operation of addition. (This group is said to be commutative because the operation is commutative.)

(b) Let ℓ be a line in a projective plane. The set of all projectivities on ℓ is a group under the operation of composition of functions.

(c) Let $\mathcal{P}$ be a projective plane. The set of all collineations of $\mathcal{P}$ is a group under the operation of composition of functions. ▮

Let us use the word "product" to denote the result of combining two elements by an operation. If G and H are elements of a group $\mathcal{G}$, the product $G \cdot H$ is also an element of $\mathcal{G}$ and must therefore have a unique inverse. An easy calculation (exercise 3) shows that $(G \cdot H)^{-1} = H^{-1} \cdot G^{-1}$; that is, the inverse of a product is the product of the inverses in reverse order.

When G is an element of a group, we write G^n for a product of n factors of G, where n is any positive integer. Since the associativity postulate ((b) of the definition of group) implies the *general* associative law (compare with Exercise 1.1.6) for products in an arbitrary group, G^n is well-defined, regardless of the association of the factors of G in this product. The result on the inverse of a product, discussed in the preceding paragraph, and a simple inductive argument yield $(G^n)^{-1} = (G^{-1})^n$. Then, if we define G^{-n} to be $(G^{-1})^n$ and G^0 to be I (the identity), the usual laws of exponents hold for powers of G (exercise 7). That is, $G^m \cdot G^k = G^{m+k}$ and $(G^m)^k = G^{mk}$ for any integers m and k, including negative integers and zero. In working with powers of G, it is important to know whether or not G is *periodic*, a notion that is made precise in the next definition. (See also exercises 4, 8, and 9.)

Definition 2.6.4. Let G be an element of the group $\mathcal{G}$. Then, G is *periodic* if and only if $G^m = I$ for some positive integer m, where I is the identity of $\mathcal{G}$. If G is periodic, the least positive integer n such that $G^n = I$ is the *period* of G. ∎

If $\mathcal{P}$ is a projective plane, the set $\mathcal{G}(\mathcal{P})$ of all bijections on $\mathcal{P}$ is a group under the operation of composition of functions. The set of all collineations of $\mathcal{P}$ is a subset of $\mathcal{G}(\mathcal{P})$ and is also a group under the same operation (Example 2.6.3 (c)). The situation just illustrated, in which one group is a subset of another group and inherits its operation from the larger group, is of frequent occurrence and is the subject of the following general definition.

Definition 2.6.5. If $\mathcal{G}$ is a group, a subset $\mathcal{H}$ of $\mathcal{G}$ is a *subgroup* of $\mathcal{G}$ if and only if all the following conditions are satisfied.

(a) The operation on $\mathcal{H}$ is the same as the operation on $\mathcal{G}$ (except restricted to $\mathcal{H}$), and $\mathcal{H}$ is closed under this operation. That is, if H and K are any elements of $\mathcal{H}$, then $H \cdot K$ (calculated in $\mathcal{G}$) is in $\mathcal{H}$.

(b) The identity I of $\mathcal{G}$ is in $\mathcal{H}$.

(c) If H is any element of $\mathcal{H}$, then H^{-1} (the inverse of H in $\mathcal{G}$) is in $\mathcal{H}$. ∎

The associativity condition of the definition of group is absent from the above definition. Nevertheless, it is evident that the operation in $\mathcal{H}$ is associative because the operation in $\mathcal{G}$ is associative. Therefore, $\mathcal{H}$ is indeed a group in its own right if it satisfies the restrictions of the preceding definition. The next example presents subgroups of the groups of Example 2.6.3.

Example 2.6.6. (a) The set of all integers (positive, negative, and zero) is a subgroup of the group of all real numbers under the operation of addition.

(b) Let ℓ be a line in a projective plane, and let P be a point on ℓ. The set of all projectivities on ℓ that fix the point P is a subgroup of the group of all projectivities on ℓ under the operation of composition. (See exercise 5a.)

(c) Let $\mathcal{P}$ be a projective plane. The set of all projective collineations of $\mathcal{P}$ is a subgroup of the group of all collineations of $\mathcal{P}$ under composition (exercise 5b). ∎

In concluding this section, we briefly discuss the role played by groups of bijections in the study of geometry. A *geometry* may be defined as a nonempty set $\mathcal{S}$, whose elements satisfy certain structural restrictions, together with a specified group of bijections on $\mathcal{S}$. Studying the geometry consists, at least in part, in ascertaining those properties of figures in $\mathcal{S}$ that are preserved by all the bijections of the group. For example, one might take $\mathcal{S}$ to be the Euclidean plane $\mathcal{E}_2$ and the group of bijections to be the set of isometries of $\mathcal{E}_2$ (exercise 12). The theorems of the resulting geometry (a part of Euclidean geometry) concern the properties, such as size and shape, of figures that are preserved by all isometries (congruences). Another example—plane projective geometry—is obtained by taking $\mathcal{S}$ to be a projective plane and using the group of collineations of $\mathcal{S}$.

Geometries may be classified by their groups of bijections; this idea originated with Felix Klein in his *Erlangen Program* of 1872. More important for our purposes is the fact that the bijections of a geometry can be used to prove theorems of the geometry. This statement can be documented by citing the book by Yaglom [32] and several exhibits of the present text—for instance, Desargues' theorem (Section 3.2), the theorem Quadrangular Sets (Section 3.3), and Pappus' theorem (Section 5.1), in each of which the proof is effected by an appeal to the underlying group of collineations.

Exercise 2.6.A

1. Prove that for any set $\mathcal{S}$ with at least three elements, the group $\mathcal{G}(\mathcal{S})$ is not commutative. Do this by actual construction of two noncommuting bijections on an *arbitrary* set containing at least three elements.

2. Let $\mathcal{G}$ be a group. Prove that the identity of $\mathcal{G}$ is unique, and that each element of $\mathcal{G}$ has a unique inverse.

3. Suppose that G and H are elements of a group $\mathcal{G}$. Prove that $(G\cdot H)\cdot(H^{-1}\cdot G^{-1}) = (H^{-1}\cdot G^{-1})\cdot(G\cdot H) = I$. Deduce that $(G\cdot H)^{-1} = H^{-1}\cdot G^{-1}$. (The uniqueness of the inverse is needed here. Why?)

4. Prove that every element of a finite group is periodic.

5. (a) Prove that the group of Example 2.6.6 (b) is a subgroup of the group of Example 2.6.3 (b).
(b) Prove that the set of all projective collineations of a projective plane $\mathcal{P}$ is a subgroup of the group of all collineations of $\mathcal{P}$.

6. Let O be a point and ℓ a line of a projective plane $\mathcal{P}$. Prove that the following are groups under composition of functions:

(a) The set of all central collineations of $\mathcal{P}$ that have axis ℓ.

(b) The set of all central collineations of $\mathcal{P}$ that have center O and axis ℓ.

7. Prove that if G is any element of a group, then $G^m \cdot G^k = G^{m+k}$, and $(G^m)^k = G^{mk}$, for any integers m and k, including negative integers and zero.

Exercise 2.6.B

8. (a) Compute the period of the homology of 13_4 whose construction was requested in Exercise 2.4.7.

(b) Compute the period of the elation of 21_5 whose construction was requested in Exercise 2.5.6.

9. Prove that a homology of a projective plane that interchanges two given distinct points is periodic with period two.

10. Let ℓ be a line of a projective plane. Prove that the group of all projectivities on ℓ (under the operation of composition) is noncommutative.

11. Prove that the intersection of two subgroups (that is, the collection of elements belonging to both subgroups) of a group is a subgroup of the group.

12. Prove that the isometries of $\mathcal{E}_2$ form a group under the operation of composition of functions. (See Exercises 1.1.8 and 1.6.11.)

13. Prove that the translations of $\mathcal{E}_2$ constitute a subgroup of the group of isometries of $\mathcal{E}_2$ (under the operation of composition).

2.7. Permutations

In preparation for the penetrating study (in the next section) of projectivities in a 21-point plane, we consider in this section some of the properties of the bijections on a finite set; such bijections are also called *permutations*. If $\mathcal{S}$ is a finite set with n elements, where n is a positive integer, the group $\mathcal{G}(\mathcal{S})$ of all permutations on $\mathcal{S}$ is finite and contains $n!$ members. The simplest permutations (other than the identity) are those that are cyclic on their noninvariant points, and, of these, the permutations with just two noninvariant points are the simplest of all.

Definition 2.7.1. Let $\mathcal{S}$ be a set with n elements, which we shall call points, and assume that $n > 1$.

(a) A *cycle* on $\mathcal{S}$ is a permutation, other than the identity, on $\mathcal{S}$ whose m noninvariant points can be labeled $P_1, P_2, \ldots, P_m$ in such a way that the permutation sends P_i into P_{i+1} for $i = 1, 2, \ldots, m-1$, and sends P_m into P_1. The *length* of the cycle is m (the number of noninvariant points), and the notation for the cycle is $(P_1, P_2, \ldots, P_m)$.

(b) A *transposition* on $\mathcal{S}$ is a cycle on $\mathcal{S}$ of length two. ∎

Underlying most work with permutations is the possibility, stated precisely in the next theorem and its corollary, of expressing a permutation as a composite of cycles.

Theorem 2.7.2. (Factorization of a Permutation) Any permutation ϕ, other than the identity, on the finite set $\mathcal{S}$ is a composite of disjoint cycles (that is, cycles with mutually disjoint sets of noninvariant points).

Proof: Let a relation $\sim$ be defined on $\mathcal{S}$ by the condition that $P \sim Q$ if and only if $P = Q\phi^j$ for some positive integer j. Since ϕ is an element of the finite group $\mathcal{G}(\mathcal{S})$, ϕ is periodic by Exercise 2.6.4; let its period be m. Then, for any P in $\mathcal{S}$, $P = P\phi^m$; hence $\sim$ is reflexive. If $P \sim Q$, then $P = Q\phi^j$, and it may be assumed that $j \leqq m$ because of the periodicity of ϕ. It follows that $Q = P\phi^{2m-j}$, with $2m - j > 0$; thus, $\sim$ is symmetric. Finally, if $P = Q\phi^j$ and $Q = R\phi^k$, then $P = R\phi^{k+j}$, so that $\sim$ is transitive. Thus, $\sim$ is an equivalence relation on $\mathcal{S}$, and, by Exercise 1.8.13, $\sim$ partitions $\mathcal{S}$ into mutually disjoint equivalence classes, with two elements of $\mathcal{S}$ belonging to the same class if and only if they are related by $\sim$. An equivalence class contains just one element precisely when that element is a fixed point of ϕ (why?).

Let $\mathcal{C}_1, \mathcal{C}_2, \ldots, \mathcal{C}_r$ be the equivalence classes that contain at least two elements each. We want to prove that, for each $\mathcal{C}_i$, there is a cycle γ_i that permutes the points of $\mathcal{C}_i$ in the same way that ϕ does, and that has all other points of $\mathcal{S}$ as fixed points. For each i from 1 to r, let P_i be a point of $\mathcal{C}_i$, and construct the sequence of points $P_i, P_i\phi, P_i\phi^2, \ldots$, until a repetition is obtained, as it must because of the finiteness of $\mathcal{S}$. The first repetition will be P_i (exercise 1), with $P_i = P_i\phi^{m_i}$. The points $P_i, P_i\phi, \ldots, P_i\phi^{m_i-1}$ exhaust $\mathcal{C}_i$ because every point of $\mathcal{C}_i$ can be obtained as $P_i\phi^j$ for some positive integer j. The required cycle γ_i is thus $(P_i, P_i\phi, \ldots, P_i\phi^{m_i-1})$.

Now let $\phi' = \gamma_1\gamma_2 \cdots \gamma_r$; we wish to show that $\phi' = \phi$. Let P be any point of $\mathcal{S}$. If $P\phi = P$, then P is not in any $\mathcal{C}_i$; so, $P\gamma_i = P$ for each i, and $P\phi' = P = P\phi$. If P is not a fixed point of ϕ, then P belongs to $\mathcal{C}_{i_1}$ for exactly one integer i_1, and $P\phi = P\gamma_{i_1}$ by the construction of γ_{i_1}. Furthermore, $P\gamma_{i_1}$ is also in $\mathcal{C}_{i_1}$; hence, both P and $P\gamma_{i_1}$ are fixed by each γ_i with $i \neq i_1$. Therefore, $P\phi' = P\gamma_1 \cdots \gamma_{i_1} \cdots \gamma_r = P\gamma_{i_1} \cdots \gamma_r = P\gamma_{i_1} = P\phi$. Thus, $\phi' = \phi$, and ϕ has been represented as a composite of the disjoint cycles $\gamma_1, \gamma_2, \ldots, \gamma_r$. ▮

Corollary: Any permutation on the finite set $\mathcal{S}$ can be represented as a composite of transpositions, provided that $\mathcal{S}$ contains at least two points.

Proof: Let ϕ be a permutation on $\mathcal{S}$. If $\phi = \iota$, then $\phi = (P, Q)(P, Q)$, where P and Q are any distinct points of $\mathcal{S}$. If $\phi \neq \iota$, then, by the theorem, ϕ is a composite of disjoint cycles. The corollary is proved by showing that any cycle can be represented as a composite of transpositions. Let the cycle be $\gamma = (P_1, P_2, \ldots, P_m)$. Then, $\gamma = (P_1, P_2)(P_1, P_3) \cdots (P_1, P_m)$, as an easy calculation confirms. (Remember that in the composite the leftmost factor is to be applied first.) ▮

Suppose that $\mathcal{S}$ has n points. We may label these points $P_1, P_2, \ldots, P_n$. If ϕ is a permutation on $\mathcal{S}$, then, for each i from 1 to n, ϕ sends P_i into P_{m_i}, where the subscripts $m_1, m_2, \ldots, m_n$ are the numbers $1, 2, \ldots, n$ in some arrangement. A convenient symbol for ϕ is

$$\begin{pmatrix} 1, & 2, & \ldots, & n \\ m_1, & m_2, & \ldots, & m_n \end{pmatrix}.$$

For instance, if $n = 4$, and if ϕ sends P_1 into P_2, P_2 into P_4, P_3 into P_1, and P_4 into P_3, we write

$$\phi = \begin{pmatrix} 1, 2, 3, 4 \\ 2, 4, 1, 3 \end{pmatrix}.$$

The next example illustrates the ideas developed in this section.

Example 2.7.3. Let $\mathcal{S}$ have eight points, labeled $P_1, P_2, \ldots, P_8$, and let ϕ be the permutation on $\mathcal{S}$ given by

$$\begin{pmatrix} 1, 2, 3, 4, 5, 6, 7, 8 \\ 4, 6, 5, 2, 8, 1, 7, 3 \end{pmatrix}.$$

To factor ϕ as a composite of disjoint cycles, we start with any non-invariant point, say P_5. The permutation ϕ sends P_5 into P_8, P_8 into

P_3, and P_3 into P_5, thus closing the cycle (P_5, P_8, P_3), which may be written simply as $(5, 8, 3)$.

Had the points P_5, P_8, P_3 exhausted the noninvariant points of ϕ, we would be finished calculating the cycles that comprise ϕ. Since that is not the case, we continue with any noninvariant point not used in any previous cycle, say P_4. Our permutation sends P_4 into P_2, P_2 into P_6, P_6 into P_1, and P_1 into P_4, thus closing the cycle $(4, 2, 6, 1)$.

Since the two cycles calculated use all the noninvariant points of ϕ, we see that $\phi = (5, 8, 3)(4, 2, 6, 1)$. The point P_7 does not appear in this factorization because it is a fixed point of ϕ.

By making different choices, we might also have written several other expressions for ϕ, such as $\phi = (2, 6, 1, 4)(8, 3, 5)$, or $\phi = (1, 4, 2, 6)(3, 5, 8)$. Notice, however, that the same cycles occur in each case, since, for example, $(4, 2, 6, 1) = (2, 6, 1, 4) = (1, 4, 2, 6)$. Quite generally, the representation of a permutation as a composite of disjoint cycles is unique to within reorderings of the factors (exercise 8).

Finally, let us write ϕ as a composite of transpositions. We use the factorization $\phi = (1, 4, 2, 6)(3, 5, 8)$. By the corollary to Theorem 2.7.2, $(1, 4, 2, 6) = (1, 4)(1, 2)(1, 6)$, and $(3, 5, 8) = (3, 5)(3, 8)$. Therefore, $\phi = (1, 4)(1, 2)(1, 6)(3, 5)(3, 8)$. ∎

Although the representation of a permutation as a composite of disjoint cycles is essentially unique (exercise 8), its representation as a composite of transpositions is not unique. For instance, the permutation ϕ of the preceding example can also be factored, using the representation $\phi = (5, 8, 3)(4, 2, 6, 1)$, as $(5, 8)(5, 3)(4, 2)(4, 6)(4, 1)$, and some of the transpositions occurring in this factorization are different from any of those in the factorization of the example. There is, however, one characteristic of a representation of a given permutation as a composite of transpositions that is not subject to variation, as the next theorem demonstrates.

Theorem 2.7.4. (Parity of a Permutation) Let ϕ be a permutation on a set $\mathcal{S}$ with n elements, where $n > 1$. The parity (that is, whether even or odd) of the number of transpositions in a composite representing ϕ is uniquely determined by ϕ.

Proof: The proof of the uniqueness of parity of ϕ is based upon an object that is introduced solely as a device to direct the argument. Consider the polynomial in n letters, $X_1, X_2, \ldots, X_n$, obtained by multiplying all possible factors of the form $(X_i - X_j)$, with $i < j$.

Written out, this polynomial, which we name Ψ, has the following appearance:

$$(X_1 - X_2)(X_1 - X_3) \cdots (X_1 - X_n)(X_2 - X_3) \cdots (X_2 - X_n) \cdots (X_{n-1} - X_n).$$

Though not numbers, the X_i are assumed to have the usual arithmetic properties of numbers. In particular, $(X_i - X_j) = -(X_j - X_i)$, and any two factors of Ψ commute.

Let the points of $\mathcal{S}$ be named $X_1, X_2, \ldots, X_n$. It is then obvious how any permutation on $\mathcal{S}$ can be applied to Ψ, with a perfectly determinable result. The plan of the proof is to show that any single transposition on $\mathcal{S}$ changes the sign of Ψ and nothing more. From this it follows that an even number of transpositions, applied successively, leaves Ψ unaltered, whereas an odd number changes the sign of Ψ. Since ϕ cannot both change the sign of Ψ and leave it unaltered, the uniqueness of the parity of ϕ will thus be established.

Let (X_i, X_j) be any transposition on $\mathcal{S}$; we investigate its effect upon Ψ. Any factor of Ψ that does not contain either X_i or X_j is unchanged. The single factor containing both X_i and X_j has its sign changed. Finally, for each factor containing X_i and X_k, where $k \neq j$, there is a factor containing X_j and X_k, and vice versa. Thus, the factors containing just one of X_i or X_j can be paired and the effect of the transposition on the product of a pair studied.

Case 1: The pair is $(X_i - X_k)$, $(X_j - X_k)$, or $(X_k - X_i)$, $(X_k - X_j)$. Then, (X_i, X_j) exchanges the two factors, with no net effect on the product of the pair.

Case 2: The pair is $(X_i - X_k)$, $(X_k - X_j)$, or $(X_k - X_i)$, $(X_j - X_k)$. Then, (X_i, X_j) interchanges the two factors and also changes the sign of each, with the result that there is again no change in the product of the pair.

Therefore, in each case, no change in the product of the pair occurs. Hence the effect of (X_i, X_j) is to change the sign of Ψ, because the single factor containing X_i and X_j has its sign changed. ∎

It is thus possible to classify each permutation on a set $\mathcal{S}$ (with at least two elements) as even or odd, depending upon the parity of the number of transpositions in a factorization of the permutation. In particular, the identity permutation is even, since it can be represented as $(X_1, X_2)(X_1, X_2)$. Uniqueness of parity of a permutation is decisive in the constructions of the next section.

Exercise 2.7.A

1. Let ϕ be a permutation. Prove that in the sequence $P, P\phi, P\phi^2, \ldots,$ the first element repeated is P.

2. Suppose that γ_1 and γ_2 are disjoint cycles on $\mathcal{S}$. Prove that $\gamma_1\gamma_2 = \gamma_2\gamma_1$.

3. Let

$$\phi = \begin{pmatrix} 1, 2, 3, 4, 5, 6 \\ 6, 5, 2, 1, 3, 4 \end{pmatrix}$$

and

$$\psi = \begin{pmatrix} 1, 2, 3, 4, 5, 6 \\ 4, 1, 2, 5, 6, 3 \end{pmatrix}.$$

Compute the composite $\phi\psi$.

4. Let ϕ be the permutation

$$\begin{pmatrix} 1, 2, 3, 4, 5, 6, 7, 8, 9 \\ 4, 5, 1, 3, 9, 8, 2, 6, 7 \end{pmatrix}.$$

(a) Factor ϕ as a composite of disjoint cycles.
(b) Factor ϕ as a composite of transpositions.
(c) Is ϕ even or odd?

5. Prove that a cycle of odd length is an even permutation and vice versa.

6. Let $\mathcal{S}$ be the set $\{1, 2, 3, 4\}$. List all the elements of $\mathcal{G}(\mathcal{S})$ and classify each one by its parity.

7. Let $\mathcal{S}$ be a finite set with at least two points. Prove that the even permutations on $\mathcal{S}$ constitute a subgroup of $\mathcal{G}(\mathcal{S})$.

Exercise 2.7.B

8. Prove that the representation of a given permutation ϕ as a composite of disjoint cycles is unique in the sense that the cycles that occur are uniquely determined by ϕ, though (by exercise 2) the order of composing them is immaterial.

9. (a) Prove that the period of a cycle is equal to its length.
(b) Prove that the period of a composite of disjoint cycles is equal to the least common multiple of the lengths of the cycles.

10. Prove that the subgroup of exercise 7 contains exactly half the elements of $\mathcal{G}(\mathcal{S})$.

11. Refer to the incidence table of 13_4 (Figure 1.9).
(a) Construct the elation of 13_4 with axis ℓ_0, center P_0, sending P_4 into P_5. Verify that your construction is a collineation.
(b) Represent your answer to part (a) as a permutation on the points 0 to 12 (ignoring its effect on lines).
(c) Is the permutation of part (b) even or odd?

2.8. The Fundamental Theorem for 21-Point Planes

In this section we use the uniqueness of parity of a permutation to establish for 21-point planes the theorem on projectivities known as the Fundamental Theorem. Additionally, we give an example of a nonprojective collineation. (Although such collineations exist in many projective planes, the simplest occur in 21-point planes.) We commence with a theorem concerning Π_2's in a 21-point plane.

Theorem 2.8.1. A Π_2 on a line ℓ of a 21-point plane $\mathcal{P}$ is an even permutation of the points on ℓ.

Proof: Let the Π_2 be π. By the theorem Fixed Points of a Π_2 (1.7.6), π has either one or two fixed points, or else $\pi = \iota$. If $\pi = \iota$, the result is apparent. There are two other possibilities.

Case 1: π has exactly one fixed point. Then, if $\pi = \ell \circ M \circ k \circ N \circ \ell$, the lines ℓ, k, and $M \cup N$ are concurrent, say at E. (See Figure 2.7.) Let P be any point on ℓ different from E, and then construct $Q = (P \cup M) \cap k$, $P\pi = (Q \cup N) \cap \ell$, and $R = (P\pi \cup M) \cap k$. Then, the points E, Q, M, $P\pi$ are triply noncollinear (why?), and the quadrangle with these points as vertices has diagonal points P, R, and N. By Theorem 1.8.5, P, R, N are collinear; hence $P = (R \cup N) \cap \ell = (P\pi)\pi = P\pi^2$. Therefore, π exchanges pairs of the four noninvariant points on ℓ, so that π is a composite of two transpositions, which is even.

Case 2: π has exactly two fixed points. Then, if P is a point on ℓ that is not fixed by π, it must be that $(P\pi)\pi \neq P$, for otherwise the fifth point on ℓ would be a third fixed point of π. Hence, P, $P\pi$, and $P\pi^2$ are all different, and $P\pi^3 = P$ (why?). Therefore, π is the cycle $(P, P\pi, P\pi^2)$, which is the same as $(P, P\pi)(P, P\pi^2)$, an even permutation. ∎

In the three lemmas and theorem to follow, we suppose that $\mathcal{P}$ is an arbitrary, but fixed, 21-point plane. Choose one line of $\mathcal{P}$ as a base

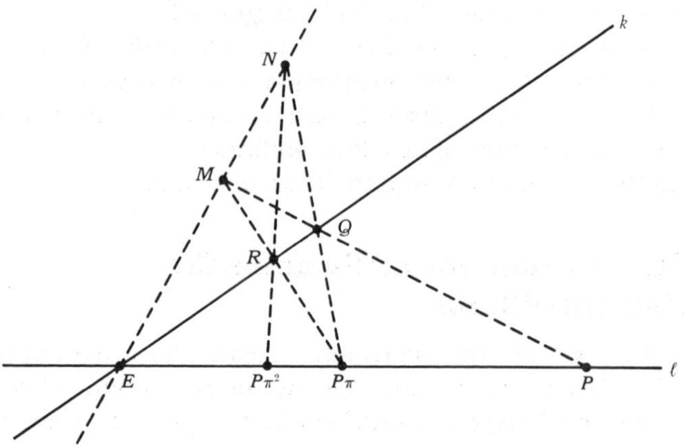

Figure 2.7

line, and call it ℓ_0. Let the points on ℓ_0 be labeled *A, B, C, D, E,* arbitrarily, but keep this labeling fixed. Let the remaining lines of $\mathcal{P}$ be named $\ell_1, \ell_2, \ldots, \ell_{20}$. For each *i* from 1 to 20, choose a single perspectivity π_i from ℓ_0 to ℓ_i, and let the points on ℓ_i be labeled *A, B, C, D, E,* according to the way in which they are mapped from ℓ_0 by the perspectivity π_i. That is, $A\pi_i$ is labeled *A*, $B\pi_i$ is labeled *B*, etc. (See Figure 2.8.) Fix these labels on the points on each line. Note that a point receives five labels, as a consequence of being on five lines; when we speak of *the* label of point *X* on line *k*, we mean the label that *X* has received in virtue of its lying on *k*. Observe also that a projectivity from one line to another, while not a permutation of points, *is* a permutation of labels of points and, as such, has a unique parity, which we shall soon prove to be even.

Lemma 2.8.2. Any perspectivity π_i' from ℓ_0 to ℓ_i is an even permutation of the labels (from points on ℓ_0 to points on ℓ_i).

Proof: If $\ell_i = \ell_0$, $\pi_i' = \iota$, and the result is obvious. Otherwise, consider the projectivity $\pi = \pi_i^{-1}\pi_i'$, where π_i is the perspectivity from ℓ_0 to ℓ_i that defines the labels on ℓ_i. Thus, by definition, π_i effects the identity permutation (which is even) of labels from points on ℓ_0 to points on ℓ_i. Now, π is a Π_2 on ℓ_i. Hence, by Theorem 2.8.1, π is an even permutation (of points as well as labels). Since $\pi_i' = \pi_i\pi$, π_i' is a composite of two even permutations of labels and is therefore even. ∎

Lemma 2.8.3. Given any lines, ℓ_i and ℓ_j, there is a perspectivity from ℓ_i to ℓ_j that effects an even permutation of the labels.

Proof: Choose a point P, not on ℓ_0, ℓ_i, or ℓ_j. (It is not assumed that these lines are necessarily different.) Let $\pi = \ell_i \circ P \circ \ell_j$. Then, also,

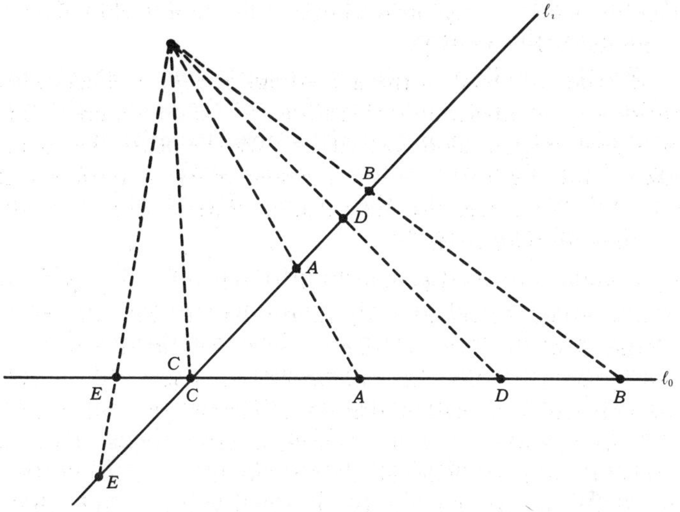

Figure 2.8

$\pi = \ell_i \circ P \circ \ell_0 \circ P \circ \ell_j$, since $P \circ \ell_0 \circ P = \iota$. The perspectivity $\ell_i \circ P \circ \ell_0$ is the inverse of $\ell_0 \circ P \circ \ell_i$ and, therefore, induces the inverse of an even (by Lemma 2.8.2) permutation of labels. Since the inverse of an even permutation is even (Exercise 2.7.7), $\ell_i \circ P \circ \ell_0$ gives an even permutation of labels. Also, $\ell_0 \circ P \circ \ell_j$ is an even permutation of labels by the previous lemma. Therefore, π, being a composite of two even permutations, is an even permutation of labels. ▮

Lemma 2.8.4. If ℓ_i and ℓ_j are any lines, then any perspectivity π' from ℓ_i to ℓ_j gives an even permutation of the labels.

Proof: Consider the projectivity $\pi_1 = \pi'\pi^{-1}$, where π is a perspectivity from ℓ_i to ℓ_j constructed in accordance with the preceding lemma. Then, π_1 is a Π_2 on ℓ_i, which is even by Theorem 2.8.1. Since π is even by Lemma 2.8.3, and since $\pi' = \pi_1\pi$, it follows that π' is even. ▮

Corollary: If ℓ_i and ℓ_j are any lines, then any projectivity π from ℓ_i to ℓ_j effects an even permutation of the labels.

Proof: Since π is a composite of perspectivities, each of which gives an even permutation of labels by the lemma, π is even. ▌

Theorem 2.8.5. (The Fundamental Theorem for 21-Point Planes) In a 21-point plane $\mathcal{P}$, any projectivity π on a line k that fixes three distinct points is the identity.

Proof: By the corollary to the preceding lemma, π effects an even permutation of the labels, and, therefore, of the points on k. Since π fixes three distinct points on k, it either fixes the other two points or exchanges them; the latter behavior would make π a transposition, which is odd. Therefore, by the theorem Parity of a Permutation (2.7.4), π fixes all points on k. ▌

The corollary to the theorem Fixed Points of a Π_2 (1.7.6) asserts that, in any projective plane, a Π_2 on a line with three distinct fixed points is the identity. For a 21-point plane, the theorem just proved is stronger, since it makes the same assertion about any projectivity on a line with three invariant points. Of course, the above theorem has so far been proved only for 21-point planes, though it is easy to see (exercise 1) that an identical theorem holds in the 7- and 13-point planes. One of our principal aims is eventually to prove the same theorem for all projective planes satisfying certain additional restrictions (Axioms 4 and 5). The general result of which the foregoing theorem is a precursor is known as the "Fundamental Theorem of Projective Geometry."

We now have enough information to construct a nonprojective collineation of 21_5. Let α be the function on the points of 21_5 given by the permutation $(3, 14)(4, 10)(8, 18)(9, 19)(11, 13)(15, 16)(17, 20)$. Here, each number is the subscript of a point of 21_5; for instance, 3 represents P_3. Since 0, 1, 2, 5, 6, 7, 12 do not appear in the factorization of α, α fixes the points with these subscripts. Clearly, α is a bijection on the points of 21_5. To see that α sends collinear points into collinear points is a matter of checking that α merely permutes the columns of the incidence table for 21_5 (Figure 1.10). Since this is so, α can be (uniquely) extended to a collineation ρ of 21_5 by the extension theorem of Exercise 2.2.10. (Or, the Extension Theorem (2.2.2) could be used, because the restriction of α to the points of 21_5 that are not on ℓ_0 satisfies the hypotheses of that theorem.)

The line ℓ_0 of 21_5 is invariant under ρ, and P_0, P_1, P_6 are invariant points on ℓ_0, while P_8 and P_{18} are exchanged by ρ. By the Fundamental Theorem for 21-Point Planes, the restriction of ρ to $\mathcal{I}(\ell_0)$ is not a projectivity. Therefore, ρ is nonprojective.

Exercise 2.8.A

1. Prove that in any 7- or 13-point plane any projectivity on a line that fixes three distinct points is the identity.

2. Show that the fixed points and fixed lines of the collineation ρ, constructed at the end of this section, form a 7-point subplane of 21_5. (See Exercise 1.8.8 for the definition of subplane.)

3. Select a labeling of the points on the line ℓ_0 of 21_5, and then pick two more lines of 21_5 and label their points by means of two perspectivities, as in the instructions preceding Lemma 2.8.2. Finally, choose any perspectivity from one of these lines to the other and verify that it is an even permutation of the labels. (Use the incidence table, Figure 1.10.)

4. Choose any line of 21_5 and construct any projectivity π on the line as a composite of three perspectivities. Use the incidence table (Figure 1.10) to verify that π gives an even permutation of the points on the chosen line.

5. Let π be a projectivity on a line k of a 21-point plane. Let the points on k be P, Q, R, S, T, and suppose that $P\pi = S$, $Q\pi = R$, and $R\pi = T$. Find $S\pi$.

Exercise 2.8.B

6. Let ρ be a collineation of 21_5 that fixes the lines ℓ_0, ℓ_5, ℓ_7, and the points P_6 and P_8. (See the incidence table, Figure 1.10.) Suppose also that ρ is not a central collineation.
    (a) Calculate $P_0\rho$.
    (b) Is ρ projective or nonprojective? Why?
    (c) Prove that $\rho^4 = \iota$.

7. Prove that in a 21-point plane a projectivity between two lines is completely determined by the specification of the images of three distinct points of the domain.

8. Show that there is at most one projective collineation of a 21-point plane that maps the triply noncollinear points A, B, C, D respectively into the triply noncollinear points A', B', C', D'.

9. Show that there is at most one nonprojective collineation of a 21-point plane that satisfies the conditions of exercise 8.

10. Use exercises 8 and 9 to show that there are at most $21 \cdot 20 \cdot 16 \cdot 9 \cdot 2 = 120{,}960$ collineations of a 21-point plane. (There actually are this many.)

11. Let k be a line of a 21-point plane.

(a) How many different projectivities on k are there?

(b) If ϕ is any even permutation on the points on k, prove that ϕ is a projectivity on k.

2.9. Consequences of the Fundamental Theorem

The assertion, "Any projectivity on a line that fixes three distinct points is the identity," has been found to be true in the 7-, 13-, and 21-point planes. This assertion, known as the "Fundamental Theorem of Projective Geometry," is not a consequence of Axioms 1–3 for projective planes in general. Indeed, we shall not be able to establish it as a universal theorem until two more axioms have been introduced. Meanwhile, it has only the status of an interesting statement that may or may not be true in a given projective plane, but that is known to be true at least in the three finite planes of smallest order. In this section, consequences of the Fundamental Theorem are investigated. First, two other equivalent forms of the statement are given.

Theorem 2.9.1. In a projective plane $\mathcal{P}$, the following assertions are equivalent.

(a) Any projectivity on a line that fixes three distinct points is the identity.

(b) Any projectivity between two lines is determined by the specification of the images of three distinct points of the domain.

(c) Any projectivity between two distinct lines that fixes the point of intersection of the two lines is a perspectivity.

Proof: The theorem is proved by showing that (a) implies (b), (b) implies (c), and (c) implies (a).

(1): (a) implies (b). That is, if (a) is assumed to be true, then it is to be shown that (b) is true. Accordingly, let k and ℓ be any lines of $\mathcal{P}$, and suppose that π_1 and π_2 are projectivities from k to ℓ that agree on three distinct points, A, B, C, on k. Then, $\pi_1\pi_2^{-1}$ is a projectivity on k that fixes A, B, and C. By (a), $\pi_1\pi_2^{-1} = \iota$, or $\pi_1 = \pi_2$, thus establishing the truth of (b).

(2): (b) implies (c). Let π be a projectivity from k to $\ell \neq k$ such that $(k \cap \ell)\pi = k \cap \ell$. Let A and B be distinct points on k, both different from $k \cap \ell$. Construct the perspectivity π' from k to ℓ that sends A into $A\pi$ and B into $B\pi$; π' exists and is unique by the theorem Construction of Perspectivities (1.7.1). Furthermore, π' agrees with π on A, B, and $k \cap \ell$. By (b), $\pi = \pi'$, and (c) is established.

(3): (c) implies (a). Let π be a projectivity on the line k, and assume that π fixes the distinct points A, B, C on k. Let $\ell \neq k$ be any other line on A, and let O be any point not on either k or ℓ. Construct the perspectivity $\pi' = k \circ O \circ \ell$, and let $\pi_1 = \pi\pi'$. Then, π_1 is a projectivity from k to ℓ that fixes $A = k \cap \ell$. By (c), π_1 is a perspectivity. Since, also, $B\pi_1 = B\pi'$ and $C\pi_1 = C\pi'$, the theorem Construction of Perspectivities guarantees (by its uniqueness assertion) that $\pi_1 = \pi'$. Therefore, $\pi\pi' = \pi'$, or $\pi = \iota$, so that (a) is established. ▌

Because of the equivalence of the three statements given in the above theorem, any one of them will henceforth be called the Fundamental Theorem, and, when reference is made to the Fundamental Theorem, it will be to whichever of the foregoing statements is most appropriate to the situation at hand.

In the next theorem we establish the existence of homologies in any projective plane $\mathcal{P}$ in which the Fundamental Theorem holds. By the Uniqueness Theorem for Central Collineations (2.4.5), if $\mathfrak{D}$ is a determining set (Definition 2.4.6) with line ℓ and point H not incident, then there is at most one homology of $\mathcal{P}$ that has $\mathfrak{D}$ as a determining set for it. If, for every such set $\mathfrak{D}$ (with ℓ and H not incident), a homology η of $\mathcal{P}$ actually exists with $\mathfrak{D}$ as a determining set for η, then $\mathcal{P}$ will be said to possess *all possible* homologies.

Theorem 2.9.2. If $\mathcal{P}$ is a projective plane in which the Fundamental Theorem is true, then $\mathcal{P}$ possesses all possible homologies.

Proof: Let $\mathfrak{D} = \{\ell, H, P, P'\}$ be any determining set in which ℓ and H are not incident. Let $k = H \cup P$, and construct $M = k \cap \ell$. Let $\mathcal{S}$ be the set of all points of $\mathcal{P}$ *except* those on k, and define a function α on $\mathcal{S}$ as follows.

(a) For each point E on ℓ, other than M, set $E\alpha = E$.

(b) For each point Q, not on ℓ or k, construct the point $R_Q = (P \cup Q) \cap \ell$, and set $Q\alpha = (R_Q \cup P') \cap (H \cup Q)$. (See Figure 2.9.)

The function α has thus been unambiguously defined, and it is easily seen to be one-to-one (exercise 1) and onto (exercise 2) from $\mathcal{S}$ to $\mathcal{S}$. We want to show that α maps three collinear points of $\mathcal{S}$ into three collinear points in all possible cases. Let S_1, S_2, S_3 be any collinear points of $\mathcal{S}$. If any two of these points coincide, the points $S_1\alpha$, $S_2\alpha$, $S_3\alpha$ are trivially collinear, so we suppose that S_1, S_2, S_3 are all different. If they lie on ℓ, their images under α are collinear because of (a) in the

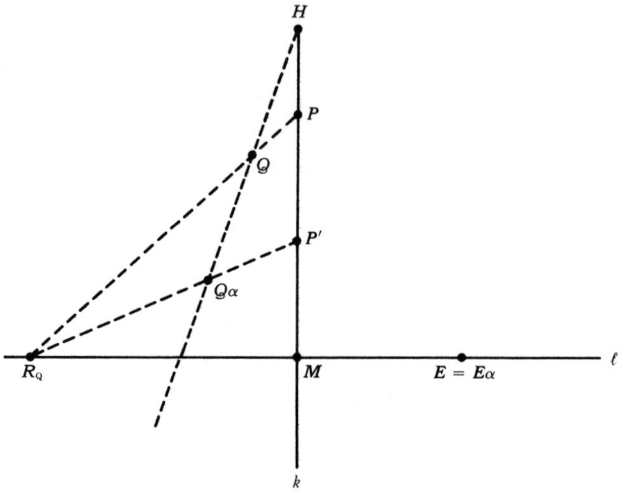

Figure 2.9

definition of α; if they lie on a line m through H, their images lie on m, and are therefore collinear, because of (b) in the definition of α. In every other case, S_1, S_2, S_3 lie on a line n, different from ℓ and not on H. Set $S = n \cap \ell$; then, S is different from at least two of S_1, S_2, S_3. For definiteness, suppose that $S \neq S_1$. We shall prove that $S_2\alpha$ lies on $S \cup S_1\alpha$, and similar reasoning would prove that $S_3\alpha$ also lies on $S \cup S_1\alpha$, thus establishing the collinearity of $S_1\alpha$, $S_2\alpha$, $S_3\alpha$. (Refer to Figure 2.10.)

If S_2 is on ℓ, then $S_2 = S$, $S_2\alpha = S$, and $S_2\alpha$ is on $S \cup S_1\alpha$; for the rest we assume that S_2 is not on ℓ. Let $o = S_1 \cup H$ and $p = S_2 \cup H$; then, $o \neq p$ (why?). Let π be the projectivity $o \circ R_1 \circ k \circ R_2 \circ p$, where $R_1 = (P \cup S_1) \cap \ell$ and $R_2 = (P \cup S_2) \cap \ell$. Then, $H\pi = H$, from which we deduce that π is a perspectivity, by the Fundamental Theorem. Furthermore, $S_1\pi = S_2$, and $(o \cap \ell)\pi = p \cap \ell$. Thus, the center of the perspectivity π is $(S_1 \cup S_2) \cap [(o \cap \ell) \cup (p \cap \ell)] = n \cap \ell = S$. Finally, since $(S_1\alpha)\pi = S_2\alpha$ (why?), we see that S, $S_1\alpha$, $S_2\alpha$ are collinear, as required.

By the Extension Theorem (2.2.2), the function α has a unique extension to a collineation η of $\mathcal{P}$. From the manner of construction of this extension, it is evident that η fixes the points M and H and sends P into P' (exercise 3). Therefore, η is the required homology that has $\mathfrak{D}$ for a determining set. ▮

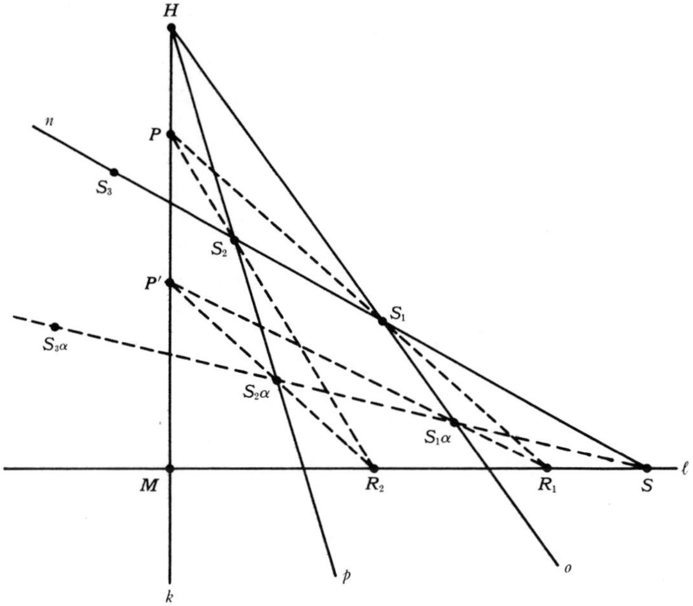

Figure 2.10

As a result of the last theorem, the 7-, 13-, and 21-point planes possess all possible homologies. (Of course, in a 7-point plane, the only possible homology is the identity (why?), which was always known to exist.) In Section 3.1 it will be proved that any projective plane that possesses all homologies also possesses all possible elations.

Exercise 2.9.A

1. Prove that the function α of the proof of Theorem 2.9.2 is one-to-one.

2. Prove that the function α of the proof of Theorem 2.9.2 is onto $\mathcal{S}$.

3. Prove that the extension of the function α, of the proof of Theorem

2.9.2, to a collineation η of $\mathcal{P}$ fixes M and H and sends P into P'. (Refer to the construction of the extension in the proof of the Extension Theorem (2.2.2).)

4. (a) How many homologies has a 13-point plane?
(b) How many homologies has a 21-point plane?

5. Let $\mathcal{P}$ be a projective plane in which the Fundamental Theorem holds, and let σ be a projective collineation of $\mathcal{P}$ that fixes the vertices of a certain quadrangle. Prove that $\sigma = \iota$.

Exercise 2.9.B

6. Let $\mathcal{P}$ be a projective plane in which the Fundamental Theorem holds. Suppose that A, B, C are distinct points on a line k of $\mathcal{P}$ and that π is a projectivity on k that sends A into B, B into C, and C into A. Let P be any point on k, and set $Q = P\pi$, $R = Q\pi$. Prove that $R\pi = P$.

7. Let $\mathcal{P}$ be a projective plane in which the Fundamental Theorem is true. Prove that any projectivity between two distinct lines of $\mathcal{P}$ can be expressed as a composite of two perspectivities.

8. Let $\mathcal{P}$ be a projective plane in which the following statement is true: "If $\pi = k \circ M \circ \ell \circ N \circ m$, where k, ℓ, m are distinct and concurrent, but M, N, and $k \cap m$ are not collinear, then π is a perspectivity." Prove that the plane $\mathcal{P}$ possesses all possible homologies.

9. Let $\mathcal{P}$ be a projective plane in which the Fundamental Theorem holds. Suppose that π is a projectivity from the point K to the point L (that is, from $\mathcal{I}(K)$ to $\mathcal{I}(L)$), and that $(K \cup L)\pi = K \cup L$. Prove that π is a perspectivity.

2.10. Projective Three-Space

In Section 1.2 we constructed the projective plane $\mathcal{E}_2{}^*$ by adjoining ideal points and an ideal line to $\mathcal{E}_2$. It is natural to carry the ideas and constructions of that section into a third dimension and to extend $\mathcal{E}_3$ (Euclidean three-space) to a space in which every plane is a projective plane, and in which every two planes intersect. Thus (exercise 6a), ideal points and lines, and an ideal plane, can be adjoined to $\mathcal{E}_3$ subject to the following conditions.

(1) To each line of $\mathcal{E}_3$ is adjoined exactly one ideal point.
(2) The ideal points adjoined to parallel lines of $\mathcal{E}_3$ are the same,

while the ideal points adjoined to distinct, nonparallel lines of $\mathcal{E}_3$ are different.

(3) To each plane of $\mathcal{E}_3$ is adjoined exactly one ideal line, which contains all the ideal points of the lines of that plane, but no other points. It follows (exercise 6b) that the ideal lines adjoined to parallel planes of $\mathcal{E}_3$ are the same, while the ideal lines adjoined to distinct, nonparallel planes of $\mathcal{E}_3$ are different.

(4) The single ideal plane contains all the ideal points and ideal lines, but no other points or lines.

$\mathcal{E}_3$ so enlarged is called *extended Euclidean three-space* and is denoted by $\mathcal{E}_3^*$. In view of conditions (1), (2), and (3), every plane of $\mathcal{E}_3^*$ that is an extension of a plane of $\mathcal{E}_3$ is an extended Euclidean plane. The ideal plane of $\mathcal{E}_3^*$ is also isomorphic to $\mathcal{E}_2^*$ (exercise 5), though that is not obvious from the above construction. (It will become apparent after we have proved Theorem 2.10.3.) Also, the following incidence properties of $\mathcal{E}_3^*$ can be readily verified (exercise 7).

2.10.1. (a) Any two distinct points determine a unique line.

(b) Any two distinct, coplanar lines intersect in a unique point.

(c) Any point and any line not on the point determine a unique plane containing them both.

(d) Any plane and any line not in the plane intersect in a unique point.

(e) Any two distinct planes intersect in a unique line and the points on that line.

$\mathcal{E}_3^*$ is a model of *projective three-space,* a brief study of which we now undertake in order to demonstrate that any plane of such a space possesses all possible homologies. This exhibit will be the final one to motivate the introduction of Axiom 4 in Section 3.1.

Since projective three-space is not an aim of this book, we do not attempt an axiomatic development of it, though such a development is surely possible. A suitable set of space axioms can be found in [26], pp. 96–100. For our purposes, it suffices to say that a projective three-space is a set $\mathcal{S}$ of points and lines, with a symmetric relation of incidence between points and lines, and in which certain distinguished subsets of points and lines are called planes. It is assumed that there exist some points and lines in $\mathcal{S}$, that not all points are in one plane, and that every line is incident with at least three distinct points. Planes are defined in such a way as to ensure that a plane $\mathcal{P}$ contains at least a line and a point not on the line, that any point on a line of $\mathcal{P}$

is itself in $\mathcal{P}$, and that any line joining two distinct points of $\mathcal{P}$ is in $\mathcal{P}$. Furthermore, enough axioms are laid down to guarantee that the incidence properties 2.10.1 above hold in $\mathcal{S}$.

In addition to $\mathcal{E}_3^*$, we could build models of projective three-space in which there are three, four, or five points on each line, and in which each plane is a 7-, 13-, or 21-point plane, respectively. In general, we see that 2.10.1 (a) and (b) ensure that every plane of a projective three-space is a projective plane, as we would expect.

There is also a modified principle of duality for projective three-space. The modification is that "point" and "line" are no longer dual terms, but that "point" and "plane" *are*, while "line" is self-dual. For example, the dual of the statement, "A point and a line not on the point determine a unique plane," is the statement, "A plane and a line not in the plane intersect in a unique point." Then, the principle of space duality asserts that the space dual of a valid theorem is also a valid theorem.

We commence the main work of this section with the definition of a perspectivity between two planes of a projective three-space.

Definition 2.10.2. If $\mathcal{P}_1$ and $\mathcal{P}_2$ are planes in a projective three-space $\mathcal{S}$, and if O is a point not in either plane, the *perspectivity* θ from $\mathcal{P}_1$ to $\mathcal{P}_2$, with *center* O, is the function from $\mathcal{P}_1$ to $\mathcal{P}_2$ defined as follows.

(a) If P is a point of $\mathcal{P}_1$, then $P\theta$ is the point in which the line $P \cup O$ intersects $\mathcal{P}_2$. (This point exists and is unique by 2.10.1 (d).)

(b) If ℓ is a line of $\mathcal{P}_1$, then $\ell\theta$ is the line in which the plane $\mathcal{P}'$, determined by ℓ and O, intersects $\mathcal{P}_2$. (This line exists and is unique by 2.10.1 (e).) ▮

Figure 2.11 illustrates the preceding definition. Observe the implicit use of 2.10.1 (a) and (c) in the construction of $P \cup O$ and the plane $\mathcal{P}'$, respectively, in the definition. The next theorem establishes the essential characteristic of a perspectivity between planes in projective space.

Theorem 2.10.3. In a projective three-space $\mathcal{S}$, a perspectivity θ from plane $\mathcal{P}_1$ to plane $\mathcal{P}_2$ is an isomorphism of $\mathcal{P}_1$ onto $\mathcal{P}_2$.

Proof: By definition, θ maps points into points and lines into lines. If P' is any point of $\mathcal{P}_2$, let P be the unique point in which $P' \cup O$ intersects $\mathcal{P}_1$ (2.10.1 (d)); then, $P\theta = P'$. If ℓ' is any line of $\mathcal{P}_2$, let ℓ be the unique line in which the plane determined by O and ℓ' intersects

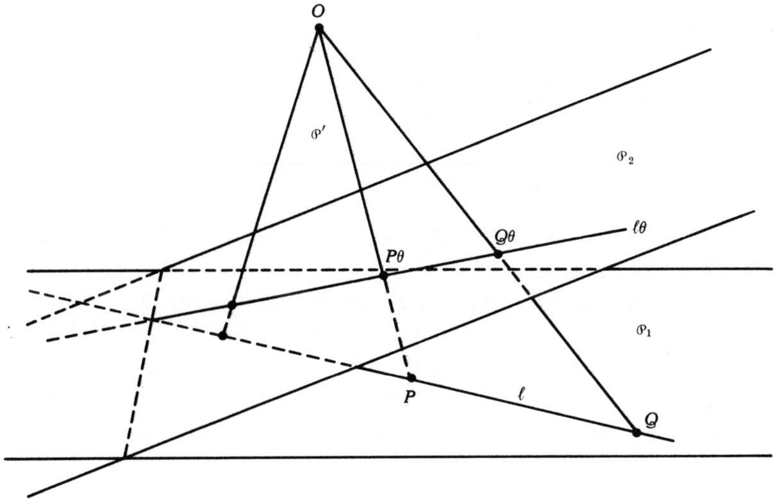

Figure 2.11

$\mathcal{P}_1$ (2.10.1 (e)). Then, $\ell\theta = \ell'$, because O and ℓ determine the same plane as do O and ℓ'. Thus, θ has been shown to be onto $\mathcal{P}_2$.

Suppose that $P\theta = Q\theta$. Then, $O \cup P$ and $O \cup Q$ intersect $\mathcal{P}_2$ in the same point $P\theta$. Therefore, $O \cup P = O \cup Q$, from which one infers (via 2.10.1 (d)) that $P = Q$. If $k\theta = \ell\theta$, the planes determined by k and O and by ℓ and O are the same, since they intersect $\mathcal{P}_2$ in the same line $k\theta$ and also have O in common (2.10.1 (c)). It follows that $k = \ell$, for both lines lie in $\mathcal{P}_1$ as well as in the common plane that they determine with O (2.10.1 (e)). Therefore, θ is one-to-one.

Since θ is a bijection, it remains to be proved that θ preserves incidence. Suppose that P and ℓ are incident in $\mathcal{P}_1$. Then, $O \cup P$ is a line of the plane $\mathcal{P}'$, determined by O and ℓ, and therefore intersects $\mathcal{P}_2$ in a point on the line of intersection of $\mathcal{P}'$ and $\mathcal{P}_2$. Thus, $P\theta$ and $\ell\theta$ are incident in $\mathcal{P}_2$. (Refer to Figure 2.11.)

It has been proved that θ satisfies all the conditions of the definition of an isomorphism (2.1.1), and, therefore, θ is an isomorphism of $\mathcal{P}_1$ onto $\mathcal{P}_2$. ▌

We are now ready to compose perspectivities between planes in a projective three-space to construct homologies of one of those planes.

Theorem 2.10.4. Every plane of a projective three-space $\mathcal{S}$ possesses all possible homologies.

Proof: Let $\mathcal{P}$ be any plane of $\mathcal{S}$, and let $\mathcal{D} = \{\ell, H, P, P'\}$ be a determining set in $\mathcal{P}$ with the line ℓ and point H not incident. It is required to prove the existence of a homology of $\mathcal{P}$ with axis ℓ, center H, sending P into P'. If $P = P'$, the identity will do; for the rest, assume that $P \neq P'$.

Since not all points of $\mathcal{S}$ are in one plane, there exists a point Q not in $\mathcal{P}$. Let $\mathcal{P}'$ be the plane determined by Q and ℓ (2.10.1 (c)). Let $k = Q \cup P$, and let O be a point on k different from both Q and P; then, O is not in either $\mathcal{P}$ or $\mathcal{P}'$ (why?). Let $m = H \cup O$ and $n = Q \cup P'$. The line k and the point P' determine a plane $\mathcal{P}_1$ (2.10.1 (c)), and n is in $\mathcal{P}_1$ because both Q and P' are. Also, the line $P \cup P'$ is in $\mathcal{P}_1$; thus, H is in $\mathcal{P}_1$ because it is on $P \cup P'$. Likewise, O, being on k, is in $\mathcal{P}_1$, and, therefore, the line $m = H \cup O$ is in $\mathcal{P}_1$. Hence, m and n intersect in a unique point O' (2.10.1 (b)). (See Figure 2.12.)

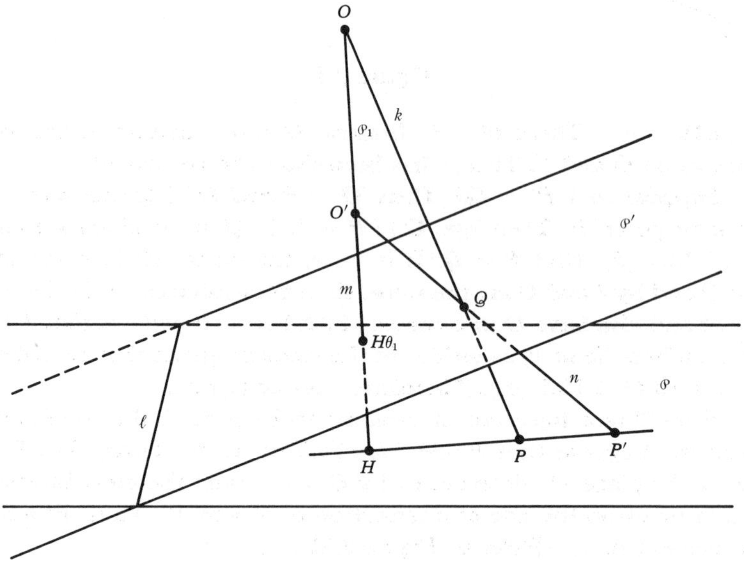

Figure 2.12

Construct the perspectivity θ_1 from $\mathcal{P}$ to $\mathcal{P}'$ with center O, and the perspectivity θ_2 from $\mathcal{P}'$ to $\mathcal{P}$ with center O'. Set $\eta = \theta_1\theta_2$; then, η is a collineation of $\mathcal{P}$, because of Theorem 2.10.3. Since every point on ℓ is fixed by both θ_1 and θ_2, η is central with axis ℓ. It is apparent that $H\eta = H$, and, since H is not on ℓ, H must be the center of η

(why?). (Of course, it is easy enough to see directly that η fixes every line on H.) Finally, since $P\theta_1 = Q$ and $Q\theta_2 = P'$, η sends P into P'. Therefore, η is the required homology of $\mathcal{P}$. ▮

Exercise 2.10.A

1. Prove that if there are $n + 1$ points on some line of a projective three-space, there are $n + 1$ points on every line of the space.

2. Prove that in a projective three-space, the cardinal number of points in any plane is the same as the cardinal number of lines on any point.

3. Prove that if there are $n + 1$ points on some line of a projective three-space, there are $n^3 + n^2 + n + 1$ points all together in the space.

4. How many lines are there in a projective three-space that has three points on each line?

5. Prove that any two planes of a projective three-space are isomorphic. Deduce that the ideal plane of $\mathcal{E}_3{}^*$ is isomorphic to $\mathcal{E}_2{}^*$.

Exercise 2.10.B

6. (a) Show how the method of extension of $\mathcal{E}_2$ to $\mathcal{E}_2{}^*$, explained in Section 1.2, can be adapted to $\mathcal{E}_3$, so that ideal points and lines, and an ideal plane, can be adjoined to $\mathcal{E}_3$ in such a way as to satisfy the conditions (1)–(4) at the beginning of this section.
(b) Show that when ideal points are adjoined to lines of $\mathcal{E}_3$ subject to condition (2) at the beginning of this section, two parallel planes are augmented by the same set of ideal points, while two distinct, nonparallel planes are augmented by two different sets of ideal points (though the two sets have one ideal point in common). Deduce that the ideal lines adjoined to parallel planes must be the same, while those adjoined to distinct, nonparallel planes must be different.

7. Prove that $\mathcal{E}_3{}^*$ has the incidence properties 2.10.1.

8. (a) Define the concept of a projectivity between two planes of a projective three-space.
(b) Define the concept of isomorphy for projective three-spaces.

9. Prove that every plane of a projective three-space possesses all possible elations.

2. Transformations of Projective Planes

10. (a) Prove that three planes of a projective three-space that do not intersect in a common line intersect in three distinct lines that are concurrent.

(b) State and prove the space dual of the statement in part (a).

Chapter 3

DESARGUESIAN PLANES

3.1. Existence of Central Collineations

Although the considerations of Sections 2.4 and 2.5 gave rather detailed information about homologies and elations, it was not possible to establish the existence of such collineations in all projective planes. However, it was proved (in Sections 2.9 and 2.10) that the 7-, 13-, and 21-point planes, and any plane of a projective three-space (a class that includes $\mathcal{E}_2^*$), possess all possible homologies. With this background in mind, we present the following axiom, in which $\mathcal{P}$ is a projective plane.

> **Axiom 4.** For every determining set $\mathfrak{D} = \{\ell, H, P, P'\}$, such that the line ℓ and the point H are not incident, there exists a homology of $\mathcal{P}$ with axis ℓ, center H, that maps P into P'. ▌

To denote a projective plane in which Axiom 4 is valid, and to draw attention to the fact that this axiom is being assumed, the term "Desarguesian plane" will be used. Although some of the definitions yet to be presented are meaningful, and a few of the theorems still to be proved are true, in any projective plane, nearly all the activity of the remainder of this book takes place in Desarguesian planes.

Although no examples of projective planes that do not satisfy Axiom 4 will be given, they are not difficult to construct [20]. In fact, there exists a hierarchy of projective planes satisfying axioms weaker than Axiom 4 but not implied by Axioms 1–3 [17].

Although Axiom 4 is not (quite) self-dual, its dual is easily deduced from Axioms 1–4 (exercise 12). Therefore, the principle of duality remains valid for the class of Desarguesian planes. In Axiom 4 only the existence of homologies has been postulated; from this assumption it will now be proved that elations also exist.

Theorem 3.1.1. (Existence of Elations) A Desarguesian plane $\mathcal{P}$ possesses all possible elations.

Proof: Let $\mathfrak{D} = \{\ell, H, P, P'\}$ be a determining set with line ℓ on point H. It is required to prove that there is an elation of $\mathcal{P}$ with axis ℓ, center H, sending P into P'. If $P' = P$, the identity suffices. For the rest of the proof, then, suppose that $P' \neq P$. Since a 7-point plane is already known (by Example 2.1.5 (Elations of a 7-Point Plane)) to possess all possible elations, we may also assume that there are at least four points on every line of $\mathcal{P}$.

Let $k = P \cup H$, and choose any line m on H that is different from both ℓ and k. Let R be any point on ℓ other than H. Construct $X = (R \cup P) \cap m$ and $X' = (R \cup P') \cap m$. Let $S = (X \cup P') \cap \ell$ and $P'' = (S \cup X') \cap k$. (See Figure 3.1.) A study of Figure 3.1 reveals that if the required elation does exist, it maps X into X' and, therefore, P' into P''. Our plan is to construct two homologies, η_1 and η_2, both with axis ℓ, such that $\eta_1\eta_2$ sends P into P' and P' into P''.

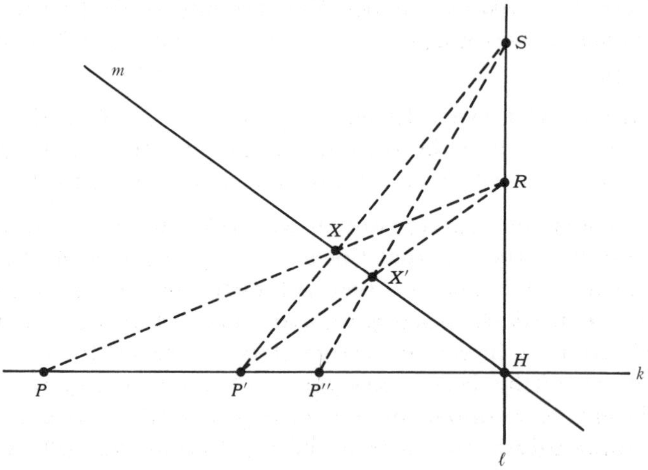

Figure 3.1

Let Q be any point on k other than P, P', and H; such a point exists by the assumption of at least four points on a line. (If $P'' \neq P$,

Q may be taken to be P''.) By Axiom 4, there is a homology η_2 with axis ℓ, center Q, sending P into P'.

Let $Y = P''\eta_2^{-1}$. Since $P'' \neq P'$ (why?), $P''\eta_2^{-1} \neq P'\eta_2^{-1}$, or $Y \neq P$. Also, Y is not on ℓ, because $Y\eta_2 = P''$, and P'' is not on ℓ. Since, additionally, $P' \neq P$, and P' is not on ℓ, Axiom 4 ensures the existence of a homology η_1, with axis ℓ, center P, sending P' into Y. Then, $\eta_1\eta_2$ is a central collineation with axis ℓ, and $P\eta_1\eta_2 = P\eta_2 = P'$; hence the center of $\eta_1\eta_2$ is on the line $P \cup P' = k$.

Because $P'\eta_1\eta_2 = Y\eta_2 = P''$, $X\eta_1\eta_2 = [(P' \cup S) \cap (P \cup R)]\eta_1\eta_2 = (P'' \cup S) \cap (P' \cup R) = X'$. Thus, the center of $\eta_1\eta_2$ is also on the line $X \cup X' = m$, implying that this center is H. It has therefore been proved that $\eta_1\eta_2$ is an elation with axis ℓ, center H, sending P into P'. ∎

As an application of the above result, we have an important commuting theorem.

Theorem 3.1.2. (Second Commuting Theorem) Let $\mathcal{P}$ be a Desarguesian plane. Suppose that ϵ_1 and ϵ_2 are elations of $\mathcal{P}$ with a common axis ℓ. Then, $\epsilon_1\epsilon_2 = \epsilon_2\epsilon_1$.

Proof: If ϵ_1 and ϵ_2 have different centers, the result follows immediately from the First Commuting Theorem (2.4.7). Suppose, then, that ϵ_1 and ϵ_2 have a common center H. We may also suppose that $\epsilon_2 \neq \iota$, since the conclusion is trivial in the contrary case.

Let ϵ_3 be an elation, different from ι, with axis ℓ and center $O \neq H$; such an elation exists by the preceding theorem. By the theorem Coaxial Collineations (2.4.4), $\epsilon_2\epsilon_3$ is an elation whose axis is ℓ, but whose center is not H. Therefore, $\epsilon_2\epsilon_3$ commutes with ϵ_1 by Theorem 2.4.7; that is, $(\epsilon_2\epsilon_3)\epsilon_1 = \epsilon_1(\epsilon_2\epsilon_3)$. But ϵ_3 and ϵ_1 also commute, since they have a common axis and different centers. Thus, $\epsilon_2\epsilon_3\epsilon_1 = \epsilon_2\epsilon_1\epsilon_3$, and, combining this with the previous equation, we have $\epsilon_1\epsilon_2\epsilon_3 = \epsilon_2\epsilon_1\epsilon_3$. Hence $\epsilon_1\epsilon_2 = \epsilon_2\epsilon_1$. ∎

We now apply Axiom 4 and the Existence of Elations theorem to derive a sequence of useful results on the extension of projectivities to projective collineations.

Theorem 3.1.3. (Extension of Perspectivities) In a Desarguesian plane $\mathcal{P}$, suppose that $\pi = k \circ H \circ m$ is a perspectivity between distinct lines k and m. Let $E = k \cap m$. Then:

(a) π can be extended to an elation of $\mathcal{P}$ with center H and axis $\ell = H \cup E$.

(b) If there are at least four points on a line in $\mathcal{P}$, π can be extended to a homology of $\mathcal{P}$ with center H and axis n, where n is any line on E that is different from k and m and not on H.

Proof: (a) Let P be any point on k other than E, and let ϵ be the elation of $\mathcal{P}$ with center H, axis ℓ, sending P into $P\pi$. The existence of ϵ is assured by the Existence of Elations theorem (3.1.1), since H, P, $P\pi$ are collinear and neither P nor $P\pi$ is on ℓ. The fact that $k = E \cup P$ implies that $k\epsilon = E \cup P\epsilon = E \cup P\pi = m$. By the theorem Projectivities Induced by Central Collineations (2.5.1), ϵ induces the perspectivity $k \circ H \circ m$. Therefore, π has been extended to the elation ϵ.

(b) Let n be as described in the statement of conclusion (b); such a line exists because there are at least four points on every line, hence at least four lines on every point, by assumption. Again, let P be any point on k other than E, and construct (by Axiom 4) the homology η, with center H, axis n, sending P into $P\pi$. Then, $k\eta = (E \cup P)\eta = E \cup P\eta = E \cup P\pi = m$. Therefore, by Theorem 2.5.1, η induces the perspectivity $k \circ H \circ m = \pi$. ▮

Corollary 1: In a Desarguesian plane, any projectivity between lines can be extended to a collineation that is a composite of central collineations.

Proof: Let π be a projectivity between two (not necessarily different) lines. Then, $\pi = \pi_1\pi_2 \cdots \pi_n$, where each π_i is a perspectivity. Each π_i that is not an identity perspectivity can be extended to a central collineation μ_i, by the theorem. If, for some i, π_i is an identity perspectivity, then it can be extended to the central collineation $\mu_i = \iota$. The collineation $\mu_1\mu_2 \cdots \mu_n$ gives the required extension of π (exercise 6). ▮

Corollary 2: In a Desarguesian plane, every projective collineation is a composite of central collineations.

Proof: Let σ be a projective collineation, and let k be any line of the plane. Then, there is a projectivity π from k to $k\sigma$ that agrees with σ on the points on k, by the definition of projective collineation (2.5.2). By Corollary 1, π can be extended to a collineation τ that is a composite of central collineations. It follows that $\sigma\tau^{-1}$ is a projective collineation that induces the projectivity $\pi\pi^{-1} = \iota$ on k. Therefore, $\sigma\tau^{-1} = \mu$, a central collineation with axis k. Finally, $\sigma = \mu\tau$, which is a composite of central collineations. ▮

Although the preceding theorem and its corollaries are quite simple, they could not be proved until the existence of the necessary central collineations was assured by Axiom 4. The next theorem sharpens the result of Corollary 1 above in the case that the projectivity is a Π_2 on a line.

Theorem 3.1.4. (Extension of a Π_2) Let π be a Π_2, not the identity, on a line k of a Desarguesian plane $\mathcal{P}$. Then:

(a) If π has just one invariant point, π can be extended to an elation of $\mathcal{P}$.

(b) If π has two distinct invariant points, π can be extended to a homology of $\mathcal{P}$.

Proof: Let $\pi = k \circ O \circ \ell \circ O' \circ k$. Since $\pi \neq \iota$, $\ell \neq k$ and $O \neq O'$. Let $M = k \cap \ell$ and $H = (O \cup O') \cap k$, so that M and H are the axial and central invariant points, respectively, of π.

(a) In this case, $M = H$. Let ϵ be the elation with center H, axis ℓ, sending O into O'. Since k is on H, it is an invariant line of ϵ, different from the axis of ϵ. By the theorem Projectivities Induced by Central Collineations (2.5.1), ϵ induces a Π_2 on k, and an expression for this Π_2 is $k \circ O \circ \ell \circ O\epsilon \circ k$. Because $O\epsilon = O'$, ϵ induces the projectivity π.

(b) Here, $M \neq H$; let η be the homology with center H, axis ℓ, sending O into O'. Again by Theorem 2.5.1, η extends π. ▌

We shall have several occasions to consider Π_2's on a line that have common invariant points. Two situations occur, and it will be helpful to have a special terminology for each of them.

Definition 3.1.5. Let π_1 and π_2 be Π_2's on a line k. Then, π_1 and π_2 have *matched* invariant points if and only if they have the same central, and also the same axial, invariant point. If the central invariant point of π_1 is the axial invariant point of π_2, and vice versa, then (and only then) π_1 and π_2 have *inversely matched* invariant points. ▌

The preceding definition is meaningful in any projective plane, but it has special significance for a Desarguesian plane, as the next theorem shows, because of the possibility of extending a Π_2 (in a Desarguesian plane) to a central collineation.

Theorem 3.1.6. (Π_2's with Matched Invariant Points) Let k be a line in a Desarguesian plane, and let A and B be any (not necessarily different) points on k. Let $\mathcal{G}$ be the set of Π_2's on k with central invariant point A and axial invariant point B. Then, $\mathcal{G}$ is a group under the operation of composition.

Proof: The identity projectivity on k is a member of $\mathcal{G}$ by prior agreement (Section 1.7), and if π is in $\mathcal{G}$, then π^{-1} is also in $\mathcal{G}$ (why?). To prove that $\mathcal{G}$ is a subgroup of the group of projectivities on k, it therefore remains to be shown that if π_1 and π_2 are any elements of $\mathcal{G}$, then $\pi_1\pi_2$ is in $\mathcal{G}$. If either π_1 or π_2 is the identity projectivity, the result is clear; for the rest of the proof, we assume that π_1 and π_2 are any elements of $\mathcal{G}$ that are both different from ι.

Let μ_1 and μ_2 be central collineations extending π_1 and π_2, respectively, constructed as in Theorem 3.1.4. (If $A = B$, μ_1 and μ_2 are elations; otherwise, they are homologies.) Then, μ_1 and μ_2 have common center A and axes on B; moreover, neither μ_1 nor μ_2 is the identity collineation. By the dual of the theorem Coaxial Collineations (2.4.4), $\mu_1\mu_2$ is a central collineation with center A and axis on B. Hence, either $\mu_1\mu_2$ induces the identity projectivity on k, or else it induces a Π_2 on k with A and B as central and axial invariant points, respectively, by the theorem Projectivities Induced by Central Collineations (2.5.1). Since, also, $\mu_1\mu_2$ induces $\pi_1\pi_2$ on k, the composite $\pi_1\pi_2$ is in $\mathcal{G}$. ∎

Corollary: Let k be a line of a Desarguesian plane, and let A, B, P, P' be points on k such that P and P' are both different from each of A and B. Then there is one and only one Π_2 on k with A and B as central and axial invariant points, respectively, that sends P into P'.

Proof: The existence of at least one such Π_2 is proved by constructing a central collineation μ with center A, axis $\ell \neq k$ on B, sending P into P', then restricting μ to $\mathcal{J}(k)$. (See also Exercise 1.7.10.) To prove the uniqueness of this Π_2, let π_1 and π_2 be Π_2's with the required properties. Then, $\pi_1\pi_2^{-1}$ is a Π_2 with A and B as central and axial invariant points, respectively, by the theorem. Furthermore, $P\pi_1\pi_2^{-1} = P$, implying that $\pi_1\pi_2^{-1} = \iota$, or $\pi_1 = \pi_2$, by the corollary to the theorem Fixed Points of a Π_2 (1.7.6). ∎

Exercise 3.1.A

1. Prove that in a Desarguesian plane a perspectivity between two points can be extended to an elation.

2. State the dual of the Second Commuting Theorem (3.1.2), and prove it without appealing to the principle of duality.

3. Let $\mathcal{P}$ be a projective plane and let k be a line of $\mathcal{P}$. Denote by $\mathcal{E}(k)$ the set of all elations of $\mathcal{P}$ that have k as an axis.

(a) Prove that $\mathcal{E}(k)$ is a group under composition.
(b) If $\mathcal{P}$ is Desarguesian, prove that $\mathcal{E}(k)$ is a commutative group.

4. How many elations are there with a given axis ℓ in a finite Desarguesian plane of order n?

5. Suppose that the Desarguesian plane $\mathcal{P}$ is finite, of order n. How many members has the group of central collineations of $\mathcal{P}$ with axis ℓ and centers on the line $k \neq \ell$?

6. For each i from 1 to n, suppose that the function β_i is an extension of the function α_i. Suppose also that $\beta = \beta_1\beta_2 \cdots \beta_n$ and $\alpha = \alpha_1\alpha_2 \cdots \alpha_n$ are both defined as composite functions. Prove that β is an extension of α.

Exercise 3.1.B

7. Let π_1 and π_2 be II_2's on a line k of a Desarguesian plane, and suppose that π_1 and π_2 have inversely matched invariant points. Prove that $\pi_1\pi_2 = \pi_2\pi_1$.

8. Let ℓ be a line in a Desarguesian plane $\mathcal{P}$, and let P and Q be distinct points not on ℓ. Let $k = P \cup Q$, and let P', Q' be distinct points on k, both different from $k \cap \ell$. Prove that there exists a unique central collineation of $\mathcal{P}$ with axis ℓ that sends P into P' and Q into Q'.

9. Let A, B, C, D be triply noncollinear points in a Desarguesian plane $\mathcal{P}$. Prove that there exists a unique elation of $\mathcal{P}$ sending A into B and C into D.

10. (a) Prove that every central collineation of a 21-point plane, when restricted to the set of points of the plane, is an even permutation of the points.
(b) Deduce that every projective collineation of a 21-point plane gives an even permutation of the points of the plane.

11. Let P and P' be points in $\mathcal{E}_2$. Show how to construct the translation τ of $\mathcal{E}_2$, sending P into P', as a composite of two central dilatations, one with ratio 2 and the other with ratio 1/2. Relate this problem to the proof of the theorem Existence of Elations (3.1.1).

12. Let $\mathcal{P}$ be any Desarguesian plane. Suppose that H and ℓ are any nonincident point and line in $\mathcal{P}$. Let k, k' be lines such that k, k', ℓ are concurrent, $k \neq \ell$, $k' \neq \ell$, and neither k nor k' is on H. Prove that there is a homology of $\mathcal{P}$ with axis ℓ, center H, sending k into k'.

Deduce that the principle of duality is valid for the class of Desarguesian planes.

3.2. Desargues' Theorem

The theorem to be proved in this section, named for Girard Desargues, has an illustrious history. Not only was it one of the first purely projective theorems known, but, also, it has classically found the widest application to one of the basic problems of projective gometry—that of establishing the collinearity of three given points. In addition, it has achieved even more renown in recent times because of its precise relation to the algebraic problem of coordinatizing a plane with a division ring. (See [4], Chapters IV, V, and VI.) To facilitate the wording of the theorem, the concept of perspective figures will first be defined.

Definition 3.2.1. Let $\mathfrak{F}_1$ and $\mathfrak{F}_2$ be figures in a projective plane. $\mathfrak{F}_1$ and $\mathfrak{F}_2$ are *perspective* from the *center* H if and only if there exists a bijection ϕ from the points of $\mathfrak{F}_1$ to the points of $\mathfrak{F}_2$ such that H, P, $P\phi$ are collinear for every point P of $\mathfrak{F}_1$. $\mathfrak{F}_1$ and $\mathfrak{F}_2$ are *perspective* from the *axis* ℓ if and only if there exists a bijection ψ from the lines of $\mathfrak{F}_1$ to the lines of $\mathfrak{F}_2$ such that ℓ, k, $k\psi$ are concurrent for every line k of $\mathfrak{F}_1$. ▮

Thus, when two figures are perspective from a point H, there is a pairing of the points of one figure with the points of the other figure in such a way that this pairing can be effected by means of lines drawn through H. Figure 3.2 exhibits two triangles that are perspective from a point.

The reader may have noticed a connection between the above definition of perspective figures and the properties of central collineations. If $\mathfrak{F}$ is a figure in a projective plane $\mathcal{P}$, and if μ is a central collineation of $\mathcal{P}$, with center H and axis ℓ, then $\mathfrak{F}$ and $\mathfrak{F}\mu$ (the figure into which $\mathfrak{F}$ is transformed by μ) are centrally perspective from H and also axially perspective from ℓ (why?). This fact is the key to our proof of Desargues' theorem.

Theorem 3.2.2. (Desargues' theorem) In a Desarguesian plane, if two triangles are perspective from a point, then they are perspective from a line, and conversely.

Proof: Since the converse is the dual, it is only necessary to prove the direct statement. Let the centrally perspective triangles be $\mathfrak{T}$ and

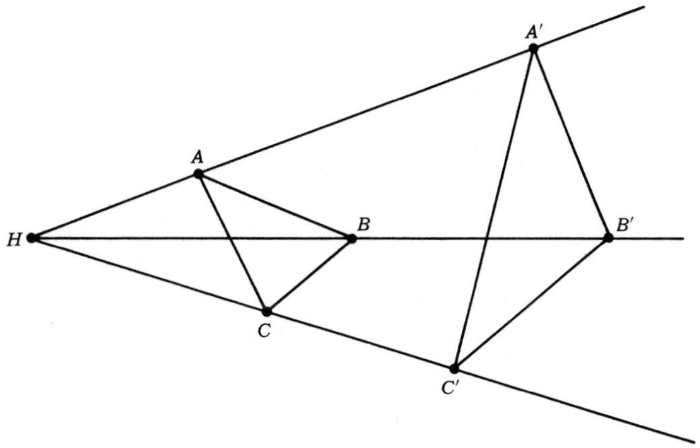

Figure 3.2

$\mathfrak{T}'$. Label their vertices A, B, C and A', B', C', respectively, in such a way that H, A, A' are collinear, H, B, B' are collinear, and H, C, C' are collinear, where H is the center of persepective. Let $k_1 = A \cup B$, $k_2 = B \cup C$, $k_3 = C \cup A$, and let k_1', k_2', k_3' be the corresponding joins of the vertices of $\mathfrak{T}'$. (See Figure 3.3.)

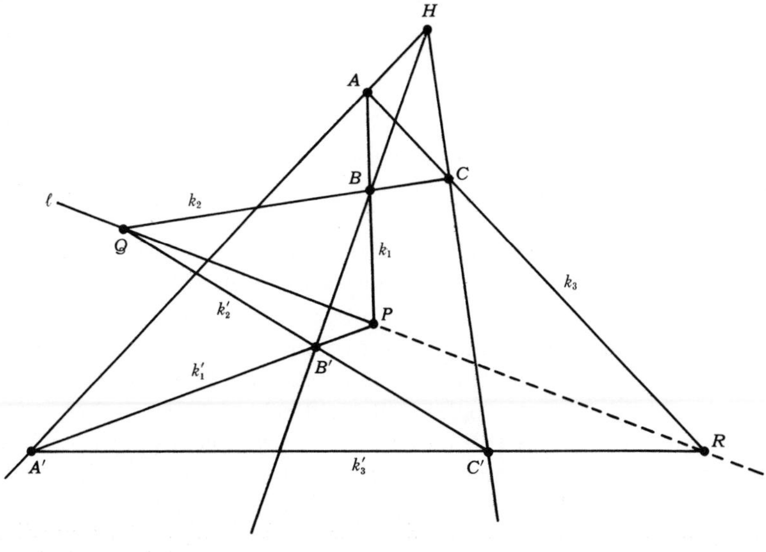

Figure 3.3

In order to prove that $\mathfrak{T}$ and $\mathfrak{T}'$ are perspective from a line, we pair k_i with k_i' for $i = 1, 2, 3$, and we seek a line ℓ such that, for each i, ℓ, k_i, k_i' are concurrent. If $k_1 = k_1'$, or if $k_2 = k_2'$, or if $k_3 = k_3'$, it is simple to find such a line ℓ (why?). We suppose, therefore, that none of these coincidences occurs. Set $P = k_1 \cap k_1'$, $Q = k_2 \cap k_2'$, and $R = k_3 \cap k_3'$. If P, Q, R are not distinct, they are surely collinear, and a line on which they lie serves as the axis ℓ of perspective. For the remainder of the proof, then, it will be assumed that P, Q, R are all different. If we let $\ell = P \cup Q$, we have to prove that R is also on ℓ.

If $H = A$, then $k_1 = H \cup B = B \cup B'$, so that $P = k_1 \cap k_1' = B'$, and, similarly, $R = C'$; since Q is on $k_2' = B' \cup C'$, the conclusion follows. Likewise, if H coincides with any vertex of either triangle, the theorem follows by an analogous argument. Therefore, for the rest it is assumed that H is different from all vertices.

On the basis of the assumptions already made, it can be seen (exercise 1) that ℓ does not lie on either B or B'. Therefore, by Axiom 4, or by the theorem Existence of Elations (3.1.1) if H lies on ℓ, there exists a central collineation μ with center H, axis ℓ, sending B into B'. Since P and Q are on ℓ, they are fixed by μ. Therefore, $k_1\mu = (B \cup P)\mu = B' \cup P = k_1'$, and $k_2\mu = (B \cup Q)\mu = B' \cup Q = k_2'$. Hence, $C\mu = [k_2 \cap (H \cup C)]\mu = k_2' \cap (H \cup C) = C'$, since $H \cup C$ is a fixed line of μ. Similarly, $A\mu = [k_1 \cap (H \cup A)]\mu = k_1' \cap (H \cup A) = A'$. Then, $k_3\mu = (A \cup C)\mu = A' \cup C' = k_3'$, implying that $k_3 \cap k_3' = R$ is on the axis of μ (why?), which is ℓ. Thus, the two triangles are perspective from the line ℓ. ▮

The adequacy of central collineations in effecting the proof of the beautiful and characteristic theorem of Desargues is the reason for the designation "Desarguesian plane" for a projective plane in which Axiom 4 holds. (See also exercise 9.) Desargues' theorem can frequently be employed to establish the collinearity of three points or the concurrency of three lines. (See, for example, exercises 2 and 3.) However, there are two kinds of difficulties that commonly arise in attempts to use the theorem. For one thing, it is often hard to decide which of many possible pairs of triangles will yield relevant new information by the application of the theorem. (See, for example, exercise 7.) The other source of discouragement is that Desargues' theorem gives only trivial information when applied to two triangles that are degenerately perspective. (See the discussion following the theorem Quadrangular Sets (3.3.2).)

In many situations in which Desargues' theorem can be applied, it is easier to find a central collineation, or perhaps two commuting central collineations, to produce the same result. Exercise 7 and the theorem Quadrangular Sets (3.3.2) exemplify this remark. After a definition, and a notation, for a special kind of figure in a projective plane, this section ends with an example illustrating all three methods, including the use of Desargues' theorem.

Definition 3.2.3. Let $\mathcal{P}$ be a projective plane with at least four points on every line. The subset $\mathcal{S} = \{k, k', A, B, C, A', B', C', P, Q, R\}$ of $\mathcal{P}$ is a *Pappus set* if and only if it satisfies all the following conditions.

(1) k and k' are distinct lines.

(2) A, B, C are distinct points on k, all different from $k \cap k'$, and A', B', C' are distinct points on k', all different from $k \cap k'$.

(3) $P = (A \cup B') \cap (A' \cup B)$, $Q = (A \cup C') \cap (A' \cup C)$, and $R = (B \cup C') \cap (B' \cup C)$. ∎

Example 3.2.4. (Restricted Pappus Property) Let $\mathcal{S}$ be a Pappus set in a Desarguesian plane, and suppose that P, Q, and $H = k \cap k'$ are collinear. Then, P, Q, and R are collinear.

Proof 1 (using Desargues' theorem): Refer to Figure 3.4. Let $\ell = P \cup Q$. The hypotheses imply that triangles $AB'C'$ and $A'BC$ are perspective from ℓ, so that, by the converse of Desargues' theorem, they are perspective from a point O. Thus, $A \cup A'$, $B' \cup B$, and $C' \cup C$ are concurrent at O. Then, triangles $AB'C$ and $A'BC'$ are perspective from O; hence they are axially perspective by Desargues' theorem. The axis of this perspective is easily calculated to lie on H, P, and R, so that R is on $H \cup P$, which, by hypothesis, is the same as $P \cup Q$. Therefore, P, Q, and R are collinear.

Proof 2 (using a central collineation): Again put $\ell = P \cup Q$, and let $O = (A \cup A') \cap (B \cup B')$. Construct the central collineation μ with center O, axis ℓ, sending B into B'. Then, $k\mu = (H \cup B)\mu = H \cup B' = k'$, and $A\mu = [(O \cup A) \cap k]\mu = (O \cup A) \cap k' = A'$. Furthermore, $A'\mu = [(B \cup P) \cap (O \cup A')]\mu = (B' \cup P) \cap (O \cup A') = A$. Thus, $k'\mu = k$, from which follows $B'\mu = B$. Finally, $C\mu = [k \cap (A' \cup Q)]\mu = k' \cap (A \cup Q) = C'$, and, similarly, $C'\mu = C$. Therefore, $(B \cup C')\mu = B' \cup C$, so that $R = (B \cup C') \cap (B' \cup C)$ is on the axis of μ, which is ℓ. (See Figure 3.4.)

Proof 3 (using two commuting elations): Set $\ell = P \cup Q$. Let ϵ_1 be

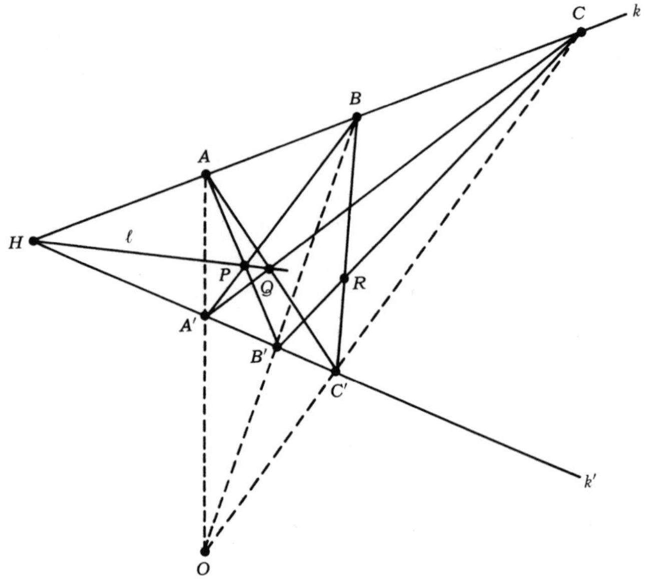

Figure 3.4

the elation with center H, axis ℓ, sending B into A, and let ϵ_2 be the elation with center H, axis ℓ, sending A into C. Then, $A'\epsilon_1 = [(B \cup P) \cap k']\epsilon_1 = (A \cup P) \cap k' = B'$, and $C'\epsilon_2 = [(A \cup Q) \cap k']\epsilon_2 = (C \cup Q) \cap k' = A'$. By the theorem Coaxial Collineations (2.4.4), $\epsilon = \epsilon_1\epsilon_2$ is a central collineation with center H, axis ℓ; by the Second Commuting Theorem (3.1.2), $\epsilon_1\epsilon_2 = \epsilon_2\epsilon_1$. Therefore, $B\epsilon = B\epsilon_1\epsilon_2 = A\epsilon_2 = C$, and $C'\epsilon = C'\epsilon_2\epsilon_1 = A'\epsilon_1 = B'$. Thus, $(B \cup C')\epsilon = C \cup B'$, so that $R = (B \cup C') \cap (C \cup B')$ is on the axis of ϵ, which is ℓ. (Refer to Figure 3.4.) ▮

Exercise 3.2.A

1. In the proof of Desargues' theorem, a stage is reached at which it has been assumed that $k_i \neq k_i'$ for $i = 1, 2, 3$, that P, Q, R are distinct, and that H is not on any vertex. With these conditions, prove that ℓ does not lie on either B or B'.

2. In a Desarguesian plane, let the diagonal points of quadrangle $PQRS$ be $A = (P \cup Q) \cap (R \cup S)$, $B = (P \cup R) \cap (Q \cup S)$, and C. Let $X = (B \cup C) \cap (S \cup R)$, $Y = (A \cup C) \cap (R \cup P)$, and $Z = (A \cup B) \cap (P \cup S)$. Prove that X, Y, Z are collinear.

3. Suppose that the points X, Y, Z are vertices of a triangle $\mathfrak{T}$ in a Desarguesian plane, and let H be any point not on any side of $\mathfrak{T}$. Let $D = (H \cup X) \cap (Y \cup Z)$, $E = (H \cup Y) \cap (X \cup Z)$, and $F = (H \cup Z) \cap (X \cup Y)$. Finally, let $A = (D \cup E) \cap (X \cup Y)$, $B = (E \cup F) \cap (Y \cup Z)$, and $C = (F \cup D) \cap (Z \cup X)$. Prove that A, B, C are collinear. (The line on which A, B, C lie is called the *trilinear polar* of H with respect to the triangle $\mathfrak{T}$.)

4. Let $\mathcal{S}$ be a Pappus set (3.2.3) in a Desarguesian plane, and suppose that $A \cup A'$, $B \cup B'$, and $C \cup C'$ are concurrent. Prove that P, Q, R, and $k \cap k'$ are collinear.

5. In a Desarguesian plane, let π be the perspectivity $k \circ H \circ k'$, where $k \neq k'$. Prove that there is a line ℓ such that for every X, Y on k, with $X \neq Y$, the point $(X \cup Y\pi) \cap (Y \cup X\pi)$ is on ℓ. (The line ℓ is called the *axis of homology* of π.)

6. In $\mathcal{E}_2$, suppose that triangles ABC and $A'B'C'$ are perspective from H, with the vertices corresponding in the order named. Suppose, further, that $A \cup B$ is parallel to $A' \cup B'$, and that $B \cup C$ is parallel to $B' \cup C'$. Assuming also that no side of one triangle coincides with the corresponding side of the other triangle, prove that $A \cup C$ is parallel to $A' \cup C'$.

Exercise 3.2.B

7. Establish the Special Pappus Property: "If $\mathcal{S}$ is a Pappus set (3.2.3) in a Desarguesian plane, and if P lies on $C \cup C'$, then P, Q, R are collinear."

8. Use Desargues' theorem to prove that if $\pi = k \circ M \circ \ell \circ N \circ m$, where k, ℓ, m are distinct but concurrent lines in a Desarguesian plane, then π is a perspectivity.

9. Use exercise 8 and the method of proof of Theorem 2.9.2 to prove that Desargues' theorem implies Axiom 4.

10. With the notation of exercise 3, prove that the line $A \cup B$ is also the trilinear polar of H with respect to the triangle DEF.

11. In a Desarguesian plane, let $\mathfrak{F}_i$ $(i = 1, 2)$ be a complete quadrangle together with its diagonal points. Suppose that $\mathfrak{F}_1$ and $\mathfrak{F}_2$ are perspective from a line in such a way that no two corresponding sides coincide. Prove that $\mathfrak{F}_1$ and $\mathfrak{F}_2$ are perspective from a point.

12. Let $\mathfrak{I}_1$, $\mathfrak{I}_2$, $\mathfrak{I}_3$ be triangles in a Desarguesian plane, so situated that each pair is perspective in a nondegenerate way from the common center H. Prove that the three axes of perspective are concurrent. (To say that $\mathfrak{I}_1$ and $\mathfrak{I}_2$ are perspective in a nondegenerate way from H means that there is a central collineation μ_1, with center H, that maps $\mathfrak{I}_1$ onto $\mathfrak{I}_2$, as in the proof of Desargues' theorem after all the special (degenerate) cases have been treated.)

3.3. Quadrangular Sets

If $\mathfrak{Q}$ is a complete quadrangle, and ℓ is a line that is not incident with any vertex of $\mathfrak{Q}$, then ℓ intersects the sides of $\mathfrak{Q}$ in the points of a *quadrangular set*. The number of distinct points in such a set can be as few as three (when the diagonal points of $\mathfrak{Q}$ are collinear and ℓ is on these points) or as many as six. This section is devoted to the establishment of a precise notation for quadrangular sets and a proof of the basic theorem concerning them.

Definition 3.3.1. Let $\mathfrak{Q}$ be a complete quadrangle with vertices Q_1, Q_2, Q_3, Q_4, and let ℓ be a line that is not on any vertex of $\mathfrak{Q}$. Let $A = (Q_1 \cup Q_2) \cap \ell$, $B = (Q_1 \cup Q_3) \cap \ell$, $C = (Q_1 \cup Q_4) \cap \ell$, $D = (Q_3 \cup Q_4) \cap \ell$, $E = (Q_2 \cup Q_4) \cap \ell$, and $F = (Q_2 \cup Q_3) \cap \ell$. (See Figure 3.5.) Then, the *ordered* sextuple $\{A, B, C, D, E, F\}$ is a *quadrangular set* determined by $\mathfrak{Q}$ and ℓ, and this fact is indicated by $\mathfrak{Q}(A, B, C; D, E, F)$. ∎

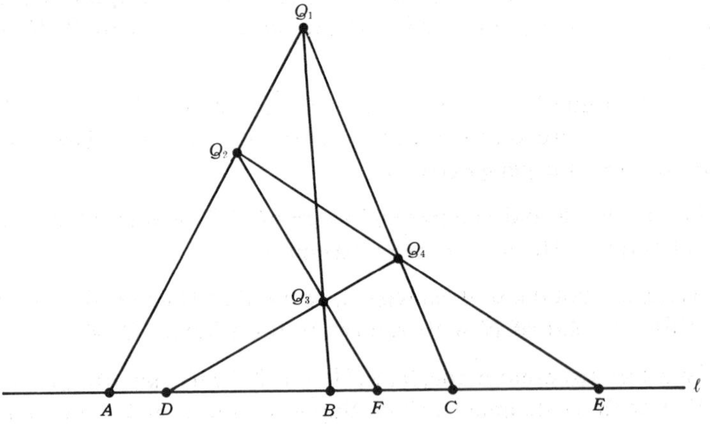

Figure 3.5

The following features of the above definition should be observed.

(1) If A, B, C, D, E, F are points in which a line, not on a vertex of $\mathcal{Q}$, intersects the sides of the quadrangle $\mathcal{Q}$, then it is fair to say, "$\mathcal{Q}(A, B, C; D, E, F)$," if and only if there is a numbering of the vertices of $\mathcal{Q}$ such that the conditions of the definition are met.

(2) A relabeling of the vertices of $\mathcal{Q}$ results in a reordering of the points of a quadrangular set. For example, if Q_1 and Q_2 were to have their names exchanged in Figure 3.5, $\mathcal{Q}(A, F, E; D, C, B)$ would result instead of $\mathcal{Q}(A, B, C; D, E, F)$. (See also exercise 1.)

(3) An easy way to remember the order of the points in a quadrangular set is to observe that A, B, C are on the sides of $\mathcal{Q}$ that join Q_1, the first vertex, to the second, third, and fourth vertices, respectively. Then, A and D are on opposite sides of $\mathcal{Q}$, B and E are on opposite sides of $\mathcal{Q}$, and C and F are on opposite sides of $\mathcal{Q}$.

(4) If $\mathcal{Q}(A, B, C; D, E, F)$, then A, B, C are distinct points, D, E, F are distinct points, $D \neq B$ or C, $E \neq A$ or C, and $F \neq A$ or B (why?).

The insistence upon a strict adherence to the ordering of a quadrangular set in accordance with the definition given above will pay dividends in simplifying statements and clarifying discussions. The importance of quadrangular sets in Desarguesian planes is due in large measure to the following theorem.

Theorem 3.3.2. (Quadrangular Sets) In a Desarguesian plane, if two quadrangular sets coincide in five of their points, then they coincide in all their points.

Proof: To say that two quadrangular sets coincide in five of their points means not only that five points on a line ℓ belong to both sets, but also that each of these five points occupies the same position in one of the sets as in the other. Since any point of a quadrangular set can be made the sixth point by a suitable relabeling of vertices (proof?), and since a corresponding relabeling of the vertices of the second quadrangle preserves the coincidence of five points, there is no loss of generality in supposing that we are given $\mathcal{Q}(A, B, C; D, E, F)$ and $\mathcal{Q}'(A, B, C; D, E, G)$, and that we are to prove that $F = G$. (See Figure 3.6.)

Set $k_1 = Q_1 \cup Q_2$ and $k_2 = Q_3' \cup Q_4'$. Construct the central collineation μ_1 with center D, axis k_1, sending E into F. Since D, E, F are distinct, and since E, F are not on k_1, μ_1 exists. Then, $Q_4\mu_1 = [(E \cup Q_2) \cap (D \cup Q_4)]\mu_1 = (F \cup Q_2) \cap (D \cup Q_4) = Q_3$. Hence, $C\mu_1 = [(Q_4 \cup Q_1) \cap (D \cup C)]\mu_1 = (Q_3 \cup Q_1) \cap (D \cup C) = B$.

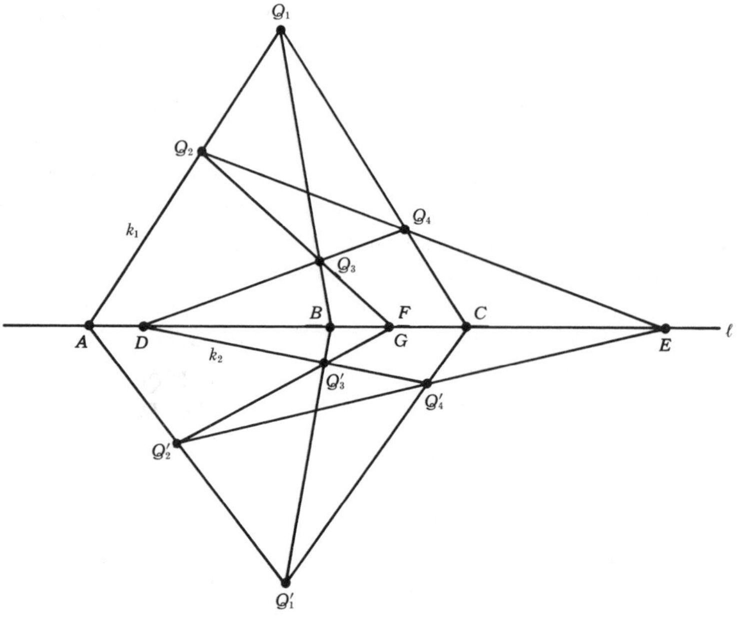

Figure 3.6

Next, construct the central collineation μ_2, with center A, axis k_2, sending B into G. Then, $Q_1'\mu_2 = [(B \cup Q_3') \cap (A \cup Q_1')]\mu_2 = (G \cup Q_3') \cap (A \cup Q_1') = Q_2'$. Hence, $C\mu_2 = [Q_1' \cup Q_4') \cap (A \cup C)]\mu_2 = (Q_2' \cup Q_4') \cap (A \cup C) = E$. We have learned that $C\mu_1\mu_2 = B\mu_2 = G$, and $C\mu_2\mu_1 = E\mu_1 = F$.

If $A = D$, μ_1 and μ_2 are elations with a common center; hence $\mu_1\mu_2 = \mu_2\mu_1$ by the dual of the Second Commuting Theorem (3.1.2). If $A \neq D$, μ_1 and μ_2 are homologies, and the center of each lies on the axis of the other. In this case, $\mu_1\mu_2 = \mu_2\mu_1$ by the First Commuting Theorem (2.4.7). In either case, $\mu_1\mu_2 = \mu_2\mu_1$, and from the preceding paragraph, $F = G$. ▮

It is tempting to try to prove the above theorem by using Desargues' theorem, since there are some easily found pairs of axially perspective triangles in Figure 3.6. The approach via Desargues' theorem works well enough when there are no coincidences among pairs of corresponding sides of the two quadrangles (see Exercise 3.2.11 and exercise 4). If, however, $Q_1 \cup Q_4 = Q_1' \cup Q_4'$, for instance, then Desargues' theorem gives only trivial information at one point, and the proof collapses. (For a correct proof based on the use of Desargues' theorem, see [26], pp. 61–63.)

It is worth emphasizing that a quadrangular set determined by a quadrangle $\mathcal{Q}$ and a line ℓ contains six points, but that some of these points will coincide (in one or more pairs) whenever ℓ lies on one or more diagonal points of $\mathcal{Q}$. However, the Quadrangular Sets theorem is valid whether the number of *different* points in each of the sets is three, four, five, or six. Indeed, some of the most important applications of the theorem are to sets with four distinct points, as we shall soon learn. The final results of this section concern the invariance of the quadrangular property under collineations and projectivities.

Theorem 3.3.3. (Quadrangular Invariance) If $\mathcal{Q}(A, B, C; D, E, F)$, and if ρ is any collineation, then $\mathcal{Q}'(A\rho, B\rho, C\rho; D\rho, E\rho, F\rho)$, where $\mathcal{Q}'$ is the quadrangle that is the image of $\mathcal{Q}$ under ρ.

Proof: Let the vertices of $\mathcal{Q}$ be Q_1, Q_2, Q_3, Q_4, and suppose that A, B, C, etc., lie on the line ℓ. Then, because $A = (Q_1 \cup Q_2) \cap \ell$, it follows that $A\rho = (Q_1\rho \cup Q_2\rho) \cap \ell\rho$, and similarly for $B\rho$, $C\rho$, etc. Since $Q_1\rho$, $Q_2\rho$, $Q_3\rho$, $Q_4\rho$ are vertices of $\mathcal{Q}'$, and since $\ell\rho$ lies on none of these vertices, the theorem is proved. ∎

Corollary: Suppose that $\mathcal{Q}(A, B, C; D, E, F)$ on a line ℓ of a Desarguesian plane, and let π be any projectivity from ℓ to any line. Then, $\mathcal{Q}'(A\pi, B\pi, C\pi; D\pi, E\pi, F\pi)$ for some quadrangle $\mathcal{Q}'$.

Proof: By Corollary 1 of the theorem Extension of Perspectivities (3.1.3), π can be extended to a (projective) collineation σ. If $\mathcal{Q}'$ is taken to be the image of $\mathcal{Q}$ under σ, the result follows from the theorem above. ∎

Exercise 3.3.A

1. Suppose that $\mathcal{Q}(A, B, C; D, E, F)$. Let X and Y be any points of this quadrangular set that are not on opposite sides of $\mathcal{Q}$. Prove that by relabeling the vertices of $\mathcal{Q}$, X and Y can be made the first and second points, respectively, of the quadrangular set based on the relabeled quadrangle. Also, prove that if neither X nor Y is a diagonal point of Q, there is only one relabeling of the vertices that suffices.

2. Let A, B, C, D, E be points on a line ℓ, not necessarily all different, but satisfying the conditions: (a) A, B, C are distinct, (b) $D \neq E$, B, or C, and (c) $E \neq A$ or C. Prove that there is a point F on ℓ such that $\mathcal{Q}(A, B, C; D, E, F)$.

3. Use the Quadrangular Sets theorem to give another proof of the Restricted Pappus Property (Example 3.2.4).

4. Use Desargues' theorem to give another proof of the Quadrangular Sets theorem in the case that no side of one quadrangle coincides with the corresponding side of the other quadrangle.

5. Let X, Y, Z be the diagonal points of a quadrangle $\mathcal{Q}$, and let $\ell = X \cup Y$. Suppose that k is a side of $\mathcal{Q}$ that lies on Z, and that P and Q are the vertices of $\mathcal{Q}$ on k. Set $U = k \cap \ell$, and prove that $\mathcal{Q}'(P, Q, U; P, Q, Z)$ for some quadrangle $\mathcal{Q}'$.

6. Suppose that $\mathcal{Q}(A, B, C; D, E, F)$ on a line ℓ. Prove that there is a projectivity π on ℓ such that $B\pi = B$, $E\pi = E$, $C\pi = A$, and $D\pi = F$.

7. Let π be a Π_2, different from the identity, on ℓ, with O and E as central and axial invariant points, respectively. Let A and B be distinct points on ℓ, both different from O and E. Prove that $\mathcal{Q}(A, B, O; B\pi, A\pi, E)$.

Exercise 3.3.B

8. (a) Define the dual concept of a quadrangular set of points, called a quadrilateral set of lines.
   (b) Suppose that $\mathcal{Q}(A, B, C; D, E, F)$ on a line ℓ in a Desarguesian plane, and let P be a point not on ℓ. Set $k_1 = P \cup A$, $k_2 = P \cup B$, $k_3 = P \cup C$, etc., and prove that $k_4, k_5, k_6, k_1, k_2, k_3$, in that order, form a quadrilateral set of lines.

9. Use the result of exercise 8b and its dual to give another proof of the corollary to the Quadrangular Invariance theorem (3.3.3).

10. Use the Quadrangular Sets theorem to give another proof of Desargues' theorem in the nondegenerate case depicted in Figure 3.3.

11. Use the Quadrangular Sets theorem to give another proof of the result in Exercise 3.1.7.

12. Let $\mathcal{P}$ be a projective plane in which any two Π_2's on a line with inversely matched invariant points commute. Prove that the Quadrangular Sets theorem holds in $\mathcal{P}$.

3.4. Harmonic Sets

If a line ℓ lies on two diagonal points of a complete quadrangle $\mathcal{Q}$, then $\mathcal{Q}$ and ℓ determine a special kind of quadrangular set of particular significance.

Definition 3.4.1. If A, B, C, D are collinear points such that $\mathcal{Q}(A, B, C; A, B, D)$, then the ordered quadruple $\{A, B, C, D\}$ is a *harmonic set,* a fact that is indicated by $\mathcal{H}(A, B; C, D)$. ▮

If $\mathcal{H}(A, B; C, D)$, then A and B are diagonal points of a quadrangle $\mathcal{Q}$, while C and D are the points in which the line $A \cup B$ intersects the sides of $\mathcal{Q}$ that do not lie on A or B. (See Figure 3.7.)

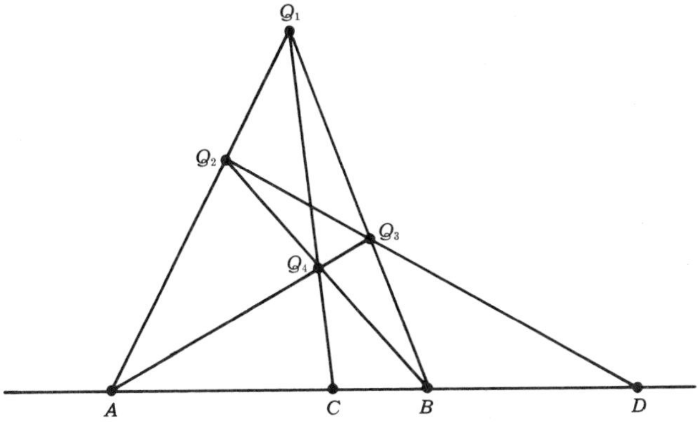

Figure 3.7

The following properties of harmonic sets are obtained as specializations of properties of quadrangular sets.

(1) If $\mathcal{H}(A, B; C, D)$, then A, B, C are distinct. If the diagonal points of $\mathcal{Q}$ are collinear, $D = C$ is the third diagonal point. If the diagonal points of $\mathcal{Q}$ are not collinear, A, B, C, D are four distinct points.

(2) The harmonic property is invariant under collineations and, in a Desarguesian plane, also under projectivities between lines. That is, if $\mathcal{H}(A, B; C, D)$, then $\mathcal{H}(A\phi, B\phi; C\phi, D\phi)$, where ϕ is any collineation, or, in a Desarguesian plane, any projectivity from the line $A \cup B$ to any line.

(3) If A, B, C are distinct points on a line ℓ of a Desarguesian plane, there is a unique point D on ℓ such that $\mathcal{H}(A, B; C, D)$ (why?). Similarly, if A, B, D are distinct points on a line ℓ in a Desarguesian plane, there is a unique point C on ℓ such that $\mathcal{H}(A, B; C, D)$.

The next theorem on harmonic sets has two important corollaries.

Theorem 3.4.2. (Equivalence of Harmonic Sets) In a Desarguesian plane, any harmonic set can be mapped onto any other harmonic set by both a projectivity and a projective collineation. That is, if $\mathcal{H}(A, B; C, D)$ and $\mathcal{H}(A', B'; C', D')$, there exist a projectivity π and a projective collineation σ such that $A\pi = A\sigma = A'$, $B\pi = B\sigma = B'$, $C\pi = C\sigma = C'$, and $D\pi = D\sigma = D'$.

Proof: A projectivity π can be constructed such that $A\pi = A'$, $B\pi = B'$, and $C\pi = C'$, by the First Existence Theorem for Projectivities (1.7.2). Then, $\mathcal{H}(A', B'; C', D\pi)$ by the invariance of the harmonic property under projectivities in a Desarguesian plane. Therefore, $D\pi = D'$, by the uniqueness of the fourth point of a harmonic set. Thus, π has the required property, and to get σ it is enough to extend π (using Corollary 1 of Theorem 3.1.3) to a projective collineation. ▌

Corollary 1: In a Desarguesian plane $\mathcal{P}$, the number of different points in a harmonic set is the same for all harmonic sets.

Proof: By the theorem, any two harmonic sets in $\mathcal{P}$ can be related by a projectivity, and this projectivity effects a bijection of one of the sets onto the other. ▌

Corollary 2: In a Desarguesian plane, if any quadrangle has collinear diagonal points, then every quadrangle has collinear diagonal points.

Proof: The number of distinct points in a harmonic set is three or four, depending upon whether the quadrangle determining the set has collinear diagonal points or not. Since every quadrangle determines at least one harmonic set in the plane, the result follows from Corollary 1. ▌

Since Axioms 1–4 do not exclude planes in which the diagonal points of a quadrangle are collinear, many of our statements concerning harmonic sets are of necessity two-part statements, depending upon whether a harmonic set has three or four distinct points. In the next theorem we learn that certain rearrangements of the points of a harmonic set yield other harmonic sets.

Theorem 3.4.3. (Harmonic Permutations) In a projective plane $\mathcal{P}$, suppose that $\mathcal{H}(A, B; C, D)$. Then:

(a) $\mathcal{H}(A, B; D, C)$.
(b) $\mathcal{H}(B, A; C, D)$.
(c) If $\mathcal{P}$ is Desarguesian, and if $C \neq D$, then $\mathcal{H}(C, D; A, B)$.

Proof: (a) In Figure 3.7, exchange the labels Q_1 and Q_2, and also exchange the labels Q_3 and Q_4. The relabeled quadrangle exhibits $\mathcal{H}(A, B; D, C)$.

(b) In Figure 3.7, exchange the labels Q_2 and Q_3 to see that $\mathcal{H}(B, A; C, D)$.

(c) Refer to Figure 3.8, in which $\mathcal{Q}$ with vertices Q_1, Q_2, Q_3, Q_4 exhibits $\mathcal{H}(A, B; C, D)$. Draw lines $k_1 = Q_1 \cup D$ and $k_2 = C \cup Q_3$, and let $P = k_1 \cap k_2$. Also, let $O = (Q_2 \cup Q_3) \cap (Q_1 \cup Q_4)$. Construct the elation ϵ with axis $\ell = A \cup B$, center A, sending Q_2 into Q_1. Then, $Q_4\epsilon = Q_3$ (why?). Therefore, $O\epsilon = [(Q_4 \cup C) \cap (Q_2 \cup D)] = (Q_3 \cup C) \cap (Q_1 \cup D) = k_2 \cap k_1 = P$. It follows that A, O, P are collinear.

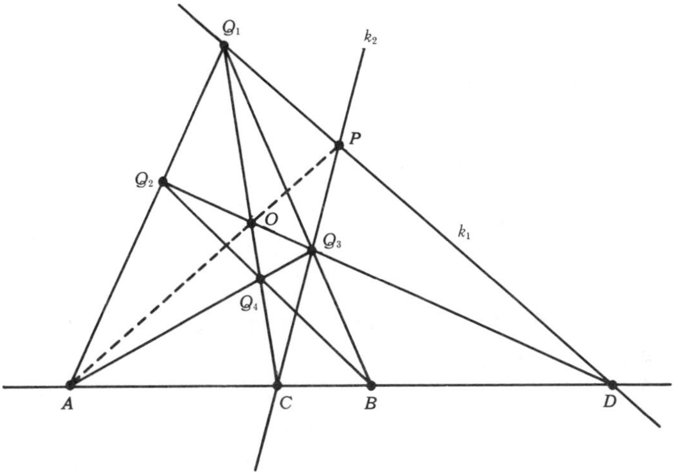

Figure 3.8

Since $C \neq D$, the points O, Q_1, Q_3, P are vertices of a quadrangle $\mathcal{Q}'$ that exhibits $\mathcal{Q}'(C, D, A; C, D, B)$. Therefore, $\mathcal{H}(C, D; A, B)$. ▌

In a Desarguesian plane, if $\mathcal{H}(A, B; C, D)$ and $C \neq D$, the operations of the above theorem yield at least eight different harmonic sets by rearrangements of the given one. (See exercise 1 and Example 3.6.3.)

The next theorem demonstrates a connection between the elations of a projective plane and harmonic sets.

Theorem 3.4.4. (Elations and Harmonic Sets) If ϵ is an elation different from the identity, with center H, axis ℓ, and if X is any point not on ℓ, then $\mathcal{H}(H, X\epsilon; X, X\epsilon^2)$.

Proof: Figure 3.9 illustrates the construction of $X\epsilon^2$ from H, ℓ, X, and $X\epsilon$. The quadrangle $Q_1Q_2Q_3Q_4$ exhibits $\mathcal{H}(H, X\epsilon; X, X\epsilon^2)$. ∎

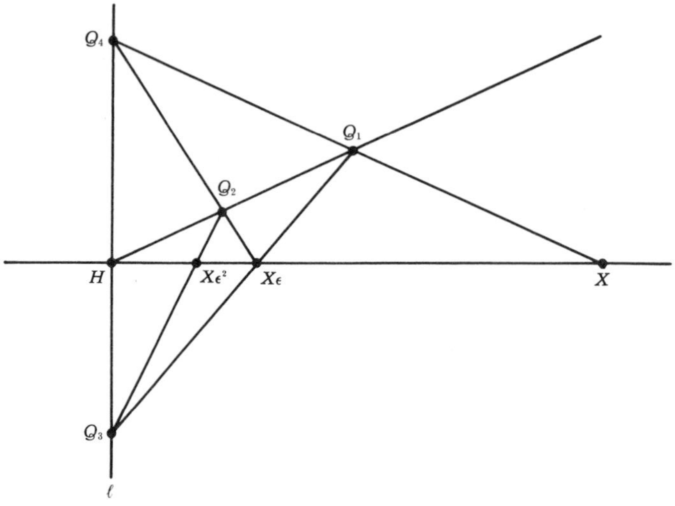

Figure 3.9

In a Desarguesian plane, there is also a certain kind of homology that is intimately related to harmonic sets.

Theorem 3.4.5. (Harmonic Homologies) Let $\mathcal{P}$ be a Desarguesian plane, and suppose that η is a homology of $\mathcal{P}$ with center H, axis ℓ.

(a) If, for some point X, different from H and not on ℓ, $\mathcal{H}(H, M; X, X\eta)$, where $M = (H \cup X) \cap \ell$, then $\eta^2 = \iota$.

(b) Conversely, if η is periodic with period two, and if X is any point different from H and not on ℓ, then $\mathcal{H}(H, M; X, X\eta)$, where $M = (H \cup X) \cap \ell$.

Proof: (a) If $\mathcal{P}$ is a plane in which the diagonal points of a quadrangle are collinear, $X\eta = X$ because $\mathcal{H}(H, M; X, X)$. Therefore, in this case, $\eta = \iota$ (why?). Hence $\eta^2 = \iota$. Note also that, for any point X, different from H and not on ℓ, $\mathcal{H}(H, M; X, X\eta)$, where $M = (H \cup X) \cap \ell$. For the remainder of part (a), we suppose that $\mathcal{P}$ is a plane in which the diagonal points of a quadrangle are not collinear.

Figure 3.10 (drawn for an arbitrary homology different from the identity) shows the construction of $X\eta^2$ from H, ℓ, X, and $X\eta$. The quadrangle $Q_1Q_2Q_3Q_4$ exhibits $\mathcal{Q}(X, X\eta, H; X\eta^2, X\eta, M)$.

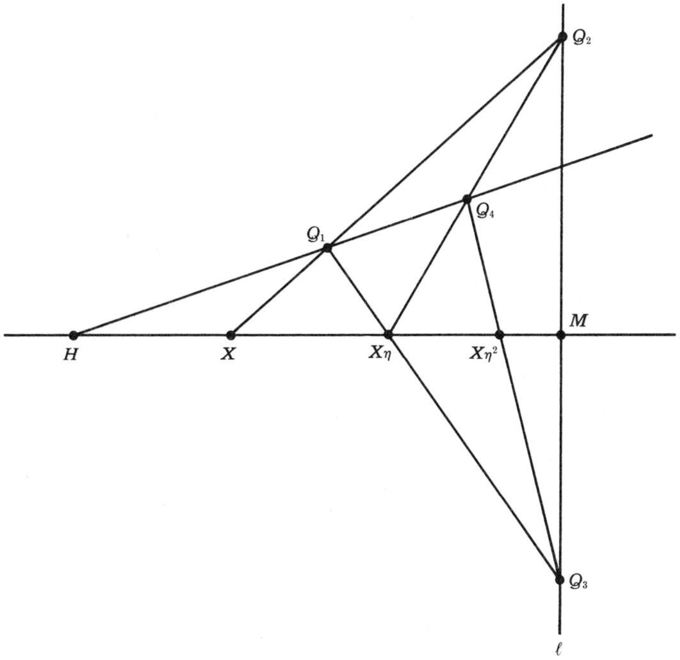

Figure 3.10

The hypothesis $\mathcal{H}(H, M; X, X\eta)$ and the assumption that $X\eta \neq X$ yield, by part (c) of the theorem Harmonic Permutations, $\mathcal{H}(X, X\eta; H, M)$, which is equivalent to $\mathcal{Q}'(X, X\eta, H; X, X\eta, M)$. A comparison of this last quadrangular set with the one of the preceding paragraph reveals (via the theorem Quadrangular Sets (3.3.2)) that $X\eta^2 = X$. Therefore, $\eta^2 = \iota$ because η^2 is a homology that fixes a point (X) different from its center H and not on its axis ℓ.

(b) The hypothesis for part (b) is that $\eta^2 = \iota$ but $\eta \neq \iota$. Let X be any point different from H and not on ℓ. Then, $X\eta \neq X$, and Figure 3.10 shows that $\mathcal{Q}(X, X\eta, H; X\eta^2, X\eta, M)$. Since $\eta^2 = \iota$, it follows that $\mathcal{H}(X, X\eta; H, M)$; hence $\mathcal{H}(H, M; X, X\eta)$, for $H \neq M$. (Observe that the diagonal points of a quadrangle in $\mathcal{P}$ are not collinear in this case.) ∎

The special kind of homology of the above theorem receives a special name in the next definition.

Definition 3.4.6. In a Desarguesian plane, a homology η (with center H, axis ℓ) is a *harmonic homology* if (and only if) for every point X different from H and not on ℓ, $\mathcal{H}(H, M; X, X\eta)$, where $M = (H \cup X) \cap \ell$. ▮

Let us agree to use the word *involution* to mean a bijection on a set that is periodic with period two. Then, the information of Theorem 3.4.5 can be summarized as follows: Let $\mathcal{P}$ be a Desarguesian plane. If the condition of Definition 3.4.6 holds for a single point X, η is a harmonic homology of $\mathcal{P}$. The diagonal points of a quadrangle in $\mathcal{P}$ are collinear if and only if the identity collineation is a harmonic homology of $\mathcal{P}$. If the diagonal points of a quadrangle in $\mathcal{P}$ are not collinear, a harmonic homology of $\mathcal{P}$ is an involution. Conversely, if the homology η of $\mathcal{P}$ is an involution, then η is a harmonic homology, and the diagonal points of a quadrangle in $\mathcal{P}$ are not collinear.

In closing this section, we remark that Axiom 4 guarantees the existence of harmonic homologies in Desarguesian planes (exercise 2), and that a harmonic homology of a Desarguesian plane is determined by its center H and axis ℓ. If X is any point different from H and not on ℓ, then $X\eta$ must be the unique point such that $\mathcal{H}(H, M; X, X\eta)$, where η is the harmonic homology, and $M = (H \cup X) \cap \ell$.

Exercise 3.4.A

1. (a) In a Desarguesian plane, suppose that $\mathcal{H}(A, B; C, D)$, with $C \neq D$. Prove that there are at least eight rearrangements of the points A, B, C, D that yield harmonic sets.
(b) In a 13-point plane, show that the four points on any line form a harmonic set in any order.

2. Let $\mathcal{P}$ be a Desarguesian plane, and let H and ℓ be any nonincident point and line in $\mathcal{P}$. Show that there is a harmonic homology of $\mathcal{P}$ with center H and axis ℓ.

3. In a Desarguesian plane, suppose that $\mathcal{H}(A, B; C, D)$, with $C \neq D$, and that $\mathcal{H}(A', B'; C', D)$, with $A' \cup D \neq A \cup D$. Prove that $A \cup A'$, $B \cup B'$, and $C \cup C'$ are concurrent.

4. In a Desarguesian plane $\mathcal{P}$, suppose that η_1 and η_2 are harmonic homologies such that the center of each lies on the axis of the other. Prove that $\eta_1\eta_2$ is a harmonic homology. Also, if the diagonal points of a quadrangle in $\mathcal{P}$ are not collinear, locate the center and axis of $\eta_1\eta_2$.

5. Let $\mathcal{P}$ be a Desarguesian plane. Prove that the diagonal points of a quadrangle in $\mathcal{P}$ are collinear if and only if every elation of $\mathcal{P}$, except the identity, is an involution.

6. Let $\mathcal{P}$ be a Desarguesian plane, and let π be a Π_2 on a line ℓ of $\mathcal{P}$, with central invariant point H and axial invariant point M. Suppose that π is an involution. Prove that $\mathcal{H}(X, X\pi; H, M)$ for every point X on ℓ, other than H and M.

7. (a) In $\mathcal{E}_2$, let A, B be distinct points, and let C be the midpoint of the segment AB. Prove that in $\mathcal{E}_2^*$ the statement $\mathcal{H}(A, B; C, I)$ is true, where I is the ideal point of $A \cup B$.

(b) Given two distinct, parallel lines in $\mathcal{E}_2$, show how to construct, by means of a straightedge alone, the midpoint of a segment on one of the lines.

(c) Let η be the harmonic homology of $\mathcal{E}_2^*$ with center H, an ordinary point, and axis the ideal line. What is the nature of the central dilatation of $\mathcal{E}_2$ that η extends?

Exercise 3.4.B

8. Use Desargues' theorem to give another proof that A, O, P of Figure 3.8 (Theorem 3.4.3 (c)) are collinear.

9. Let $\mathcal{P}$ be a Desarguesian plane in which the diagonal points of a quadrangle are not collinear.

(a) Let η be a harmonic homology of $\mathcal{P}$, and let μ be a central collineation of $\mathcal{P}$ with the same axis as η. Prove that $\mu\eta$ is a harmonic homology if and only if μ is an elation.

(b) Deduce that the composite of two harmonic homologies of $\mathcal{P}$ with a common axis is an elation.

10. Let $\mathcal{P}$ be a Desarguesian plane, and let η_1 be the harmonic homology of $\mathcal{P}$ with center H, axis ℓ. If η_2 is any homology with center H, axis ℓ, prove that $\eta_1\eta_2 = \eta_2\eta_1$.

11. (a) Define a harmonic set of lines.

(b) Let $\mathcal{P}$ be a Desarguesian plane, and let $\pi = k \circ O \circ \ell$, where k and ℓ are distinct lines of $\mathcal{P}$. Let $m = O \cup (k \cap \ell)$, and let n be the axis of homology of π, defined in Exercise 3.2.5. Prove that $\mathcal{H}(k, \ell; m, n)$.

(c) In $\mathcal{E}_2$, let k and ℓ be distinct intersecting lines, and let $P = k \cap \ell$. Let m and n be the lines that bisect the angles formed at P by k and ℓ. Prove that $\mathcal{H}(k, \ell; m, n)$ in $\mathcal{E}_2^*$.

12. Let O, A, B, C be triply noncollinear points in a Desarguesian plane, and put $X = (O \cup A) \cap (B \cup C)$, $Y = (O \cup B) \cap (A \cup C)$, and $Z = (O \cup C) \cap (A \cup B)$. Let X', Y', Z' be the points such that $\mathcal{H}(B, C; X, X')$, $\mathcal{H}(A, C; Y, Y')$, and $\mathcal{H}(A, B; Z, Z')$. Prove that X', Y', Z' are collinear.

13. Let A, B, C be vertices of a triangle in a Desarguesian plane, and assume that D, D', E, E', F, F' are points such that $\mathcal{H}(B, C; D, D')$, $\mathcal{H}(A, C; E, E')$, and $\mathcal{H}(A, B; F, F')$. Prove that D', E', F' are collinear if and only if $A \cup D$, $B \cup E$, and $C \cup F$ are concurrent.

3.5. Conjugacy

The work that lies ahead of us necessitates generalizing and amplifying the concept of conjugacy that was introduced in Section 2.5. Our first aim is to understand what is meant by the conjugate of a collineation τ (of the projective plane $\mathcal{P}$) by the collineation ρ of $\mathcal{P}$. The easiest way to gain a correct understanding of this idea is to view it as a natural extension of the notion of the conjugate of a projectivity π by the collineation ρ. Let us summarize the development in the relevant part of Section 2.5 as follows: Suppose that π is a projectivity with domain $\mathcal{I}(k)$. Then, there is a projectivity π', with domain $\mathcal{I}(k\rho)$, that acts just like π with its domain (and codomain) moved by ρ. More specifically, if P is any point on k, π sends P into $P\pi$, and π' sends $P\rho$ (P moved by ρ) into $(P\pi)\rho$ ($P\pi$ moved by ρ).

Evidently, then, we want the conjugate of τ by ρ to be a collineation τ' that acts just like τ with its domain (and codomain) moved by ρ. It is not obvious that such a collineation exists, but, if it does, it has the following property: Let P be any point and ℓ any line of $\mathcal{P}$; since τ sends P into $P\tau$ and ℓ into $\ell\tau$, τ' must send $P\rho$ (P moved by ρ) into $(P\tau)\rho$ ($P\tau$ moved by ρ) and $\ell\rho$ into $(\ell\tau)\rho$. That is, $(P\rho)\tau' = (P\tau)\rho$ for every point P, and $(\ell\rho)\tau' = (\ell\tau)\rho$ for every line ℓ. Thus, $\rho\tau' = \tau\rho$, or $\tau' = \rho^{-1}\tau\rho$. Since $\rho^{-1}\tau\rho$ is indeed a collineation, and since it sends $P\rho$ into $(P\tau)\rho$ and $\ell\rho$ into $(\ell\tau)\rho$, we see that it is exactly the object that we are seeking. The collineation $\tau' = \rho^{-1}\tau\rho$ is the *conjugate* (or *transform*) of τ by ρ.

Suppose now that σ is a projective collineation. If k is any line, the restriction of σ to $\mathcal{I}(k)$ is a projectivity; let π represent this projectivity. If $\sigma' = \rho^{-1}\sigma\rho$, the restriction of σ' to $\mathcal{I}(k\rho)$ is readily calculated to be $\rho^{-1}\pi\rho$, which is a projectivity by the corollary to the theorem Conjugate of an Elementary Correspondence (2.5.3). Therefore, by the Criterion for Projective Collineations (2.5.4), σ' is a projective collineation. Since the argument does not depend upon whether ρ is projective, we have learned that any conjugate of a projective collineation is a projective collineation. The next theorem strengthens this result for central collineations.

Theorem 3.5.1. (Conjugate of a Central Collineation) Let μ be a central collineation of the projective plane $\mathcal{P}$, and let $\mathcal{D} = \{\ell, H, P, P'\}$ be a determining set for μ. Let ρ be any collineation of $\mathcal{P}$. Then, $\mu' = \rho^{-1}\mu\rho$ is a central collineation, and $\mathcal{D}' = \{\ell\rho, H\rho, P\rho, P'\rho\}$ is a determining set for μ'.

Proof: That $\mathcal{D}'$ is a determining set (Definition 2.4.6) follows easily from the hypotheses that $\mathcal{D}$ is a determining set and that ρ is a collineation (verify!). Let k be any line on $H\rho$; then, $k\rho^{-1}$ is on $H\rho\rho^{-1} = H$. Therefore, $k\rho^{-1}\mu = k\rho^{-1}$; hence $k\rho^{-1}\mu\rho = k$, proving that μ' is a central collineation with center $H\rho$. A dual argument shows that $\ell\rho$ is an axis for μ'. Finally, $P\rho\mu' = P\rho\rho^{-1}\mu\rho = P\mu\rho = P'\rho$, proving that $\mathcal{D}'$ is a determining set for μ'. ∎

In defining the conjugate of a collineation τ by a collineation ρ to be $\rho^{-1}\tau\rho$, we have used two of the group properties of the set of collineations of a projective plane—closure under composition and the existence of inverses. It is evident that this definition of conjugate can be generalized to apply to the elements of any group; the indicated generalization, presented in the next definition, has great utility in the study of groups. (The notion of the conjugate of a collineation can also be extended in another direction; see exercise 12.)

Definition 3.5.2. Let $\mathcal{G}$ be a group. If G_1 and G_2 are elements of $\mathcal{G}$, then G_2 is a *conjugate* of G_1 in $\mathcal{G}$ if and only if there is an element H in $\mathcal{G}$ such that $G_2 = H^{-1} \cdot G_1 \cdot H$. ∎

If G_2 is conjugate to G_1 in the group $\mathcal{G}$, we also say that G_2 is related to G_1 by the relation of *conjugacy*. The relation thus defined on an arbitrary group $\mathcal{G}$ is an equivalence relation (exercise 1). (See also exercise 10.) We now give an example of the calculation of the conjugate of one group element by another.

Example 3.5.3. Let $\mathcal{G}$ be the group of all permutations on the set $\mathcal{S} = \{1, 2, 3\}$. Let $\phi = (1, 2)$ (a transposition on $\mathcal{S}$) and $\psi = (1, 3, 2)$ (a three-cycle on $\mathcal{S}$). Let $\phi' = \psi^{-1}\phi\psi$; we want to calculate the effect of ϕ' on each point of $\mathcal{S}$. First, ψ^{-1} is easily computed to be the three-cycle $(1, 2, 3)$. Then, $1\phi' = 1\psi^{-1}\phi\psi = 2\phi\psi = 1\psi = 3$, $2\phi' = 2\psi^{-1}\phi\psi =$

$3\phi\psi = 3\psi = 2$, and $3\phi' = 3\psi^{-1}\phi\psi = 1\phi\psi = 2\psi = 1$. Therefore, ϕ' is the transposition $(1, 3)$. Observe that ϕ transposes 1 and 2 and fixes 3, that ψ sends 1, 2, 3 into 3, 1, 2, respectively, and that ϕ' transposes 3 and 1 and fixes 2; thus, ϕ' acts just like ϕ with its domain moved by ψ. In particular, ϕ' is a transposition, as is ϕ. (See also exercises 6 and 7.) ∎

From the preceding example, and from the discussion of the conjugate of a collineation, we surmise that when two elements of a group are conjugate, they possess many common characteristics. One significant attribute that a group element may have is the property of being periodic (Definition 2.6.4). The next theorem shows that the period of a periodic element is shared by all its conjugates. (See also exercise 4.)

Theorem 3.5.4. (Period of a Conjugate) Let $\mathcal{G}$ be a group, and suppose that G_1' and G_2' are conjugates, by the single element H, of the elements G_1 and G_2, respectively, of $\mathcal{G}$. Then:

(a) $G_1' \cdot G_2' = H^{-1} \cdot (G_1 \cdot G_2) \cdot H$. (The product of the conjugates is the conjugate of the product.)

(b) If G_1 is periodic with period n, then G_1' is also periodic with period n.

Proof: (a) Since $G_1' = H^{-1} \cdot G_1 \cdot H$ and $G_2' = H^{-1} \cdot G_2 \cdot H$, it follows that $G_1' \cdot G_2' = H^{-1} \cdot G_1 \cdot H \cdot H^{-1} \cdot G_2 \cdot H = H^{-1} \cdot (G_1 \cdot G_2) \cdot H$.

(b) The method of part (a), applied to the product $G_1' \cdot G_1'$, yields $(G_1')^2 = H^{-1} \cdot (G_1)^2 \cdot H$. Then, induction shows that $(G_1')^k = H^{-1} \cdot (G_1)^k \cdot H$ for any positive integer k. If G_1 is periodic with period n, then $(G_1)^n = I$ (the identity of $\mathcal{G}$); hence $(G_1')^n = H^{-1} \cdot (G_1)^n \cdot H = H^{-1} \cdot I \cdot H = I$, also. Therefore, G_1' is periodic, with period not exceeding n. Since $G_1 = H \cdot G_1' \cdot H^{-1}$, a repetition of the argument shows that the period of G_1 is not greater than the period of G_1'. Thus, the period of G_1' is n. ∎

Suppose that $\mathcal{G}$ is a group, that G is an element of $\mathcal{G}$, and that $\mathcal{H}$ is a nonempty subset of $\mathcal{G}$. Then, the set $\mathcal{K}$, consisting of all elements of $\mathcal{G}$ of the form $G^{-1} \cdot H \cdot G$, where H may be any element of $\mathcal{H}$, is called the conjugate, or transform, of $\mathcal{H}$ by G and is designated by $G^{-1} \cdot \mathcal{H} \cdot G$. The next theorem concerns a transform of a *subgroup*.

Theorem 3.5.5. (Conjugate Subgroups) Let $\mathcal{G}$ be a group, $\mathcal{H}$ a subgroup of $\mathcal{G}$, and $\mathcal{K} = G^{-1} \cdot \mathcal{H} \cdot G$, where G is an element of $\mathcal{G}$. Then, $\mathcal{K}$ is a subgroup of $\mathcal{G}$, and there is a bijection Φ, from $\mathcal{H}$ to $\mathcal{K}$, with the property that $(H_1 \cdot H_2)\Phi = (H_1\Phi) \cdot (H_2\Phi)$ for any elements H_1, H_2 of $\mathcal{H}$.

Proof: First it must be proved that $\mathcal{K}$ is a subgroup of $\mathcal{G}$. Let K_1 and K_2 be any elements of $\mathcal{K}$. Then, $K_1 = G^{-1} \cdot H_1 \cdot G$, and $K_2 = G^{-1} \cdot H_2 \cdot G$, for some elements H_1, H_2 in $\mathcal{H}$. Therefore, $K_1 \cdot K_2 = G^{-1} \cdot H_1 \cdot H_2 \cdot G$, and, since $H_1 \cdot H_2$ is in $\mathcal{H}$ (because $\mathcal{H}$ is a subgroup), it follows that $K_1 \cdot K_2$ is in $\mathcal{K}$. Because I (the identity of $\mathcal{G}$) is in $\mathcal{H}$, $G^{-1} \cdot I \cdot G = I$ is in $\mathcal{K}$. Finally, if $K_3 = G^{-1} \cdot H_3 \cdot G$ is in $\mathcal{K}$ (where H_3 is some element of $\mathcal{H}$), then $K_3^{-1} = G^{-1} \cdot H_3^{-1} \cdot G$ is also in $\mathcal{K}$, for H_3^{-1} is in $\mathcal{H}$. By the definition of subgroup (2.6.5), $\mathcal{K}$ is a subgroup of $\mathcal{G}$.

Next, define a function Φ, from $\mathcal{H}$ to $\mathcal{K}$, as follows: For each H in $\mathcal{H}$, set $H\Phi = G^{-1} \cdot H \cdot G$. The function Φ is onto K, by the definition of $\mathcal{K}$. If $H_1\Phi = H_2\Phi$, then $G^{-1} \cdot H_1 \cdot G = G^{-1} \cdot H_2 \cdot G$; hence $H_1 \cdot G = H_2 \cdot G$, and $H_1 = H_2$. Therefore, Φ is a bijection.

For the last conclusion of the theorem, observe that $(H_1 \cdot H_2)\Phi = G^{-1} \cdot H_1 \cdot H_2 \cdot G = G^{-1} \cdot H_1 \cdot G \cdot G^{-1} \cdot H_2 \cdot G = (H_1\Phi) \cdot (H_2\Phi)$ if H_1 and H_2 are any elements of $\mathcal{H}$. ▌

The subgroups $\mathcal{H}$ and $\mathcal{K}$ of the preceding theorem provide a special example of two *isomorphic* groups, according to the next definition.

Definition 3.5.6. The group $\mathcal{K}$ is *isomorphic* to the group $\mathcal{H}$ if and only if there exists a bijection Φ, from $\mathcal{H}$ to $\mathcal{K}$, with the property that $(H_1 \cdot H_2)\Phi = (H_1\Phi) \cdot (H_2\Phi)$ for any elements, H_1 and H_2, in $\mathcal{H}$. A bijection Φ satisfying this condition is an *isomorphism* of $\mathcal{H}$ onto $\mathcal{K}$. ▌

In the equation $(H_1 \cdot H_2)\Phi = (H_1\Phi) \cdot (H_2\Phi)$ of the above definition, observe that the product $H_1 \cdot H_2$ is calculated in $\mathcal{H}$, whereas the product $(H_1\Phi) \cdot (H_2\Phi)$ is calculated in $\mathcal{K}$. Since $\mathcal{H}$ and $\mathcal{K}$ are not necessarily subgroups of a single group, the two product operations may be quite different. (For an example, see exercise 11.) If the group $\mathcal{K}$ is isomorphic to the group $\mathcal{H}$, then we may also say that $\mathcal{K}$ is related to $\mathcal{H}$ by the relation of *isomorphy*. The relation thus defined on the set of all groups is an equivalence relation (exercise 2). Since a group is completely determined by its elements and the specification of all products of ordered pairs of these elements, we see that two groups that are isomorphic are in fact abstractly identical.

An isomorphism from one projective plane to another is a bijection characterized by the equations $(P \cup Q)\theta = P\theta \cup Q\theta$ and $(k \cap \ell)\theta = k\theta \cap \ell\theta$ (Equations 2.1.4). An isomorphism from one group to another is a bijection characterized by $(H_1 \cdot H_2)\Phi =$

$(H_1\Phi)\cdot(H_2\Phi)$. The similarity of structure of these equations is evident and helps to explain why we have used the same terminology for the two situations. In a group, the operation is product $(\cdot)$, and an isomorphism preserves this operation. In a projective plane, we can view join $(\bigcup)$ and intersection $(\bigcap)$ as the basic operations, and an isomorphism preserves these operations. (Join and intersection are not binary operations in the strict sense of the definition given at the beginning of Section 2.6. However, it should be clear how the concept of operation can be generalized to include an operation from one set to another. For example, join is an operation from the set of points of a projective plane to the set of lines of the plane.) Quite generally, an isomorphism of a mathematical system $\mathcal{A}$ (consisting of a set in which certain operations are prescribed) onto a mathematical system $\mathcal{B}$ of the same type (that is, having operations satisfying the same postulates as those in $\mathcal{A}$) is a bijection of $\mathcal{A}$ onto $\mathcal{B}$ that preserves all the relevant operations. In Section 3.8 we shall meet isomorphisms of certain mathematical systems (division rings) having two binary operations.

Exercise 3.5.A

1. Let $\mathcal{G}$ be any group. Prove that conjugacy is an equivalence relation on $\mathcal{G}$.

2. Prove that isomorphy is an equivalence relation on the set of all groups.

3. Let τ and τ' be collineations of a projective plane, and suppose that τ' is the conjugate of τ by the collineation ρ. Prove that if P is a fixed point of τ, then $P\rho$ is a fixed point of τ', and that if ℓ is a fixed line of τ, then $\ell\rho$ is a fixed line of τ'.

4. Let π be a projectivity on a line ℓ in a projective plane, and suppose that π is periodic with period n. If ρ is a collineation of the plane, and if $\pi' = \rho^{-1}\pi\rho$, prove that π' is also periodic with period n.

5. Let $\mathcal{G}$ be a group, and let G_1 and G_2 be any elements of $\mathcal{G}$. Prove that $G_2\cdot G_1$ is conjugate in $\mathcal{G}$ to $G_1\cdot G_2$.

6. Let $\mathcal{S} = \{1, 2, 3, 4\}$. Let ϕ and ψ be the permutations on $\mathcal{S}$ given by $\phi = (1, 4, 2, 3)$ and $\psi = (2, 3)(1, 4)$. Calculate the conjugate of ϕ by ψ.

Exercise 3.5.B

7. Let $\mathcal{S}$ be a finite set with n ($\geqq 2$) elements, and let ϕ be the m-cycle $(P_1, P_2, \ldots, P_m)$ on $\mathcal{S}$, where $2 \leqq m \leqq n$. Let ψ be any permutation on $\mathcal{S}$. Prove that the m-cycle $(P_1\psi, P_2\psi, \ldots, P_m\psi)$ is the conjugate of ϕ by ψ.

8. Let H be a point and ℓ a line not on H in a projective plane $\mathcal{P}$, and suppose that ρ is a collineation of $\mathcal{P}$. Prove that the group of homologies of $\mathcal{P}$ with center H, axis ℓ, is isomorphic to the group of homologies of $\mathcal{P}$ with center $H\rho$, axis $\ell\rho$.

9. Let $\mathcal{G}$ be the group of all permutations on the set $\mathcal{S} = \{1, 2, 3\}$. Let $\mathcal{H} = \{\iota, (1, 2)\}$ and $\mathcal{K} = \{\iota, (2, 3)\}$, where ι is the identity permutation on $\mathcal{S}$. Prove that $\mathcal{H}$ and $\mathcal{K}$ are subgroups of $\mathcal{G}$ (under composition) and that they are isomorphic.

10. Since conjugacy is an equivalence relation on a group, it decomposes the group into disjoint equivalence classes (Exercise 1.8.13), called *conjugate classes*. List all the conjugate classes in the group of all permutations on the set $\mathcal{S} = \{1, 2, 3\}$.

11. Let $\mathcal{G}_1$ be the group of all positive real numbers under the operation of multiplication. Let $\mathcal{G}_2$ be the group of all real numbers under the operation of addition. Prove that the function Φ, from $\mathcal{G}_1$ to $\mathcal{G}_2$, defined by $x\Phi = \log_{10} x$ for each x in $\mathcal{G}_1$, is an isomorphism of $\mathcal{G}_1$ onto $\mathcal{G}_2$.

12. Let θ be an isomorphism of the projective plane $\mathcal{P}$ onto the projective plane $\mathcal{P}'$, and suppose that τ is a collineation of $\mathcal{P}$. Set $\tau' = \theta^{-1}\tau\theta$.

(a) Prove that τ' is a collineation of $\mathcal{P}'$.

(b) If P is any point of $\mathcal{P}$, show that τ' sends $P\theta$ into $(P\tau)\theta$.

(c) If τ is a central collineation, with determining set $\mathcal{D} = \{\ell, H, P, P'\}$, prove that τ' is also a central collineation and that $\mathcal{D}' = \{\ell\theta, H\theta, P\theta, P'\theta\}$ is a determining set for τ'.

3.6. Projective Equivalence of Quadrangles

Although the concept of conjugate of a collineation is meaningful in any projective plane, it is not very useful in a plane that has few collineations. In a Desarguesian plane $\mathcal{P}$, however, the concept is extremely powerful, primarily because of the richness (as evidenced by our next theorem) of the collineation group of $\mathcal{P}$.

Theorem 3.6.1. (Quadrangle Mapping Theorem) If $\mathcal{Q}$ and $\mathcal{Q}'$ are any quadrangles in a Desarguesian plane $\mathcal{P}$, there is a projective collineation of $\mathcal{P}$ that maps $\mathcal{Q}$ onto $\mathcal{Q}'$, with the vertices of $\mathcal{Q}$ being transformed in any prescribed order into the vertices of $\mathcal{Q}'$.

Proof: Let the vertices of $\mathcal{Q}$ be Q_1, Q_2, Q_3, Q_4, and those of $\mathcal{Q}'$ be Q_1', Q_2', Q_3', Q_4', where the numberings indicate the order in which the vertices are to be mapped. A projective collineation that sends Q_i into Q_i' for each i will meet the requirements, since all sides of a quadrangle are determined by the vertices.

First construct $A = (Q_1 \cup Q_2) \cap (Q_3 \cup Q_4)$ and then construct $A' = (Q_1' \cup Q_2') \cap (Q_3' \cup Q_4')$. A, Q_1, Q_2 are distinct points on the line $k = Q_1 \cup Q_2$, and there exists (by the First Existence Theorem for Projectivities (1.7.2)) a projectivity π, from k to $Q_1' \cup Q_2'$ that sends A, Q_1, Q_2 into A', Q_1', Q_2', respectively. Extend π to a projective collineation σ_1. Figure 3.11 shows the relation of the quadrangle $\mathcal{Q}\sigma_1$ ($\mathcal{Q}$ transformed by σ_1) to $\mathcal{Q}'$.

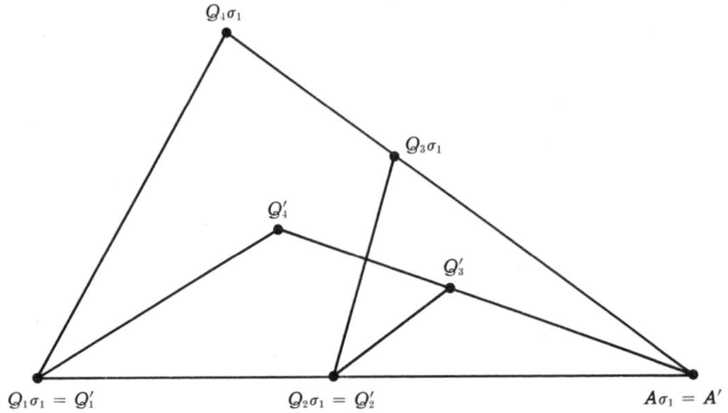

Figure 3.11

If $Q_3\sigma_1 = Q_3'$, take $\sigma_2 = \iota$ (the identity collineation). Otherwise, let H be a point, different from $Q_3\sigma_1$ and Q_3', on the line $Q_3\sigma_1 \cup Q_3'$, and construct the central collineation σ_2, with center H, axis $Q_1' \cup Q_2'$, sending $Q_3\sigma_1$ into Q_3'. In either case, then, $Q_i\sigma_1\sigma_2 = Q_i'$ for $i = 1, 2, 3$ (why?).

Let σ_3 be the homology with center Q_3', axis $Q_1' \cup Q_2'$, sending $Q_4\sigma_1\sigma_2$ into Q_4'; σ_3 exists because $Q_4\sigma_1\sigma_2$ and Q_4' are both on the line $A' \cup Q_3'$, are both different from Q_3' (why?), and are not on $Q_1' \cup Q_2'$.

(If $\mathcal{Q}_4\sigma_1\sigma_2 = \mathcal{Q}_4'$, $\sigma_3 = \iota$.) Then, $\mathcal{Q}_i\sigma_1\sigma_2\sigma_3 = \mathcal{Q}_i'$ for $i = 1, 2, 3, 4$, and the projective collineation $\sigma_1\sigma_2\sigma_3$ effects the desired mapping. ▮

A slight refinement of the above theorem is obtained by observing that the collineation σ_1 of the proof can be constructed as a composite of three or fewer central collineations, since the projectivity π is a composite of three or fewer perspectivities. Therefore, $\sigma_1\sigma_2\sigma_3$ is a composite of five or fewer central collineations; this number will, however, be improved upon in Section 4.6. The next theorem demonstrates the power of the Quadrangle Mapping Theorem in combination with the idea of conjugacy.

Theorem 3.6.2. (Conjugacy of Elations) In a Desarguesian plane, any two elations, different from the identity, are conjugate.

Proof: Let ϵ_1 and ϵ_2 be elations, both different from ι, and suppose that, for $i = 1, 2$, ϵ_i has $\mathfrak{D}_i = \{\ell_i, H_i, P_i, P_i'\}$ for a determining set. For $i = 1, 2$, let R_i and S_i be distinct points on ℓ_i, both different from H_i. Since P_i, P_i', R_i, S_i are triply noncollinear for $i = 1, 2$ (why?), there exists, by the Quadrangle Mapping Theorem, a collineation σ such that $P_1\sigma = P_2$, $P_1'\sigma = P_2'$, $R_1\sigma = R_2$, and $S_1\sigma = S_2$.

Because $\ell_1 = R_1 \cup S_1$, $\ell_1\sigma = R_2 \cup S_2 = \ell_2$; because $H_1 = (P_1 \cup P_1') \cap \ell_1$, $H_1\sigma = (P_2 \cup P_2') \cap \ell_2 = H_2$. Therefore, $\sigma^{-1}\epsilon_1\sigma$ is an elation with $\{\ell_2, H_2, P_2, P_2'\} = \mathfrak{D}_2$ as a determining set, by the theorem Conjugate of a Central Collineation (3.5.1). It follows that $\sigma^{-1}\epsilon_1\sigma = \epsilon_2$. ▮

Corollary 1: In a Desarguesian plane $\mathcal{P}$, if any elation different from the identity is periodic, with period p, then every elation of $\mathcal{P}$, other than the identity, is periodic with period p.

Proof: This corollary is an immediate consequence of the above theorem and the theorem Period of a Conjugate (3.5.4). ▮

Corollary 2: In a Desarguesian plane, the period of a periodic elation, other than the identity, is a prime number.

Proof: Let ϵ be a periodic elation with period $p > 1$. Suppose that $p = nm$, where n and m are positive integers and $n < p$. Then, since $\epsilon^p = \iota$, we have $\epsilon^{nm} = (\epsilon^n)^m = \iota$; but, ϵ^n is an elation and is not ι because $n < p$. Therefore, the period of ϵ^n is also p by Corollary 1. Because $(\epsilon^n)^m = \iota$, m must be at least as large as p; hence $n = 1$. Thus, in any factorization of p as a product of two positive integers, one of the factors is 1 and the other is p, which means that p is a prime. ▮

The prime number of Corollary 2, which is unique for any particular Desarguesian plane $\mathcal{P}$ by Corollary 1, is called the *characteristic* of $\mathcal{P}$. In view of Exercise 3.4.5, a Desarguesian plane $\mathcal{P}$ has characteristic 2 if and only if the diagonal points of every quadrangle in $\mathcal{P}$ are collinear. A Desarguesian plane with no periodic elation, other than the identity, is said to have characteristic zero.

The preceding theorem is decisive in determining the possible orders of a finite Desarguesian plane $\mathcal{P}$. If ϵ is any elation of $\mathcal{P}$ different from the identity, then the elations $\epsilon, \epsilon^2, \epsilon^3, \ldots$, cannot all be different, because of the assumed finiteness of $\mathcal{P}$. Therefore, $\epsilon^j = \epsilon^i$ for some $j > i$; hence $\epsilon^{j-i} = \iota$, and ϵ is periodic. Thus, $\mathcal{P}$ has a nonzero characteristic p, which is a prime number. The *order* of $\mathcal{P}$ may very well be larger than p, however. In any event, the order is some positive integral power of p, which may be seen as follows: The order of $\mathcal{P}$ is the same as the number of elations with a given center H and axis ℓ. This set of elations is a finite group (under composition) in which every element except the identity has period p. Now, a standard result of group theory ([13], pp. 43–44) asserts that if $\mathcal{G}$ is a finite group, and if the prime q divides the order (number of elements) of $\mathcal{G}$, then $\mathcal{G}$ has an element of period q. Applied to our group of elations with center H, axis ℓ, this theorem implies that p is the only prime divisor of the order of the elation group, which is the same as the order of $\mathcal{P}$. Therefore, the order of $\mathcal{P}$ is p^k for some positive integer k.

The group of elations of a finite Desarguesian plane with center H, axis ℓ, is so simple in its structure that an elementary number-theoretic argument can also be used to prove that its order is p^k (exercise 7). Furthermore, it is true that for any prime p and any positive integer k, there exists a unique (to within isomorphisms) Desarguesian plane of order p^k, though a complete proof of this statement will not be given. (See Section 4.8 and [16], pp. 314–325.) This section concludes with an application of the concept of characteristic to harmonic sets.

Example 3.6.3. Suppose that $\mathcal{H}(A, B; C, D)$ in a Desarguesian plane $\mathcal{P}$. If $\mathcal{P}$ has characteristic 3, then A, B, C, D form a harmonic set in any of their 24 arrangements. If the characteristic of $\mathcal{P}$ is neither 2 nor 3, exactly eight permutations of A, B, C, D yield harmonic sets.

Proof: Let ℓ be a line on A different from $A \cup B$. Construct the elation ϵ, with axis ℓ, center A, sending C into B; then, $\mathcal{H}(A, B; C, B\epsilon)$

by the theorem Elations and Harmonic Sets (3.4.4). Therefore, $B\epsilon = D$ by the uniqueness of the fourth point of a harmonic set in a Desarguesian plane. Another application of Theorem 3.4.4, this time to the elation ϵ^2, yields $\mathcal{H}(A, D; C, D\epsilon^2)$, since $C\epsilon^2 = B\epsilon = D$. (Note that $D \neq C$, because, in any case, we are supposing that the characteristic of $\mathcal{P}$ is not 2.) If the elation ϵ^{-2} is applied to the last harmonic set, there results $\mathcal{H}(A, C; C\epsilon^{-2}, D)$ because of the invariance of the harmonic property under collineations.

Now, suppose that $\mathcal{P}$ has characteristic 3. Then, $\epsilon^3 = \iota$; hence $D\epsilon^2 = D\epsilon^{-1} = B$, and $C\epsilon^{-2} = C\epsilon = B$. From the preceding paragraph, we see that $\mathcal{H}(A, D; C, B)$ and $\mathcal{H}(A, C; B, D)$, as well as the hypothesized $\mathcal{H}(A, B; C, D)$. The operations of the theorem Harmonic Permutations (3.4.3) applied to these three harmonic sets give, as harmonic sets, all 24 arrangements of A, B, C, D (verify!).

Conversely, if the characteristic of $\mathcal{P}$ is not 3, then $\epsilon^3 \neq \iota$, and $\mathcal{H}(A, D; C, B)$ and $\mathcal{H}(A, C; B, D)$ are both false (why?). If the characteristic of $\mathcal{P}$ is not 2 either, as we are assuming, the 16 arrangements obtainable from A, D, C, B and A, C, B, D by the operations of Theorem 3.4.3 all yield sets that are not harmonic (proof?), from which it follows that only the eight arrangements coming from A, B, C, D via the operations of that theorem give harmonic sets. ▮

Exercise 3.6.A

1. Give the characteristics of the following planes.

(a) 7_3.

(b) 13_4.

(c) 21_5.

(d) A Desarguesian plane with 91 points all together.

2. Prove that there is no Desarguesian plane with 11 points on a line.

3. Prove that in a Desarguesian plane of characteristic zero there are infinitely many points on every line.

4. Let $\mathcal{P}$ be a Desarguesian plane.

(a) Prove that any collineation of $\mathcal{P}$ that is conjugate to a harmonic homology of $\mathcal{P}$ is a harmonic homology.

(b) Prove that any two harmonic homologies of $\mathcal{P}$ are conjugate.

5. Suppose that $\mathcal{H}(A, B; C, D)$ in a Desarguesian plane of characteristic 2. What permutations of A, B, C, D yield harmonic sets?

Exercise 3.6.B

6. Let ℓ_1 and ℓ_2 be any lines in a Desarguesian plane $\mathcal{P}$, and let H_1 and H_2 be any points of $\mathcal{P}$ that are not on ℓ_1, ℓ_2, respectively. Prove that the group of homologies with center H_1, axis ℓ_1, is isomorphic to the group of homologies with center H_2, axis ℓ_2.

7. Let $\mathcal{P}$ be a finite Desarguesian plane of characteristic p, a prime. For the following, all elations have the same axis and center in $\mathcal{P}$.

(a) If ϵ_1 and ϵ_2 are elations such that $\epsilon_2^k = \epsilon_1^m$, where $1 \leqq k < p$, prove that $\epsilon_2 = \epsilon_1^{m'}$ for a suitable positive integer m'.

(b) If $\epsilon_1 \neq \iota$ and $\epsilon_2 \neq \iota$, and if ϵ_2 is not a power of ϵ_1, prove that the set of elations $\{\epsilon_1^i\epsilon_2^j\}$ contains exactly p^2 members.

(c) Continuing (b), prove that if ϵ_3 is not contained in the set $\{\epsilon_1^i\epsilon_2^j\}$, then the set $\{\epsilon_1^i\epsilon_2^j\epsilon_3^n\}$ has exactly p^3 members.

(d) Prove that the order of $\mathcal{P}$ is p^k for some positive integer k.

8. Suppose that $\mathcal{P}$ is a Desarguesian plane and that $\mathcal{P}' \cong \mathcal{P}$.

(a) Prove that $\mathcal{P}'$ is Desarguesian.

(b) Prove that the characteristic of $\mathcal{P}'$ is the same as the characteristic of $\mathcal{P}$.

(Use the results of Exercise 3.5.12.)

9. Let $\mathcal{P}$ be a Desarguesian plane, and suppose that there is a certain line ℓ in $\mathcal{P}$ such that any projectivity on ℓ with three distinct fixed points is the identity. Prove that the Fundamental Theorem holds in $\mathcal{P}$.

10. Let $\mathcal{A}$ be an affine plane, and let $\mathcal{P}$ be its projective extension. (Refer to Exercises 1.5.6 and 2.2.11.) An *affinity* of $\mathcal{A}$ is the restriction to $\mathcal{A}$ of a collineation ρ of $\mathcal{P}$ that fixes the line of $\mathcal{P}$ that is not in $\mathcal{A}$. (Thus, the restriction of ρ to $\mathcal{A}$ is a function on $\mathcal{A}$.) Suppose that $\mathcal{P}$ is Desarguesian, and let ABC and $A'B'C'$ be any triangles in $\mathcal{A}$. Prove that there is an affinity of $\mathcal{A}$ that sends A into A', B into B', and C into C'.

3.7. Construction of the Division Ring

In this section the geometric structure of a Desarguesian plane $\mathcal{P}$ is used to create an algebraic structure in the set of all points, except one, on a line of $\mathcal{P}$. The algebraic structure so developed is that of a mathematical system known as a division ring. The reason for omitting one of the points on the chosen line from this algebraic system will be evident from the nature of the constructions. (The point omitted is analogous to the ideal point of an ordinary line of $\mathcal{E}_2^*$.)

Let $\mathcal{P}$ be an arbitrary Desarguesian plane, and let k be a line of $\mathcal{P}$. Select a point on k, and name it ∞. Let $\mathcal{S}$ be the set of points on k other than ∞. Choose two distinct points of $\mathcal{S}$, and name them 0 and 1. Finally, let ℓ be a line on ∞ different from k. For the remainder of this section, the choices of $\mathcal{P}$, k, ∞, $\mathcal{S}$, 0, 1, and ℓ will not be changed.

The first task is to define an addition operation $+$ on $\mathcal{S}$. For each point X in $\mathcal{S}$, let ϵ_X be the elation with axis ℓ, center ∞, sending 0 into X. If A and B are any points of $\mathcal{S}$, *define* $A + B = A\epsilon_B$. (Figure 3.12 illustrates the construction of $A + B$.) Thus defined, addition in $\mathcal{S}$ has the customary properties, as the next theorem shows.

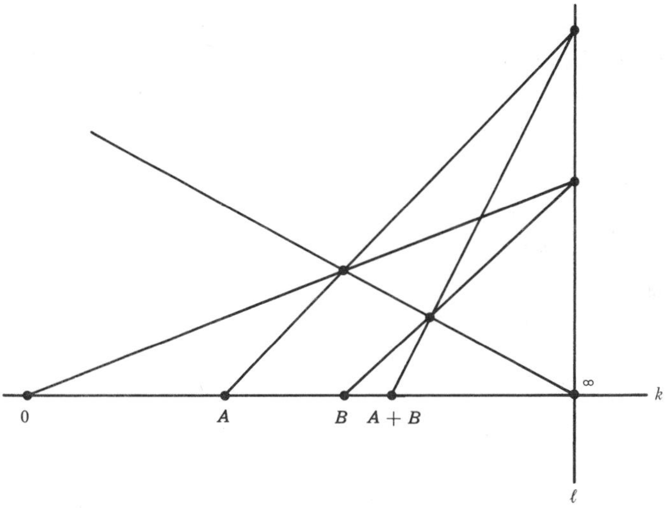

Figure 3.12

Theorem 3.7.1. The elements of $\mathcal{S}$, under the operation $+$, form a commutative group.

Proof: (a) The closure of $\mathcal{S}$ under $+$ is evident from the definition, since $A + B = A\epsilon_B$ is an element of $\mathcal{S}$ for any A, B in $\mathcal{S}$.

(b) Associativity of addition: Let A, B, C be any points of $\mathcal{S}$. Then, $\epsilon_B\epsilon_C$ is an elation with axis ℓ, center ∞, and $0\epsilon_B\epsilon_C = B\epsilon_C =$

$B + C = 0\epsilon_{B+C}$. Therefore, $\epsilon_B\epsilon_C = \epsilon_{B+C}$ (why?); hence $(A + B) + C = (A + B)\epsilon_C = A\epsilon_B\epsilon_C = A\epsilon_{B+C} = A + (B + C)$, and associativity is proved.

(c) Additive identity: Since $\epsilon_0 = \iota$, $A\epsilon_0 = A$ for any A in $\mathcal{S}$. Thus, $A + 0 = A$. Also, $0 + A = 0\epsilon_A = A$ by definition of addition (and of ϵ_A). Therefore, 0 is the additive identity of $\mathcal{S}$.

(d) Additive inverses: Let A be any point of $\mathcal{S}$; ϵ_A^{-1} is an elation with axis ℓ, center ∞, and it sends A into 0. Let $B = 0\epsilon_A^{-1}$; then, $\epsilon_B = \epsilon_A^{-1}$. Now, $B + A = B\epsilon_A = 0\epsilon_A^{-1}\epsilon_A = 0$, and $A + B = A\epsilon_B = 0\epsilon_A\epsilon_A^{-1} = 0$. Thus, B is the additive inverse of A, which we shall also denote by $-A$.

(e) Commutativity of addition: Let A and B be any points of $\mathcal{S}$. Then, $A + B = A\epsilon_B = 0\epsilon_A\epsilon_B = 0\epsilon_B\epsilon_A = B\epsilon_A = B + A$, since $\epsilon_A\epsilon_B = \epsilon_B\epsilon_A$ by the Second Commuting Theorem (3.1.2). ▮

Our success in using elations to define a satisfactory addition in $\mathcal{S}$ encourages the attempt to employ homologies to define multiplication. This effort will also be successful, with one mild reservation—the multiplication so defined will not necessarily be commutative.

For each X different from 0 in $\mathcal{S}$, let η_X be the homology with axis ℓ, center 0, sending 1 into X. Then, for each $A \neq 0$ and each

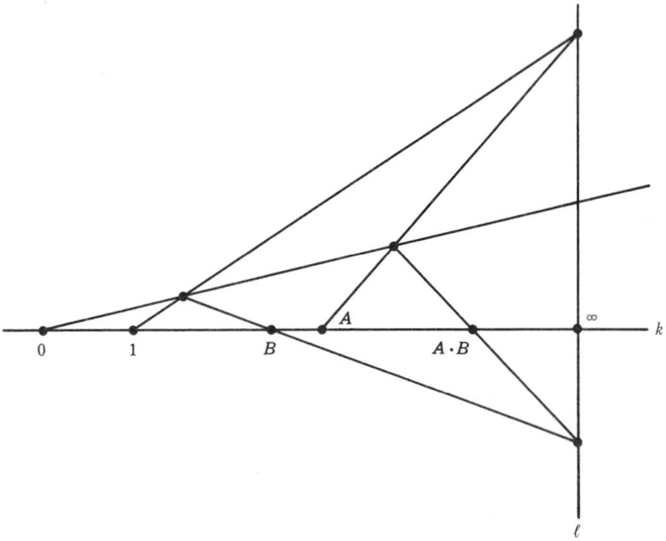

Figure 3.13

B in $\mathcal{S}$, *define* $A \cdot B = B\eta_A$. (Figure 3.13 illustrates the construction of $A \cdot B$.) Note that $A \cdot 0 = 0$ by this definition, but the product $0 \cdot B$ has not yet been defined. To complete the definition of multiplication in $\mathcal{S}$, set $0 \cdot B = 0$ for every B in $\mathcal{S}$.

Theorem 3.7.2. The elements of $\mathcal{S}$ that are different from 0 form a group under multiplication.

Proof: (a) Closure under multiplication: If A, B are elements of $\mathcal{S}$ different from 0, then $A \cdot B = B\eta_A$ is an element of $\mathcal{S}$ that is different from 0 (why?).

(b) Associativity of multiplication: Let A, B, C be any elements of $\mathcal{S}$ different from 0. Then, $\eta_B\eta_A$ is a homology with axis ℓ, center 0; further, $1\eta_B\eta_A = B\eta_A = A \cdot B = 1\eta_{A \cdot B}$. Therefore, $\eta_B\eta_A = \eta_{A \cdot B}$, and from this it follows that $(A \cdot B) \cdot C = C\eta_{A \cdot B} = C\eta_B\eta_A = (B \cdot C)\eta_A = A \cdot (B \cdot C)$.

(c) Multiplicative identity: Since $\eta_1 = \iota$, $1 \cdot A = A\eta_1 = A$ for every A in $\mathcal{S}$. Also, $A \cdot 1 = 1\eta_A = A$ if $A \neq 0$, and $0 \cdot 1 = 0$ by definition. Therefore, 1 is the multiplicative identity for all of $\mathcal{S}$.

(d) Multiplicative inverses: Let A be any element of $\mathcal{S}$ different from 0; η_A^{-1} is a homology with axis ℓ, center 0, and $A\eta_A^{-1} = 1$. Set $B = 1\eta_A^{-1}$, so that $\eta_B = \eta_A^{-1}$. Then, $B \cdot A = A\eta_B = A\eta_A^{-1} = 1$, and $A \cdot B = B\eta_A = 1\eta_B\eta_A = 1$. Thus, B is the multiplicative inverse of A, which we shall also denote by A^{-1}. ▮

The associativity of multiplication, proved above for the elements of $\mathcal{S}$ that are different from 0, in fact holds throughout $\mathcal{S}$ (exercise 1). That commutativity of multiplication is not a consequence of Axioms 1–4 will be demonstrated in Section 4.8. (The desirability of having a commutative multiplication will lead to the introduction of Axiom 5 in Chapter 5.)

Although it would have been possible, and apparently less awkward, to define multiplication by the equation $A \cdot B = A\eta_B$ for $B \neq 0$, the necessities of Chapter 4 dictate the choice of $A \cdot B = B\eta_A$ for $A \neq 0$. The homologies with center 0, axis ℓ, generate what may be called the left-multiplications (by elements other than 0) in $\mathcal{S}$. Since multiplication may not be commutative, these same homologies may not generate the right-multiplications in $\mathcal{S}$, so that the information of the next lemma is welcome.

Lemma 3.7.3. Let m be a line on 0 different from k. For each $X \neq 0$ in $\mathcal{S}$, let η^X be the homology with center ∞, axis m, sending 1 into X. Then, for any $B \neq 0$ and any A in $\mathcal{S}$, $A \cdot B = A\eta^B$.

Proof: If $A = 0$, $0\eta^B = 0 = 0 \cdot B$, so that the lemma is correct in this case. If $A \neq 0$, then $A\eta^B = 1\eta_A\eta^B = 1\eta^B\eta_A = B\eta_A = A \cdot B$. That $\eta_A\eta^B = \eta^B\eta_A$ is a consequence of the First Commuting Theorem (2.4.7), since each of η_A, η^B has its center on the axis of the other. ▮

From the definitions of addition and multiplication using elations and homologies, it seems that something can be proved concerning the interaction of the two operations, and this is indeed so, as the next theorem shows.

Theorem 3.7.4. In $\mathcal{S}$, multiplication is both left- and right-distributive with respect to addition. That is, for arbitrary elements A, B, C in $\mathcal{S}$, it is true that:

(a) $A \cdot (B + C) = A \cdot B + A \cdot C$, and

(b) $(B + C) \cdot A = B \cdot A + C \cdot A$.

Proof: (a) Left-distributivity: If $A = 0$, then $A \cdot (B + C) = 0$, $A \cdot B = 0$, $A \cdot C = 0$, and the result follows. If $A \neq 0$, the collineation $\eta_A^{-1}\epsilon_C\eta_A$ is, by the theorem Conjugate of a Central Collineation (3.5.1), an elation with axis ℓ, center ∞. Since $0\eta_A^{-1}\epsilon_C\eta_A = 0\epsilon_C\eta_A = C\eta_A = A \cdot C$, it is seen that $\eta_A^{-1}\epsilon_C\eta_A = \epsilon_{A \cdot C}$; hence $\epsilon_C\eta_A = \eta_A\epsilon_{A \cdot C}$. Therefore, $A \cdot (B + C) = (B + C)\eta_A = B\epsilon_C\eta_A = B\eta_A\epsilon_{A \cdot C} = (A \cdot B)\epsilon_{A \cdot C} = A \cdot B + A \cdot C$.

(b) Right-distributivity: If $A = 0$, then $(B + C) \cdot A = 0$, $B \cdot A = 0$, $C \cdot A = 0$, and the result follows. If $A \neq 0$, the collineation $(\eta^A)^{-1}\epsilon_C\eta^A$ is, also by Theorem 3.5.1, an elation with axis ℓ, center ∞. Since $0(\eta^A)^{-1}\epsilon_C\eta^A = 0\epsilon_C\eta^A = C\eta^A = C \cdot A$, it is seen that $(\eta^A)^{-1}\epsilon_C\eta^A = \epsilon_{C \cdot A}$, or $\epsilon_C\eta^A = \eta^A\epsilon_{C \cdot A}$. Therefore, $(B + C) \cdot A = (B + C)\eta^A = B\epsilon_C\eta^A = B\eta^A\epsilon_{C \cdot A} = (B \cdot A)\epsilon_{C \cdot A} = B \cdot A + C \cdot A$. ▮

When the results of this section are collected, it is found that $\mathcal{S}$, endowed with the operations of addition and multiplication that have been defined, is a *division ring*, according to the following definition.

Definition 3.7.5. A *division ring* is a set $\mathcal{R}$ containing at least two distinct elements, together with two binary operations on $\mathcal{R}$, called addition $(+)$ and multiplication $(\cdot)$ (also indicated by juxtaposition of the elements being multiplied), subject to the following postulates.

A. The elements of $\mathcal{R}$ form a commutative group under the operation $+$, the identity element of this group being named 0.

M. If a and b are any elements of $\mathcal{R}$, ab is an element of $\mathcal{R}$. Further, multiplication is associative in $\mathcal{R}$; that is, $(ab)c = a(bc)$ for any elements a, b, c in $\mathcal{R}$. Finally, the elements of

$\mathcal{R}$ different from 0 form a group under multiplication, the identity element of this group being named 1.

D. For arbitrary a, b, c in $\mathcal{R}$, the two distributive laws hold: $a(b + c) = ab + ac$, and $(b + c)a = ba + ca$. ▮

Examples of division rings familiar to the reader are the rational numbers, the real numbers, and the complex numbers; in all these division rings multiplication is commutative. Additional examples of division rings (also with commutative multiplication) can be constructed by using the planes 7_3, 13_4, 21_5, and the plane of Exercise 1.4.4, together with the methods of this section (exercises 3, 4, 11, and 12). A division ring in which multiplication is commutative is called a *field*. In Section 4.8 there will be given a construction of a certain division ring that is not a field, as well as a method for building Desarguesian planes over arbitrary division rings, thus proving the existence of Desarguesian planes in which multiplication is not commutative.

Exercise 3.7.A

1. Prove that multiplication is associative in all of $\mathcal{S}$, where $\mathcal{S}$ is the division ring constructed in this section.

2. If A and B are elements of $\mathcal{S}$ different from 0, prove that $\eta^A\eta^B = \eta^{A \cdot B}$, where η^A, η^B are as defined in Lemma 3.7.3.

3. By using the plane 7_3 and the constructions of this section, make a division ring with two elements. Write the addition and multiplication tables for this division ring, and show that it is a field.

4. Carry out the program of exercise 3 with the plane 13_4, thus making a three-element division ring. Is it a field?

5. (a) In any division ring, prove that if $ab = 0$, then either $a = 0$ or $b = 0$.

(b) In any division ring, prove that $a(-b) = (-a)b = -(ab)$ for any elements a and b.

6. Here the notation of this section is used.

(a) Let B be an arbitrary point of $\mathcal{S}$, and let a function α_B be defined on $\mathcal{I}(k)$ as follows: $X\alpha_B = X + B$ for each X in $\mathcal{S}$, and $(\infty)\alpha_B = \infty$. Prove that α_B is a projectivity on k.

(b) Let B be an element of $\mathcal{S}$ different from 0, and let a function β_B be defined on $\mathcal{I}(k)$ as follows: $X\beta_B = B \cdot X$ if X is in $\mathcal{S}$, and $(\infty)\beta_B = \infty$. Prove that β_B is a projectivity on k.

(c) Let B be an element of $\mathcal{S}$ different from 0, and let a function γ_B be defined on $\mathcal{J}(k)$ as follows: $X\gamma_B = X \cdot B$ if X is in $\mathcal{S}$, and $(\infty)\gamma_B = \infty$. Prove that γ_B is a projectivity on k.

Exercise 3.7.B

7. Let η be the harmonic homology with axis ℓ, center 0, in the notation of this section. Prove that, for every X in $\mathcal{S}$, $X\eta = -X$.

8. Use the results of exercises 5b and 7 to construct another proof of the result given in Exercise 3.4.10.

9. Let A and B be any elements of $\mathcal{S}$ (the division ring of this section) such that $A \neq 0$ or 1 and $B \neq 0$ or 1. Prove that $\mathcal{Q}(1, A, \infty; A \cdot B, B, 0)$.

10. Let A and B be any elements of $\mathcal{S}$ that are both different from 0. Prove that $\mathcal{Q}(0, A, \infty; B + A, B, \infty)$.

11. Carry out the program of exercise 3 for the plane 21_5, thus constructing a four-element division ring. Prove that this division ring is a field.

12. Using the incidence table for a 31-point plane that you have saved from Exercise 1.4.4, carry out the program of exercise 3 for this plane, thus constructing a five-element division ring. Prove that this division ring is a field.

3.8. Uniqueness of the Division Ring

The first aim of this section is to establish the equivalence of any two division rings created in the Desarguesian plane $\mathcal{P}$ by the method of the last section. Let k, ∞, $\mathcal{S}$, 0, 1, ℓ be as in Section 3.7. In $\mathcal{S}$, multiplication is governed by the group $\mathcal{H}$ of homologies with center 0, axis ℓ, and addition is governed by the group $\mathcal{E}$ of elations with center ∞, axis ℓ. Now, choose any line k', any distinct points $0'$, $1'$, ∞', on k', and any line ℓ', other than k', on ∞'. In the set of points on k' other than ∞', construct a second division ring $\mathcal{S}'$, whose multiplication and addition are respectively determined by the group $\mathcal{H}'$ of homologies with center $0'$, axis ℓ', and the group $\mathcal{E}'$ of elations with center ∞', axis ℓ'. We shall produce a collineation that maps $\mathcal{S}$ onto $\mathcal{S}'$ and simultaneously transforms $\mathcal{H}$ into $\mathcal{H}'$ and $\mathcal{E}$ into $\mathcal{E}'$. The isomorphy of the (conjugate) groups $\mathcal{H}$ and $\mathcal{H}'$ and of the (conjugate) groups $\mathcal{E}$ and $\mathcal{E}'$ ensures the equivalence of $\mathcal{S}$ and $\mathcal{S}'$. (Compare with Exercise 3.6.6.)

Let R and S be distinct points on ℓ, both different from ∞, and let R' and S' be distinct points on ℓ', both different from ∞'. By the Quadrangle Mapping Theorem (3.6.1), there is a collineation σ of $\mathcal{P}$ such that $R\sigma = R'$, $S\sigma = S'$, $0\sigma = 0'$, and $1\sigma = 1'$. Then, $k\sigma = k'$, $\ell\sigma = \ell'$, $(\infty)\sigma = \infty'$ (why?), and the restriction of σ to the points of $\mathcal{S}$ is a bijection from $\mathcal{S}$ to $\mathcal{S}'$. If X is any point of $\mathcal{S}$, and if ϵ_X is the elation with axis ℓ, center ∞, sending 0 into X, then $\sigma^{-1}\epsilon_X\sigma$ is the elation with axis ℓ', center ∞', sending $0'$ into $X\sigma$, by the theorem Conjugate of a Central Collineation (3.5.1). Therefore, $\sigma^{-1}\epsilon_X\sigma = \epsilon'_{X\sigma}$, the elation that generates the addition of $X\sigma$ in the division ring $\mathcal{S}'$. Similarly, if $X \neq 0$ is a point of $\mathcal{S}$, then $\sigma^{-1}\eta_X\sigma = \eta'_{X\sigma}$, the homology that generates the left-multiplication by $X\sigma$ in $\mathcal{S}'$.

In $\mathcal{S}'$, $A\sigma + B\sigma = (A\sigma)\epsilon'_{B\sigma} = (A\sigma)\sigma^{-1}\epsilon_B\sigma = A\epsilon_B\sigma = (A + B)\sigma$. Also, if $A\sigma \neq 0'$, $A\sigma \cdot B\sigma = (B\sigma)\eta'_{A\sigma} = (B\sigma)\sigma^{-1}\eta_A\sigma = B\eta_A\sigma = (A \cdot B)\sigma$. If $A\sigma = 0'$, then $A\sigma \cdot B\sigma = 0' = 0\sigma = (0 \cdot B)\sigma = (A \cdot B)\sigma$, since $A = 0$. Thus, the restriction of σ to the points of $\mathcal{S}$ is a bijection from $\mathcal{S}$ to $\mathcal{S}'$ with the following properties.

(a) $(A + B)\sigma = A\sigma + B\sigma$ for all A, B in $\mathcal{S}$.

(b) $(A \cdot B)\sigma = A\sigma \cdot B\sigma$ for all A, B in $\mathcal{S}$.

Such a function is an *isomorphism* of $\mathcal{S}$ onto $\mathcal{S}'$, in accordance with the next definition.

Definition 3.8.1. The division ring $\mathcal{R}'$ is *isomorphic* to the division ring $\mathcal{R}$ if and only if there is a bijection Φ from $\mathcal{R}$ to $\mathcal{R}'$ that has both the following properties.

(a) $(a + b)\Phi = a\Phi + b\Phi$ for all a, b in $\mathcal{R}$.

(b) $(ab)\Phi = (a\Phi)(b\Phi)$ for all a, b in $\mathcal{R}$.

A bijection Φ satisfying these conditions is an *isomorphism* of $\mathcal{R}$ onto $\mathcal{R}'$. ▮

In the equation (a) of the above definition, observe that the sum $a + b$ is calculated in $\mathcal{R}$, while the sum $a\Phi + b\Phi$ is calculated in $\mathcal{R}'$, which may have a different addition operation. A similar remark applies to equation (b). However, an important special case of the definition occurs when $\mathcal{R}$ and $\mathcal{R}'$ are the same division ring, with the same operations of addition and multiplication; in this case, the bijection Φ is called an *automorphism* of $\mathcal{R}$. If the division ring $\mathcal{R}'$ is isomorphic to the division ring $\mathcal{R}$, we may also say that $\mathcal{R}'$ is related to $\mathcal{R}$ by the relation of *isomorphy*. The relation thus defined on the set of all division rings is an equivalence relation (exercise 1c).

An isomorphism of division rings preserves the two relevant operations—addition and multiplication. (Compare with the discussion of isomorphisms at the end of Section 3.5.) Thus, two division rings that are isomorphic are algebraically indistinguishable, and it is in this sense that we have proved the following theorem.

Theorem 3.8.2. (Uniqueness of the Division Ring) A Desarguesian plane $\mathcal{P}$ determines a unique (to within isomorphisms) division ring $\mathcal{R}$, which can be constructed in the set of all points, except one, on any line of $\mathcal{P}$ in the manner of Section 3.7. ∎

Example 3.8.3. We prove that the division ring associated with $\mathcal{E}_2{}^*$ is (isomorphic to) the field of real numbers. In $\mathcal{E}_2$, construct a Cartesian coordinate system, and let k be the x-axis of this coordinate system. Let ∞ be the ideal point of k, and let ℓ be the ideal line of $\mathcal{E}_2{}^*$.

For each nonzero real number r, let η_r be the homology of $\mathcal{E}_2{}^*$ with axis ℓ, center $[0, 0]$, sending $[1, 0]$ into $[r, 0]$. Our first task is to discover the effect of η_r upon the ordinary points of k. This happens to be a task for which we are well prepared by Proposition 2.3.5. For, δ_r, the central dilatation of $\mathcal{E}_2$ with center $[0, 0]$ and ratio r, has, by Proposition 2.3.5, a unique extension to a central collineation η (with center $[0, 0]$) of $\mathcal{E}_2{}^*$, and η evidently has axis ℓ. Since $[1, 0]\delta_r =$ $[r, 0]$, the Uniqueness Theorem for Central Collineations (2.4.5) implies that the extension of δ_r is the homology η_r. Therefore, for every ordinary point $[b, 0]$ on k, $[b, 0]\eta_r = [b, 0]\delta_r = [rb, 0]$.

Next, for each real number t, let ϵ_t be the elation of $\mathcal{E}_2{}^*$ with center ∞, axis ℓ, sending $[0, 0]$ into $[t, 0]$. Now, τ_t, the translation of $\mathcal{E}_2$ by $[t, 0]$, has, also by Proposition 2.3.5, a unique extension to a central collineation ϵ (with center ∞) of $\mathcal{E}_2{}^*$, and ϵ evidently has axis ℓ. Since $[0, 0]\tau_t = [t, 0]$, Theorem 2.4.5 implies that the extension of τ_t is the elation ϵ_t. Therefore, for each ordinary point $[b, 0]$ on k, $[b, 0]\epsilon_t = [b, 0]\tau_t = [b + t, 0]$.

Let $\mathcal{S}$ be the division ring constructed in the set of all points, except ∞, on the line k in the manner of Section 3.7, using k, ∞, $[0, 0]$, $[1, 0]$, ℓ of $\mathcal{E}_2{}^*$ in the roles of k, ∞, 0, 1, ℓ, respectively, of the previous section. Let $\mathcal{R}$ be the field of real numbers, and define a function Φ from $\mathcal{R}$ to $\mathcal{S}$ as follows: $a\Phi = [a, 0]$ for each real number a. Then, Φ is a bijection from $\mathcal{R}$ to $\mathcal{S}$.

If a, b are any numbers of $\mathcal{R}$, $(a + b)\Phi = [a + b, 0] = [a, 0]\epsilon_b$ from above. Observing that $[a, 0] = a\Phi$ and that ϵ_b is the elation that would have been named $\epsilon_{b\Phi}$ in Section 3.7, we see that $[a, 0]\epsilon_b =$

$(a\Phi)\epsilon_{b\Phi} = a\Phi + b\Phi$, where this addition takes place in $\mathcal{S}$. Thus, $(a + b)\Phi = a\Phi + b\Phi$.

If $a = 0$, then $a\Phi = [0, 0]$, the zero element of $\mathcal{S}$; hence $(ab)\Phi = 0\Phi = (0\Phi)\cdot(b\Phi)$ (in $\mathcal{S}$) for any b in $\mathcal{R}$. If $a \neq 0$, and if b is any number of $\mathcal{R}$, then $(ab)\Phi = [ab, 0] = [b, 0]\eta_a$ from above. Because $[b, 0]\eta_a = (a\Phi)\cdot(b\Phi)$ in $\mathcal{S}$ (why?), it follows that $(ab)\Phi = (a\Phi)\cdot(b\Phi)$ for all a, b in $\mathcal{R}$.

Therefore, Φ is an isomorphism of $\mathcal{R}$ onto $\mathcal{S}$, and, since (by Theorem 3.8.2) $\mathcal{S}$ is isomorphic to the division ring $\mathcal{R}'$ associated with $\mathcal{E}_2^*$, we see that $\mathcal{R}'$ is isomorphic to $\mathcal{R}$ (exercise 1c). ▌

The (unique) division ring associated with a Desarguesian plane $\mathcal{P}$ may be thought of as having an existence independent of $\mathcal{P}$; it is for this reason that we have used $\mathcal{R}$ to denote it in Theorem 3.8.2, rather than the letter $\mathcal{S}$ employed in Section 3.7. If we regard $\mathcal{R}$ as being detached from $\mathcal{P}$ after its construction, it will be helpful to name its elements (which will henceforth be called *numbers*) with small italic letters, such as a, b.

Our viewpoint, then, is the following: A division ring has been constructed in the set $\mathcal{S}$. It is then extracted from $\mathcal{S}$, simultaneously having its name changed to $\mathcal{R}$ and the names of its elements from A, B, etc., to a, b, etc. We now regard $\mathcal{R}$ as a set of *coordinates* for the points of $\mathcal{S}$, with the points 0 and 1 having the coordinates 0 and 1, respectively, the point A having the coordinate a, etc. (The use of 0 and 1 as names for points of $\mathcal{S}$ as well as for numbers of $\mathcal{R}$ is a convenience that is partially justified by exercise 3.) The essential feature of this coordinate system in $\mathcal{S}$ is that if A has coordinate a and B has coordinate b, then $A + B$ has coordinate $a + b$, and $A\cdot B$ has coordinate ab. That is, the function from $\mathcal{R}$ to $\mathcal{S}$ that assigns to each element a of $\mathcal{R}$ that point of $\mathcal{S}$ with coordinate a is an isomorphism of $\mathcal{R}$ onto the division ring $\mathcal{S}$. We are led to make the following definition.

Definition 3.8.4. Let $\mathcal{P}$ be a Desarguesian plane, and let $\mathcal{R}$ be the division ring associated with $\mathcal{P}$. Suppose that the division ring $\mathcal{S}$ has been constructed in the set of all points except one on a line k of $\mathcal{P}$. If an isomorphism Φ of $\mathcal{R}$ onto $\mathcal{S}$ is prescribed, then $\mathcal{S}$ is said to be *coordinatized* by Φ (and $\mathcal{R}$), and Φ is a *coordinatization* of $\mathcal{S}$. The point $a\Phi$ is said to have coordinate a in the coordinate system determined by Φ, where a is any number of $\mathcal{R}$. ▌

Theorem 3.8.2 guarantees that the set $\mathcal{S}$ of the above definition has at least one coordinatization, but it may have more than one. Quite generally, there are as many as there are automorphisms of $\mathcal{R}$, as the next theorem proves.

Theorem 3.8.5. Let Φ be a coordinatization of $\mathcal{S}$ (Definition 3.8.4).

(a) If Ψ is any coordinatization of $\mathcal{S}$, then $\Psi = \Theta\Phi$, where Θ is some automorphism of $\mathcal{R}$.

(b) Conversely, if Θ is any automorphism of $\mathcal{R}$, then $\Psi = \Theta\Phi$ is a coordinatization of $\mathcal{S}$.

Proof: (a) Let $\Theta = \Psi\Phi^{-1}$. Since Φ^{-1} is an isomorphism of $\mathcal{S}$ onto $\mathcal{R}$ (exercise 1a), $\Psi\Phi^{-1}$ is an isomorphism of $\mathcal{R}$ onto $\mathcal{R}$ (exercise 1b). Thus, Θ is an automorphism of $\mathcal{R}$, and $\Psi = \Theta\Phi$.

(b) Since Θ is an automorphism of $\mathcal{R}$, $\Theta\Phi$ is an isomorphism of $\mathcal{R}$ onto $\mathcal{S}$ (exercise 1b); that is, $\Psi = \Theta\Phi$ is a coordinatization of $\mathcal{S}$. ▌

Exercise 3.8.A

1. Let $\mathcal{R}$, $\mathcal{R}'$, $\mathcal{R}''$ be division rings.

(a) If Φ is an isomorphism of $\mathcal{R}$ onto $\mathcal{R}'$, prove that Φ^{-1} is an isomorphism of $\mathcal{R}'$ onto $\mathcal{R}$.

(b) If Φ is an isomorphism of $\mathcal{R}$ onto $\mathcal{R}'$ and ψ is an isomorphism of $\mathcal{R}'$ onto $\mathcal{R}''$, prove that $\Phi\Psi$ is an isomorphism of $\mathcal{R}$ onto $\mathcal{R}''$.

(c) Prove that isomorphy is an equivalence relation on the set of all division rings.

2. In a Desarguesian plane $\mathcal{P}$, prove that the multiplicative group of nonzero numbers of $\mathcal{R}$ (the division ring associated with $\mathcal{P}$) is isomorphic to $\mathcal{H}(H, \ell)$, the group of homologies with center H, axis ℓ, for any choice of nonincident H and ℓ. (Use the result of Exercise 3.6.6.)

3. Prove that in any isomorphism of one division ring onto another, the additive and multiplicative identities of one ring are mapped upon the additive and multiplicative identities, respectively, of the other ring. In particular, conclude that any coordinatization of $\mathcal{S}$ (Definition 3.8.4) assigns to the points 0 and 1 of $\mathcal{S}$ the coordinates 0 and 1, respectively.

4. Suppose that Φ is an automorphism of the division ring $\mathcal{R}$, and let x be any nonzero number of $\mathcal{R}$. Prove that $(x^{-1})\Phi = (x\Phi)^{-1}$.

5. (a) Let $\mathcal{P}$ be a Desarguesian plane of characteristic p, and let $\mathcal{R}$ be the division ring associated with $\mathcal{P}$. If x is any number of $\mathcal{R}$, prove that $px = 0$, where px is defined to be $x + x + \cdots + x$ (p summands).

(b) Prove that $\mathcal{E}_2^*$ has no periodic elation.

(c) Prove that the diagonal points of a complete quadrangle in $\mathcal{E}_2^*$ are never collinear.

6. Let a be a nonzero element of the division ring $\mathcal{R}$. Let a function Φ be defined on $\mathcal{R}$ by the equation $x\Phi = a^{-1}xa$ for each x in $\mathcal{R}$.

(a) Prove that Φ is an automorphism of $\mathcal{R}$. (It is called an *inner* automorphism.) Also, prove that Φ is the identity automorphism if and only if a commutes (in multiplication) with every element of $\mathcal{R}$.

(b) Prove that if Φ and Ψ are inner automorphisms of $\mathcal{R}$, then Φ^{-1} and $\Phi\Psi$ are inner automorphisms of $\mathcal{R}$. Deduce that the inner automorphisms of $\mathcal{R}$ form a group under composition.

Exercise 3.8.B

7. (a) Let $\mathcal{R}$ be a field with p elements, where p is a prime. Prove that the only automorphism of $\mathcal{R}$ is the identity.

(b) Find an automorphism, different from the identity, of the field of four elements whose construction was requested in Exercise 3.7.11.

8. (a) Prove that the only automorphism of the field of rational numbers is the identity.

(b) Prove that the only automorphism of the field of real numbers is the identity.

9. Here the notation is that of Section 3.7.

(a) Let A and B be any points of $\mathcal{S}$, with $A \neq 0$. Then, $A \cdot B = B\eta_A$. Prove that if ℓ' is any line on ∞ other than k and ℓ, and if η'_A is the homology with center 0, axis ℓ', sending 1 into A, then $B\eta'_A = A \cdot B$, also.

(b) Establish a result analogous to that of part (a) for addition in $\mathcal{S}$. Hence, prove that the arithmetic operations in $\mathcal{S}$ are completely determined by the assignments of 0, 1, ∞.

10. Let ρ be any collineation of $\mathcal{P}$ that fixes the points 0, 1, ∞ on k, in the notation of Section 3.7. Prove that the restriction of ρ to $\mathcal{S}$ is an automorphism of the division ring $\mathcal{S}$. (Use the method of the first part of this section, together with the results of exercise 9.)

3. Desarguesian Planes

11. Again the notation is that of Section 3.7.

(a) Let π be a Π_2 on k with central invariant point 0, axial invariant point ∞, sending 1 into A, where $A \neq 0$. Prove that $B\pi = A \cdot B$ for every B in $\mathcal{S}$.

(b) Let π' be a Π_2 on k with central and axial invariant points at ∞, sending 0 into B. Prove that $A\pi' = A + B$ for every A in $\mathcal{S}$.

(c) Deduce that the arithmetic operations in $\mathcal{S}$ could have been defined by using Π_2's on k. (Compare with [33], pp. 120–127.)

Chapter 4

COORDINATES IN A DESARGUESIAN PLANE

4.1. Homogeneous Coordinates

In the first seven sections of this chapter, $\mathcal{P}$ is an arbitrary Desarguesian plane. Our first goal is to construct a coordinate system for all the points of $\mathcal{P}$. The natural inclination is to attempt to represent each point of $\mathcal{P}$ by an ordered pair of numbers from $\mathcal{R}$ (the division ring associated with $\mathcal{P}$). That such an attempt must fail for the plane 21_5, for example, is easily demonstrated by comparing the number of points of 21_5 (21) with the number of ordered pairs of numbers of the four-element field associated with 21_5 ($4^2 = 16$). There simply aren't enough ordered pairs to represent all the points, and the same thing is true for any finite Desarguesian plane, as a similar counting argument shows (exercise 1).

For an infinite plane $\mathcal{P}$, there still aren't enough ordered pairs of numbers of $\mathcal{R}$ to take care of all the points if we want the coordinate system to have the customary properties. Consider $\mathcal{E}_2^*$, whose associated division ring is (by Example 3.8.3) the field of real numbers. We know how to coordinatize $\mathcal{E}_2$ in a satisfactory way, and we would want a coordinate system for $\mathcal{E}_2^*$ to be some kind of extension of a coordinate system for $\mathcal{E}_2$. But, when the points of $\mathcal{E}_2$ are represented by ordered pairs of real numbers (through introduction of a Cartesian coordinate system, for instance), all ordered pairs of real numbers are used up. What sort of coordinate representation is possible, then, for the ideal points of $\mathcal{E}_2^*$?

A clue to the solution of our problem for $\mathcal{E}_2^*$ (and for the general

Desarguesian plane as well) can be discovered by focusing our attention on the lines of $\mathcal{E}_2$ rather than on the points, for the principle of duality suggests that if points of $\mathcal{E}_2^*$ are to have coordinates, then so should lines. But, $\mathcal{E}_2$ already has all the lines of $\mathcal{E}_2^*$ except the ideal line. Thus, if we can find coordinates for lines of $\mathcal{E}_2$, only one additional set of coordinates would have to be invented to take care of the lines of $\mathcal{E}_2^*$, and coordinates of points in $\mathcal{E}_2^*$ could then be obtained by dualization.

It is a familiar fact that (in the presence of a coordinate system) a line k in $\mathcal{E}_2$ can be represented by an equation $xk + ym + n = 0$, with the point $[x, y]$ of $\mathcal{E}_2$ being on k if and only if its coordinates satisfy this equation. (Since multiplication of real numbers is commutative, it makes no difference whether we write $xk + ym + n = 0$ or $kx + my + n = 0$. However, if we were working over a division ring whose multiplication is not commutative, the two equations would not in general be equivalent. We have chosen the form $xk + ym + n = 0$ with an eye to the needs of the remainder of this chapter; this form is in part dictated by the decision to use the right-hand notation for functions—$X\phi$ rather than $\phi(X)$.) Now, the numbers k, m, n determine the line k, and we might take them as coordinates for k, writing

$$[k] = \begin{bmatrix} k \\ m \\ n \end{bmatrix}$$

to mean that this ordered (column-) triple is a coordinate triple for k. (We shall write coordinates of lines in columns to distinguish them from coordinates of points, which we shall write in rows.) Note, however, that

$$\begin{bmatrix} kr \\ mr \\ nr \end{bmatrix}$$

is an equally good coordinate triple for k for any $r \neq 0$, because $x(kr) + y(mr) + (nr) = 0$ is also an equation for k if $r \neq 0$. This property of coordinates of lines in $\mathcal{E}_2$ is called *homogeneity*.

We have learned that lines of $\mathcal{E}_2$ can, in a natural way, be assigned homogeneous coordinates, and that these coordinates take the form of *classes* of ordered *triples* of real numbers. That is, a line k (with equation $xk + ym + n = 0$) is assigned the class of all triples of the form

$$\begin{bmatrix} kr \\ mr \\ nr \end{bmatrix}$$

for $r \neq 0$. (Again, whether the multiplier r is put on the right or left is immaterial for real numbers, but not for the elements of a non-commutative division ring. The right-hand notation has been chosen because it is the more advantageous for our later work.) Observe that if k, m, n are any real numbers such that not both k and m are zero, there is a line of $\mathcal{E}_2$ with coordinate triple

$$\begin{bmatrix} k \\ m \\ n \end{bmatrix},$$

but that no line of $\mathcal{E}_2$ has the coordinate triple

$$\begin{bmatrix} 0 \\ 0 \\ r \end{bmatrix}$$

for any r (why?). These facts suggest assigning the class of triples of the form

$$\begin{bmatrix} 0 \\ 0 \\ r \end{bmatrix}$$

$(r \neq 0)$ to the ideal line of $\mathcal{E}_2^*$. If this were done, each line of $\mathcal{E}_2^*$ would be represented by a unique class of triples and each class of triples (with not all members 0) would represent a unique line of $\mathcal{E}_2^*$.

Since there are just enough classes of triples (with not all members 0) to represent the lines of $\mathcal{E}_2^*$, the principle of duality leads us to represent points also by classes of (row-) triples. The following procedure produces a homogeneous coordinate system in $\mathcal{E}_2^*$ that is a natural extension of a coordinate system in $\mathcal{E}_2$.

Let a Cartesian coordinate system be given in $\mathcal{E}_2$. Let P be any point of $\mathcal{E}_2$, and suppose that P has Cartesian coordinates $[p, q]$. We assign to P, as a point of $\mathcal{E}_2^*$, the triple $[p, q, 1]$; since point-coordinates are to be homogeneous, too, we also give to P the class of all triples $[rp, rq, r]$ for $r \neq 0$. (The multiplier r is put on the left in point-triples to satisfy future needs.) If k is a line of $\mathcal{E}_2$, with Cartesian equation $xk + ym + n = 0$, we assign to k, as a line of $\mathcal{E}_2^*$, the class of triples

$$\begin{bmatrix} kr \\ mr \\ nr \end{bmatrix}$$

for $r \neq 0$. It is then easy to see (exercise 2a) that the point X of $\mathcal{E}_2$ is on k if and only if $xk + ym + zn = 0$, where $[x, y, z]$ is a coordinate triple for X. If I is the ideal point of k (in $\mathcal{E}_2^*$), we assign to I the class of triples $[rm, -rk, 0]$ for $r \neq 0$. It follows (exercise 2b) that the coordinates of I satisfy the equation $xk + ym + zc = 0$ for any c, which is in accord with the fact that I is on every line of $\mathcal{E}_2$ that is parallel to k. Since k could have been any line of $\mathcal{E}_2$, all ideal points have been assigned coordinate triples. The coordinates of every ideal point (and of no ordinary point) are seen (exercise 2c) to satisfy the equation $x \cdot 0 + y \cdot 0 + zr = 0$ $(r \neq 0)$, which justifies assigning to the ideal line of $\mathcal{E}_2^*$ the class of all triples

$$\begin{bmatrix} 0 \\ 0 \\ r \end{bmatrix}$$

for $r \neq 0$.

The discussion of $\mathcal{E}_2^*$ in this section has served to give us a method of attacking the problem of coordinatizing the general Desarguesian plane $\mathcal{P}$. The actual details of the construction of a coordinate system in $\mathcal{P}$ will be taken up in the next section. We end this section with a summary of ideas that we shall use in that construction.

(1) Points of $\mathcal{P}$ will be represented by classes of ordered (row-) triples of numbers of $\mathcal{R}$. Let us set down here the definitions of the row-triple relations and operations that we shall need.

(a) Equality: $[a, b, c] = [d, e, f]$ if and only if $a = d$, $b = e$, and $c = f$.

(b) (Left-) multiplication by a number: $r[a, b, c] = [ra, rb, rc]$.

(c) Addition: $[a, b, c] + [d, e, f] = [a + d, b + e, c + f]$.

(d) (Left-) equivalence: Let a relation $\sim$ be defined on the set of row-triples of numbers of the division ring $\mathcal{R}$ as follows: $[d, e, f] \sim [a, b, c]$ if and only if $[d, e, f] = r[a, b, c]$ for some $r \neq 0$. Then, $\sim$ is an equivalence relation (exercise 3a).

(2) Lines of $\mathcal{P}$ will have equations of the form $xk + ym + zn = 0$, and will be represented by classes of (right-) equivalent (column-) triples of numbers of $\mathcal{R}$. The reader can easily supply definitions of equality, right-multiplication by a number, addition, and right-equivalence for column-triples (exercise 3b).

(3) If $[x, y, z]$ is one coordinate triple for X, and if this triple satisfies the equation $xk + ym + zn = 0$, then any other triple for X (namely, $[rx, ry, rz]$ for some $r \neq 0$) satisfies the same equation. A similar remark applies to coordinates of lines. (The truth of these remarks depends upon the consistency of our choices of the form of equations of lines and of classes of left-equivalent triples to represent points, right-equivalent triples to represent lines. See exercise 7.)

(4) The coordinate system that we constructed for $\mathcal{E}_2^*$ depended upon a Cartesian coordinate system in $\mathcal{E}_2$, though any linear coordinate system in $\mathcal{E}_2$ would have served as well. A linear coordinate system in $\mathcal{E}_2$ is determined by the x- and y-axes and the unit points on these axes; equivalently, (exercise 4a), it is determined by the x- and y-axes and the point that is to be $[1, 1]$. Since this second approach requires putting a number scale on only one line, it is the method that we shall use for $\mathcal{P}$. When $\mathcal{E}_2$ is viewed as a subset of $\mathcal{E}_2^*$, the construction of a linear coordinate system in $\mathcal{E}_2$ also makes implicit use of the knowledge of which line of $\mathcal{E}_2^*$ is the ideal line. Thus, our coordinate system for $\mathcal{P}$ will be based upon a line ℓ_∞ (analogous to the ideal line of $\mathcal{E}_2^*$), lines ℓ_I and ℓ_J (analogous to the x- and y-axes of $\mathcal{E}_2$), and a unit point U (analogous to $[1, 1]$ in $\mathcal{E}_2$). The elements ℓ_∞, ℓ_I, ℓ_J, U will in turn be determined by a choice of four triply noncollinear base points—see exercise 4b and the beginning of the next section.

(5) The success of our assignment of the triples $[rm, -rk, 0]$ to the ideal point of the line of $\mathcal{E}_2$ with Cartesian equation $xk + ym + n = 0$ depended upon commutativity of multiplication of real numbers (why?). Although the same basic idea will be used to assign coordinates of points on ℓ_∞ in $\mathcal{P}$, a bit more care will be necessitated by the possible noncommutativity of multiplication in $\mathcal{R}$. (See Phase 3 of the next section.)

Exercise 4.1.A

1. Let $\mathcal{P}$ be a finite Desarguesian plane, $\mathcal{R}$ its associated division ring. Prove that there are more points in $\mathcal{P}$ than there are ordered pairs of numbers of $\mathcal{R}$.

2. Suppose that the points and lines of $\mathcal{E}_2^*$ have been assigned coordinate triples as described in this section.

(a) If $[x, y, z]$ and

$$\begin{bmatrix} k \\ m \\ n \end{bmatrix}$$

are triples for the point X and line k, respectively, of $\mathcal{E}_2$, prove that X is on k if and only if $xk + ym + zn = 0$.
(b) If $[i, j, 0]$ and

$$\begin{bmatrix} k \\ m \\ n \end{bmatrix}$$

are triples for the ideal point I and the ordinary line k, respectively, prove that I is on k if and only if $ik + jm = 0$.
(c) If the point X has coordinate triple $[x, y, z]$, prove that X is on the ideal line if and only if $zr = 0$ for $r \neq 0$.

3. Let $\mathcal{R}$ be a division ring.
(a) Prove that left-equivalence (defined in statement (1) (d) of this section) is an equivalence relation on the set of row-triples of numbers of $\mathcal{R}$.
(b) Define equality, right-multiplication by a number, addition, and right-equivalence for column-triples of numbers of $\mathcal{R}$. Prove that right-equivalence is an equivalence relation.

4. Let a linear coordinate system be given in $\mathcal{E}_2$.
(a) Show that this system is determined by the x- and y-axes and the point $[1, 1]$.
(b) Show that this system is also determined by the points $[0, 0]$, $[1, 1]$, and the ideal points (in $\mathcal{E}_2^*$) of the x- and y-axes.

5. Suppose that $\mathcal{E}_2^*$ has been coordinatized in the manner of this section, and let P and Q be the points with coordinate triples $[4, 1, 2]$ and $[-1, -2, 3]$, respectively. Find a coordinate triple for the line $P \cup Q$.

Exercise 4.1.B

6. Let $\mathcal{P}$ be a finite Desarguesian plane, $\mathcal{R}$ its associated division ring. Prove that the number of points of $\mathcal{P}$ is equal to the number of (left-) equivalence classes of row-triples of numbers of $\mathcal{R}$, excluding the class of the triple $[0, 0, 0]$.

7. Let $\mathcal{P}$ be a Desarguesian plane, $\mathcal{R}$ its associated division ring.
(a) Show that the definition of equivalence for point-triples as left-equivalence, coupled with the possible noncommutativity of multiplication in $\mathcal{R}$, rules out the form $kx + my + nz = 0$ for the equation of a line of $\mathcal{P}$. (This can be done by showing that, for some choice of k, m, n, x, y, z in a noncommutative division

ring $\mathcal{R}$, there is a number r of $\mathcal{R}$ such that $kx + my + nz = 0$, but $k(rx) + m(ry) + n(rz) \neq 0$.)

(b) Show that the choice of $xk + ym + zn = 0$ as the form of an equation of a line in $\mathcal{P}$, coupled with the possible noncommutativity of multiplication in $\mathcal{R}$, dictates the choice of the definition of equivalence for line-triples as right-equivalence.

8. Consider Model 4 (Section 1.4). In $\mathcal{E}_3$, let a Cartesian coordinate system be established with its origin at the point O.

(a) From analytic geometry, each line on O is associated with a class of (equivalent) ordered triples of direction numbers, proportional to the cosines of the angles that the line makes with the coordinate axes. Show how this fact gives rise to a homogeneous coordinate system for the "points" of Model 4.

(b) A plane on O can be specified by the class of direction number triples of the line through O perpendicular to that plane. Show how this fact gives rise to homogeneous coordinates for the "lines" of Model 4.

(c) If $[x, y, z]$ and

$$\begin{bmatrix} k \\ m \\ n \end{bmatrix}$$

are coordinate triples for the "point" X and the "line" k, respectively, of Model 4, assigned according to the scheme of (a) and (b), show that X is on k if and only if $xk + ym + zn = 0$.

9. In Section 3.8 we learned how to coordinatize the points of a set $\mathcal{S}$ on a line k of $\mathcal{P}$ by means of numbers of $\mathcal{R}$. When $\mathcal{S}$ is so coordinatized, the point ∞ on k receives no coordinate from $\mathcal{R}$. Show how a coordinatization of $\mathcal{S}$ gives rise to an assignment of (left-) equivalence classes of ordered *pairs* of numbers of $\mathcal{R}$ to the points on k (including ∞), thus putting all points on k on an equal footing with respect to coordinates. (Use all classes of pairs except the class of the pair $[0, 0]$.)

4.2. Construction of the Coordinate System

We are now ready to create for our Desarguesian plane $\mathcal{P}$ a coordinate system with the following properties.

(a) Every point is represented by a class of (left-) equivalent triples of numbers (not all 0) of $\mathcal{R}$ (the division ring associated with $\mathcal{P}$).

(b) Each line k of $\mathcal{P}$ has an equation of the form $xk + ym +$

$zn = 0$, satisfied by the coordinates of those, and only those, points that lie on k.

To commence the construction of a coordinate system in $\mathcal{P}$, let O, U, I, J be triply noncollinear points, and set $\ell_I = O \cup I$, $\ell_J = O \cup J$, $\ell_U = O \cup U$, $\ell_\infty = I \cup J$, and $\infty = \ell_U \cap \ell_\infty$. (See Figure 4.1.) Let $\mathcal{S}$ be the set of points on ℓ_U other than ∞. With ℓ_U, O, U, ∞, ℓ_∞ here assuming the roles of k, 0, 1, ∞, ℓ, respectively, of Section 3.7, use the method of that section to construct the division ring in $\mathcal{S}$. By the Uniqueness of the Division Ring (Theorem 3.8.2), there exists at least one coordinatization of $\mathcal{S}$ (Definition 3.8.4); let Φ be a coordinatization of $\mathcal{S}$, and keep Φ fixed. The rest of the development of a coordinate system in $\mathcal{P}$ is divided into five phases. For notational convenience, $[X]$ will indicate a coordinate triple for the point X, and $[X] = [x, y, z]$ will mean that $[x, y, z]$ is one member of the class of coordinate triples for X.

Phase 1: To assign coordinates to all points not on ℓ_∞. Let P be any such point. Then, $P_1 = (P \cup J) \cap \ell_U$ and $P_2 = (P \cup I) \cap \ell_U$ are both different from ∞, and therefore belong to $\mathcal{S}$. Consequently,

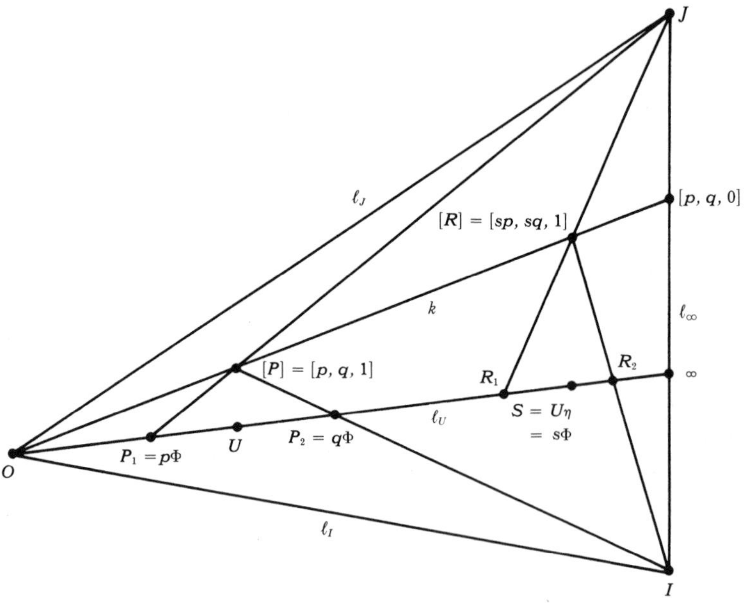

Figure 4.1

$P_1 = p\Phi$, and $P_2 = q\Phi$ for unique numbers, p and q, in $\mathcal{R}$. Assign to P the class of triples equivalent to $[p, q, 1]$. (See Figure 4.1.) Note that if P is on ℓ_U, then $p = q$; thus, for each x in $\mathcal{R}$, $[x\Phi] = [x, x, 1]$. In particular, $[O] = [0, 0, 1]$, and $[U] = [1, 1, 1]$.

No two different points have received the same class of coordinate triples by the above assignments (exercise 1a). Moreover, a point not on ℓ_∞ has no triple with 0 as its third element. In Phase 3 the points on ℓ_∞ will be given triples with third members 0; before these assignments can be made, we need to develop equations for lines on O.

Phase 2: To show that lines on O have equations of the form $xk + ym + zn = 0$. If the triple $[0, 0, 1]$ satisfies this equation, we see that $n = 0$. Therefore, letting k be any line on O, we want to show that $xk + ym = 0$ is an equation for k for some choice of k and m. Let P be a point on k other than O and $k \cap \ell_\infty$, and suppose that $[P] = [p, q, 1]$. Since $P \neq O$, not both p and q are 0; assume, for Phases 2 and 3, that $q \neq 0$. (The argument is similar for $p \neq 0$. See exercise 4a.) Then,

4.2.1. $x - y(q^{-1}p) = 0$

is an equation satisfied by both $[0, 0, 1]$ and $[p, q, 1]$, and we shall prove that this equation is fulfilled by the coordinates of those, and only those, points that lie on k. (Figure 4.1 also illustrates Phases 2 and 3.)

Let R be any point on k other than O and $k \cap \ell_\infty$, and let $R_1 = (R \cup J) \cap \ell_U$, $R_2 = (R \cup I) \cap \ell_U$. Let η be the homology with axis ℓ_∞, center O, sending P into R. If $P_1 = (P \cup J) \cap \ell_U$ and $P_2 = (P \cup I) \cap \ell_U$, then $P_1\eta = (R \cup J) \cap \ell_U = R_1$, and $P_2\eta = R_2$. Suppose that $U\eta = S = s\Phi$. From Section 3.7, $P_1\eta = S \cdot P_1$, and $P_2\eta = S \cdot P_2$, where the products are computed in the division ring $\mathcal{S}$. Since $P_1 = p\Phi$ and $P_2 = q\Phi$, and since Φ is an isomorphism, $S \cdot P_1 = (s\Phi) \cdot (p\Phi) = (sp)\Phi$, and $S \cdot P_2 = (sq)\Phi$. Therefore, $R_1 = P_1\eta = S \cdot P_1 = (sp)\Phi$, and $R_2 = (sq)\Phi$; hence $[R] = [sp, sq, 1]$, and these coordinates for R satisfy Equation 4.2.1.

Conversely, let T be a point other than O such that $[T] = [t, u, 1]$ and $t - u(q^{-1}p) = 0$. Set $s = uq^{-1}$, so that $t = sp$ and $u = sq$; $s \neq 0$ because not both t and u are 0. If η is the homology with axis l_∞, center O, sending U into $s\Phi$, then $[P\eta] = [sp, sq, 1]$, as is seen by repeating the argument of the preceding paragraph (with $R = P\eta$).

Thus, $[P\eta] = [T]$; hence $P\eta = T$ (exercise 1c), proving that T is on $O \cup P = k$.

Therefore, a point not on ℓ_∞ lies on k if and only if any one of its coordinate triples satisfies Equation 4.2.1. In Phase 3 the points on ℓ_∞ will be assigned triples in such a way that $k \cap \ell_\infty$ is the one and only point on ℓ_∞ whose coordinates satisfy 4.2.1.

Phase 3: To assign coordinates to the points on ℓ_∞. Let k and P be the same as in Phase 2; then, the point $k \cap \ell_\infty$ is assigned the class of triples equivalent to $[p, q, 0]$. This assignment is independent of the choice of P, different from O and $k \cap \ell_\infty$, on k, because, by Phase 2, if R is any such point on k, then $[R] = [sp, sq, 1]$ for some $s \neq 0$, and the triple $[sp, sq, 0]$ is equivalent to $[p, q, 0]$. The triple $[p, q, 0]$ clearly satisfies Equation 4.2.1. Conversely, if T is such that $[T] = [t, u, 0]$ and $t - u(q^{-1}p) = 0$, then $t = sp$ and $u = sq$ for $s = uq^{-1}$ $(\neq 0)$; hence, $[T] = s[p, q, 0]$, and $T = k \cap \ell_\infty$ (exercise 1b).

Since k was an arbitrary line on O, $k \cap \ell_\infty$ could have been any point on ℓ_∞. Therefore, every point of $\mathcal{P}$ has been assigned a unique class of coordinate triples. Also, no two different points have received the same class of triples (exercise 1), and every triple with not all elements 0 is a coordinate triple for a unique point of $\mathcal{P}$ (exercise 2).

Phase 4: To show that lines on ∞ have linear equations. The line ℓ_∞ evidently has equation $z = 0$, for points on ℓ_∞ (and no other points) have triples with third members 0. Let m be any line, other than ℓ_∞, on ∞, and let A be a point, other than ∞, on m. Suppose that $[A] = [a, b, 1]$; from Phase 3, $[\infty] = [1, 1, 0]$. The equation

4.2.2. $$x - y + z(b - a) = 0$$

is satisfied by both $[a, b, 1]$ and $[1, 1, 0]$, and we shall prove that this equation is fulfilled by the coordinates of those, and only those, points that lie on m. (Figure 4.2 is drawn for Phase 4.)

Let R be any point on m except ∞, and let $R_1 = (R \cup J) \cap \ell_U$, $R_2 = (R \cup I) \cap \ell_U$. Let ϵ be the elation with axis ℓ_∞, center ∞, sending A into R. If $A_1 = (A \cup J) \cap \ell_U$ and $A_2 = (A \cup I) \cap \ell_U$, then $A_1\epsilon = (R \cup J) \cap \ell_U = R_1$, and $A_2\epsilon = R_2$. Suppose that $O\epsilon = S = s\Phi$. From Section 3.7, $A_1\epsilon = A_1 + S$, and $A_2\epsilon = A_2 + S$, where the sums are computed in $\mathcal{S}$. Since $A_1 = a\Phi$ and $A_2 = b\Phi$, and since Φ is an isomorphism, $A_1 + S = a\Phi + s\Phi = (a + s)\Phi$, and $A_2 + S = (b + s)\Phi$. Thus, $R_1 = A_1\epsilon = A_1 + S = (a + s)\Phi$, and $R_2 = (b + s)\Phi$;

hence $[R] = [a + s, b + s, 1]$, and these coordinates for R satisfy Equation 4.2.2.

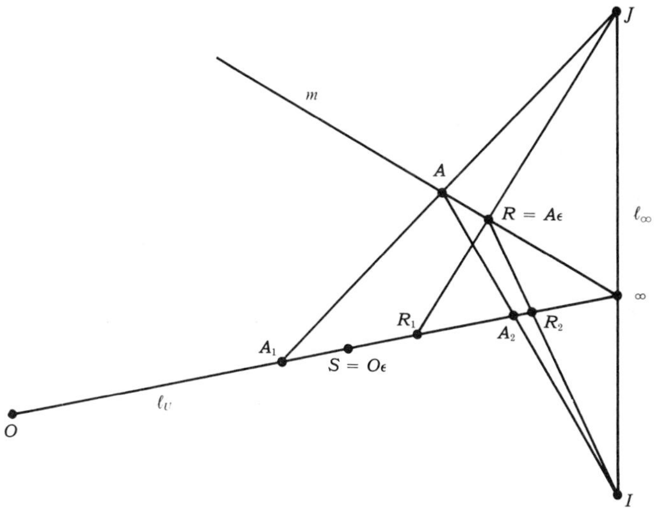

Figure 4.2

Conversely, let T be a point such that $[T] = [t, u, 1]$ and $t - u + (b - a) = 0$. If ϵ is the elation with axis ℓ_∞, center ∞, sending O into $(t - a)\Phi$, then $[A\epsilon] = [a + t - a, b + t - a, 1] = [t, u, 1]$, as is seen by repeating the argument of the last paragraph (with $R = A\epsilon$ and $s = t - a$). Therefore, $[A\epsilon] = [T]$; hence $A\epsilon = T$, and T is on m. Finally, if T is on ℓ_∞, with $[T] = [t, u, 0]$, and if $t - u = 0$, then $[t, u, 0] = t[1, 1, 0]$; hence $T = \infty$, which is on m.

Phase 5: To show that lines not on ∞ have linear equations. Let n be any line not on ∞, and let $C = n \cap \ell_U$, $E = n \cap \ell_\infty$. Suppose that $[C] = [c, c, 1]$ and $[E] = [e, f, 0]$. Not both e and f are 0; assume, for this and the next paragraph, that $f \neq 0$. (The argument is similar for $e \neq 0$. See exercise 4b.) Then, both $[c, c, 1]$ and $[e, f, 0]$ satisfy the equation

4.2.3. $x - y(f^{-1}e) - z(c - cf^{-1}e) = 0$,

and we shall prove that this is an equation for n. (Figure 4.3 is drawn for Phase 5.)

Let ϵ' be the elation with axis ℓ_∞, center ∞, sending C into O. Since $n = C \cup E$, $n\epsilon' = O \cup E$, which has equation $x - y(f^{-1}e) = 0$ by Phases 2 and 3. Let T be any point not on ℓ_∞, with $[T] = [t, u, 1]$. An argument like that in Phase 4 shows that $[T\epsilon'] = [t - c, u - c, 1]$. If T is on n, then $T\epsilon'$ is on $n\epsilon'$; hence $(t - c) - (u - c)(f^{-1}e) = 0$, which, with a slight rearrangement, proves that $[t, u, 1]$ satisfies Equation 4.2.3. Conversely, if $t - u(f^{-1}e) - (c - cf^{-1}e) = 0$, then $(t - c) - (u - c)(f^{-1}e) = 0$, so that $T\epsilon'$ is on $n\epsilon'$, and T is on n. Finally, if V is on ℓ_∞, with $[V] = [v, w, 0]$, and if $v - w(f^{-1}e) = 0$, then $v = se$ and $w = sf$, where $s = wf^{-1}$ $(\neq 0)$. Therefore, $[V] = s[e, f, 0]$; hence $V = E$, which is on n.

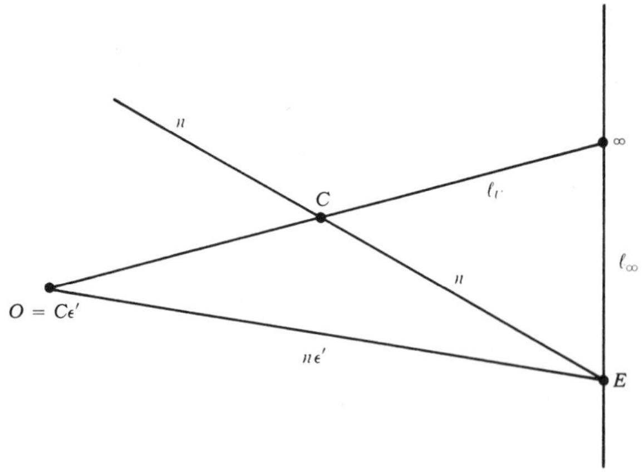

Figure 4.3

In this section a system of homogeneous coordinates for the points of $\mathcal{P}$ has been constructed, and it has been established that an arbitrary line k has equation $xk + ym + zn = 0$ for some choice of k, m, n (not all 0). We assign to k the class of (right-) equivalent column-triples of the form

$$\begin{bmatrix} kr \\ mr \\ nr \end{bmatrix}$$

for $r \neq 0$. In order to justify this assignment of homogeneous coordinates to lines of $\mathcal{P}$, it must be demonstrated that the linear equation of a line is unique to within right-multiplications by any $r \neq 0$. The algebraic proof of this uniqueness is the first concern of the next section.

Exercise 4.2.A

1. (a) Show that no two different points not on ℓ_∞ are assigned the same class of coordinate triples.
(b) Show that no two different points on ℓ_∞ are assigned the same class of coordinate triples.
(c) Deduce that if $[P] = [Q]$, then $P = Q$.

2. Show that every row-triple with not all elements 0 is a coordinate triple for a unique point of $\mathcal{P}$ in the coordinate system created in this section.

3. Find equations for the lines ℓ_U, ℓ_I, ℓ_J, and coordinates for the points I and J of this section.

4. (a) Work through Phases 2 and 3 again on the assumption that $p \neq 0$, replacing Equation 4.2.1 with the equation $x(p^{-1}q) - y = 0$.
(b) Work through Phase 5 again on the assumption that $e \neq 0$, replacing Equation 4.2.3 with $x(e^{-1}f) - y - z\,(ce^{-1}f - c) = 0$. Use the result of part (a).

5. Establish a homogeneous coordinate system in the plane 7_3, and give equations for all lines, too. Use $O = P_0$, $U = P_1$, $I = P_2$, and $J = P_5$.

6. Compare the construction of a coordinate system in $\mathcal{E}_2{}^*$ presented in Section 4.1 with the method of Phases 1–3 of this section.

Exercise 4.2.B

7. (a) Let η be a homology with axis ℓ_∞, center O, and suppose that $[U\eta] = [a, a, 1]$, where $a \neq 0$. Prove that if $[X] = [x, y, z]$, then $[X\eta] = [x, y, za^{-1}]$.
(b) Let ϵ be an elation with axis ℓ_∞, center ∞, and suppose that $[O\epsilon] = [b, b, 1]$. Prove that if $[X] = [x, y, z]$, then $[X\epsilon] = [x + zb, y + zb, z]$.

8. Carry out the instructions of exercise 5 for the plane 13_4, using $O = P_0$, $U = P_1$, $I = P_2$, $J = P_5$.

9. Carry out the instructions of exercise 5 for the plane 21_5, using $O = P_0$, $U = P_1$, $I = P_2$, $J = P_5$.

10. With the notation of this section, suppose that a new coordinatization Ψ is chosen for the set $\mathcal{S}$ on the line ℓ_U, and that the construction of the coordinate system is repeated with Ψ replacing Φ, everything else being unchanged. Prove that if $[X]_1 = [x, y, z]$ in the original coordinate system, then $[X]_2 = [x\Theta, y\Theta, z\Theta]$ $(= [x, y, z]\Theta)$ in the new coordinate system, where $\Theta = \Phi\Psi^{-1}$, and where $[X]_1$, $[X]_2$ denote triples for the same point X in the original and new coordinates systems, respectively.

11. Suppose that $\mathcal{A}$ is an affine plane whose projective extension $\mathcal{P}$ (defined in Exercise 1.5.6) is Desarguesian. Show how a coordinate system can be constructed in $\mathcal{A}$ such that points of $\mathcal{A}$ are represented by ordered pairs of numbers of $\mathcal{R}$ (the division ring associated with P), and lines of $\mathcal{A}$ have equations of the form $xk + ym + n = 0$.

12. Let α be a function defined on the points of $\mathcal{P}$ by $[X\alpha] = [x\Phi, y\Phi, z\Phi]$, where X is an arbitrary point of $\mathcal{P}$, with $[X] = [x, y, z]$, and where Φ is any automorphism of $\mathcal{R}$. (Observe that α is *well-defined* by this prescription. That is, the value of $X\alpha$ is independent of the particular triple chosen to represent X (proof?).) Prove that α has an extension to a collineation of $\mathcal{P}$.

4.3. Coordinates on a Line

Relative to the coordinate system in $\mathcal{P}$ constructed in the last section, an aribtrary line k has been shown to have an equation $xk + ym + zn = 0$ for some choice of k, m, n (not all 0). The first business of this section is to establish the essential uniqueness of this linear equation for k. Let A and D be distinct points on k, with $[A] = [a, b, c]$ and $[D] = [d, e, f]$. Then, the numbers k, m, n simultaneously satisfy:

4.3.1. (a) $ak + bm + cn = 0$.
(b) $dk + em + fn = 0$.

We shall prove that Equations 4.3.1 determine the triple

$$\begin{bmatrix} k \\ m \\ n \end{bmatrix}$$

to within a right-multiplication by any $r \neq 0$. The argument is algebraic, depending only on the properties of a division ring, plus the fact that $[a, b, c]$ and $[d, e, f]$ are inequivalent row-triples.

Not all of a, b, c are 0. For definiteness, suppose that $a \neq 0$.

Then, 4.3.1 (a) is equivalent to $k + a^{-1}bm + a^{-1}cn = 0$, from which it follows that $dk + da^{-1}bm + da^{-1}cn = 0$. Subtract this last equation from 4.3.1 (b) to get

4.3.2. $(e - da^{-1}b)m + (f - da^{-1}c)n = 0.$

Suppose, for a moment, that *both* $e - da^{-1}b = 0$ *and* $f - da^{-1}c = 0$, and set $r = da^{-1}$. Then, $d = ra$, $e = rb$, and $f = rc$. Hence $[d, e, f] = r[a, b, c]$, contrary to the hypothesis that A and D are distinct points of $\mathcal{P}$. Thus, the coefficients of m and n in Equation 4.3.2 are not both 0.

Again for definiteness, assume that $e - da^{-1}b \neq 0$, and, to shorten the writing, set $g = e - da^{-1}b$ and $h = f - da^{-1}c$. Then, 4.3.2 is equivalent to $m = -g^{-1}hn$, and 4.3.1 (a) yields $k = -a^{-1}(bm + cn) = a^{-1}(bg^{-1}h - c)n$. Therefore,

4.3.3. $$\begin{bmatrix} k \\ m \\ n \end{bmatrix} = \begin{bmatrix} a^{-1}(bg^{-1}h - c) \\ -g^{-1}h \\ 1 \end{bmatrix} n$$

is a necessary condition that k, m, n satisfy both of Equations 4.3.1, under the assumptions that $a \neq 0$ and $e - da^{-1}b \neq 0$. Conversely, it is simple to verify that the triple on the right in 4.3.3 does satisfy Equations 4.3.1 for any choice of n. (Of course, the trivial solution for $n = 0$ is of no interest.)

Calculations similar to the above yield analogous solutions, also unique to within right-multiplications, in case $e - da^{-1}b = 0$ but $f - da^{-1}c \neq 0$, and in the cases that arise when $a = 0$ but b or c is not 0 (exercise 1). If the division ring $\mathcal{R}$ associated with $\mathcal{P}$ is a field, the substitution $n = agr$ $(r \neq 0)$ in 4.3.3, and subsequent simplification, give (exercise 2):

4.3.4. $$\begin{bmatrix} k \\ m \\ n \end{bmatrix} = \begin{bmatrix} bf - ce \\ cd - af \\ ae - bd \end{bmatrix} r\,.$$

Since Equation 4.3.4 involves no multiplicative inverses, it provides the solution of Equations 4.3.1 in all cases when $\mathcal{R}$ is a field.

The essential uniqueness of the linear equation of k justifies assigning to k, as homogeneous line-coordinates, a class of (right-) equivalent column-triples, as has been done in 4.3.3 (and in 4.3.4, when $\mathcal{R}$ is a field). The statement

$$[k] = \begin{bmatrix} k \\ m \\ n \end{bmatrix}$$

will mean that

$$\begin{bmatrix} k \\ m \\ n \end{bmatrix}$$

is one member of the class of coordinate triples for k.

If $[X] = [x, y, z]$ and

$$[k] = \begin{bmatrix} k \\ m \\ n \end{bmatrix},$$

the necessary and sufficient condition for X and k to be incident is that $xk + ym + zn = 0$. If X is regarded as a fixed point and k as a variable line on X, the equation just written may be thought of as an equation of the point X. Thus, points also possess linear equations, and the duality between points and lines assumes a highly gratifying form in homogeneous coordinates. The reader can dualize the calculations of the first part of this section, interchanging left- and right-multiplications, and so compute the coordinates of the point of intersection of two distinct lines whose line-coordinates are given.

Our next task is to show how the coordinate system of $\mathcal{P}$ induces in any pencil of points a homogeneous coordinate system of *pairs* of numbers. Let k be an arbitrary line, with equation $xk + ym + zn = 0$, and let A and D be distinct points on k, with $[A] = [a, b, c]$ and $[D] = [d, e, f]$; then, Equations 4.3.1 hold. Let u and v be any numbers of R; multiply 4.3.1 (a) on the left by u and 4.3.1 (b) on the left by v, and add to get

4.3.5. $(ua + vd)k + (ub + ve)m + (uc + vf)n = 0\,.$

Thus, $[ua + vd,\ ub + ve,\ uc + vf]$ represents a point on k whenever at least one of its members is not 0, and we want to prove that, conversely, every point on k has such a representation. If P is an arbitrary point on k, with $[P] = [p, q, r]$, our job is to solve the equations

4.3.6. (a) $ua + vd = p$
(b) $ub + ve = q$
(c) $uc + vf = r$

for u and v. The plan is to solve two of the equations in 4.3.6 for u and v, then to show that the numbers obtained also satisfy the third equation.

As in the earlier work of this section, suppose that $a \neq 0$ and that $e - da^{-1}b \neq 0$; it is then evident that we should solve 4.3.6 (a) and (b) for u and v. (Similar calculations, using appropriate pairs of equations from 4.3.6, yield like results in the other cases (exercise 3).)

Equation 4.3.6 (a) is equivalent to $u + vda^{-1} = pa^{-1}$; hence $ub + vda^{-1}b = pa^{-1}b$. Subtract the last equation from 4.3.6 (b) to get $v(e - da^{-1}b) = q - pa^{-1}b$, so that $v = (q - pa^{-1}b)g^{-1}$, and $u = pa^{-1} - vda^{-1} = pa^{-1} - (q - pa^{-1}b)g^{-1}da^{-1}$, where $g = e - da^{-1}b$. Therefore, for 4.3.6 (a) and (b) to hold, u and v must be the (unique) numbers just computed; conversely, these numbers satisfy both 4.3.6 (a) and (b), as can easily be verified. With these values for u and v, $(ua + vd)k + (ub + ve)m + rn = 0$, because P is on k. A comparison of the last equation with 4.3.5 (which was shown to hold for any numbers u and v in $\mathcal{R}$) reveals that $(uc + vf)n = rn$. Hence $uc + vf = r$, since, from 4.3.3 (which expresses the coordinates of $A \cup D = k$ when $a \neq 0$ and $e - da^{-1}b \neq 0$, as we are assuming here), $n \neq 0$. Thus, 4.3.6 (c) is also fulfilled. Moreover, not both u and v are 0, for not all of p, q, r are 0.

Conversely, let $[p, q, r] = [ua + vd, ub + ve, uc + vf]$. The expressions for u and v (in terms of $p, q, r, a, b, c, d, e, f$) derived in the last paragraph show that if $p = q = r = 0$, then $u = v = 0$. Consequently, if not both u and v are 0, not all of p, q, r are 0; hence $[p, q, r]$ represents a point P of $\mathcal{P}$, and P is on k because of Equation 4.3.5, which holds for all numbers u, v in $\mathcal{R}$.

By setting $\mathbf{A} = [a, b, c]$ and $\mathbf{D} = [d, e, f]$, and by using the operations of left-multiplication of triples by numbers and addition of triples (defined in statements (1) (b) and (c) of Section 4.1), we can write $[ua + vd, ub + ve, uc + vf] = u[a, b, c] + v[d, e, f] = u\mathbf{A} + v\mathbf{D}$. Note that $\mathbf{A}$ stands for the specific triple $[a, b, c]$, while $[A]$ is a generic symbol for any triple representing A. With the aid of these conventions, the highly significant theorem that has been proved in the last several paragraphs is now formally stated.

Theorem 4.3.7. Let $k = A \cup D$, with $[A] = [a, b, c] = \mathbf{A}$ and $[D] = [d, e, f] = \mathbf{D}$. If P is any point on k, with $[P] = [p, q, r] = \mathbf{P}$, then $\mathbf{P} = u\mathbf{A} + v\mathbf{D}$ for unique numbers u, v, not both 0, in $\mathcal{R}$. Conversely, if u and v are any numbers, not both 0, in $\mathcal{R}$, then $u\mathbf{A} + v\mathbf{D}$ is a triple for a (unique) point on k. ▮

If $\mathbf{P} = u\mathbf{A} + v\mathbf{D}$, then $s\mathbf{P} = (su)\mathbf{A} + (sv)\mathbf{D}$ for any s in $\mathcal{R}$. This fact and the uniqueness of the solution of Equations 4.3.6 justify assigning to P, as a point on k, the class of pairs $[su, sv]$ $(= s[u, v])$ for all $s \neq 0$ (that is, the class of pairs left-equivalent to $[u, v]$). A homogeneous coordinate system is thus *induced* on $\mathcal{g}(k)$, determined by the *first base point* A, the *second base point* D, and the triples $\mathbf{A}$ and $\mathbf{D}$, respectively, for them. The method provided by an induced coordinate system for representing (triples for) points on a line as linear combinations of (triples for) two base points is extraordinarily useful in analytic projective geometry, as we shall have frequent occasion to observe. Our immediate goal (to be attained in the next section) is to establish equations for projectivities; to reach that goal we must know not only how to construct induced coordinate systems, but also how two such systems on the same pencil are related.

Suppose, then, that a *second* coordinate system, specified by first base point A', second base point D', and triples $\mathbf{A}'$ and $\mathbf{D}'$, respectively, is constructed on $\mathcal{g}(k)$. Let P be any point on k, with $[P] = [p, q, r] = \mathbf{P}$. By Theorem 4.3.7, $\mathbf{P} = u\mathbf{A} + v\mathbf{D} = u'\mathbf{A}' + v'\mathbf{D}'$ for unique numbers u, v, u', v', and we write $[P] = [u, v]$ and $[P]' = [u', v']$ to indicate that $[u, v]$ is a pair for P in the first, and $[u', v']$ a pair for P in the second, coordinate system on $\mathcal{g}(k)$. (No confusion arises from the use of $[P]$ to mean either a triple for P, as a point of $\mathcal{P}$, or a pair for P, as a point on k. The context clarifies the meaning.) Also, there exist unique numbers a_1, d_1, a_2, d_2 such that $\mathbf{A} = a_1\mathbf{A}' + d_1\mathbf{D}'$ and $\mathbf{D} = a_2\mathbf{A}' + d_2\mathbf{D}'$. Hence, $\mathbf{P} = u(a_1\mathbf{A}' + d_1\mathbf{D}') + v(a_2\mathbf{A}' + d_2\mathbf{D}') = (ua_1 + va_2)\mathbf{A}' + (ud_1 + vd_2)\mathbf{D}'$. The uniqueness of u' and v' implies that $u' = ua_1 + va_2$ and $v' = ud_1 + vd_2$, or

4.3.8. $[u', v'] = u[a_1, d_1] + v[a_2, d_2]$.

Equation 4.3.8, which gives analytic form to the relation between two induced coordinate systems on $\mathcal{g}(k)$, underlies the work of the next section. In this equation, $[a_1, d_1]$ and $[a_2, d_2]$ are inequivalent pairs, because they represent (in the second coordinate system) the distinct points A and D.

In the first coordinate system on $\mathcal{g}(k)$, $[A] = [1, 0]$, $[D] = [0, 1]$, and the pair $[1, 1]$ represents the point on k that has the triple $\mathbf{A} + \mathbf{D}$ in the coordinate system of $\mathcal{P}$. The selection of the triples $\mathbf{A}$ and $\mathbf{D}$ for A and D, respectively, determines the point to be represented by $[1, 1]$ in the coordinate system on $\mathcal{g}(k)$. Moreover, if G is *any* point on k

other than A and D, triples for A and D can be so chosen that $[G]' = [1, 1]$ in the coordinate system determined by A, D, and the newly selected triples. To see this, assume that $[G] = g_1\mathbf{A} + g_2\mathbf{D}$, with both g_1 and g_2 different from 0, and let $A' = A$, $D' = D$, $\mathbf{A}' = g_1\mathbf{A}$, $\mathbf{D}' = g_2\mathbf{D}$ determine a second coordinate system on $\mathcal{J}(k)$. Then, since $\mathbf{A} = g_1^{-1}\mathbf{A}'$ and $\mathbf{D} = g_2^{-1}\mathbf{D}'$, Equation 4.3.8 yields $[G]' = g_1[g_1^{-1}, 0] + g_2[0, g_2^{-1}] = [1, 1]$.

The point G such that $[G] = \mathbf{A} + \mathbf{D}$ may be called the *third base point* of the coordinate system determined by A, D, $\mathbf{A}$, and $\mathbf{D}$. The phrase, "the induced coordinate system on $\mathcal{J}(k)$ determined by A ($\mathbf{A}$), D ($\mathbf{D}$), G," will henceforth convey the information that A is the first base point, D the second base point, $\mathbf{A}$ and $\mathbf{D}$ the triples selected to represent A and D, respectively, and G the point represented by $\mathbf{A} + \mathbf{D}$. It is interesting to note that the specification of A, D, and G determines the coordinate system on $\mathcal{J}(k)$ to within an *inner* automorphism of $\mathcal{R}$ (exercise 4).

Exercise 4.3.A

1. (a) Solve Equations 4.3.1 with the assumptions that $a \neq 0$ and $f - da^{-1}c \neq 0$.
(b) Solve Equations 4.3.1 with the assumption that $b \neq 0$ (two cases).
(c) Solve Equations 4.3.1 with the assumption that $c \neq 0$ (two cases).

2. Assuming that $\mathcal{R}$ is a field, derive Equation 4.3.4 from Equation 4.3.3.

3. Solve Equations 4.3.6 in each of the cases enumerated in exercise 1.

4. Let A, D, G be distinct points on k.
(a) Prove that if $\mathbf{A}$ and $\mathbf{D}$ are triples for A and D, respectively, such that $[G] = \mathbf{A} + \mathbf{D}$, and if $\mathbf{A}'$ and $\mathbf{D}'$ are also triples for A and D, respectively, such that $[G] = \mathbf{A}' + \mathbf{D}'$, then $\mathbf{A}' = s\mathbf{A}$ and $\mathbf{D}' = s\mathbf{D}$ for the *same* $s \neq 0$.
(b) If two induced coordinate systems on $\mathcal{J}(k)$ are determined by (first) A ($\mathbf{A}$), D ($\mathbf{D}$), G, and (second) A ($\mathbf{A}'$), D ($\mathbf{D}'$), G, show that Equation 4.3.8 then becomes $[u', v'] = [us^{-1}, vs^{-1}] = s^{-1}[sus^{-1}, svs^{-1}]$ for some $s \neq 0$.
(c) Deduce that a coordinate system on $\mathcal{J}(k)$ with A, D, G as first, second, third base points, respectively, is determined by this

assignment of base points to within an *inner* automorphism of $\mathcal{R}$ (defined in Exercise 3.8.6).

5. Let A, B, C be noncollinear points, with coordinate triples **A**, **B**, **C**, respectively. Prove that if $u\mathbf{A} + v\mathbf{B} + w\mathbf{C} = [0, 0, 0]$, then $u = v = w = 0$.

6. (a) Find a coordinate triple for the line $A \cup B$, where $[A] = [1, 2, 1]$ and $[B] = [2, -2, 1]$. ($2 = 1 + 1$, $3 = 2 + 1$, etc. Observe that $2 \cdot \mathrm{x} = \mathrm{x} \cdot 2$, $3 \cdot \mathrm{x} = \mathrm{x} \cdot 3$, etc., for any x in $\mathcal{R}$.)
(b) Find a triple for the point $m \cap n$, if

$$[m] = \begin{bmatrix} 1 \\ 1 \\ 2 \end{bmatrix} \quad \text{and} \quad [n] = \begin{bmatrix} -2 \\ 1 \\ 1 \end{bmatrix}.$$

Exercise 4.3.B

7. (a) Let $\pi_1 = \ell_I \circ O_1 \circ \ell_\infty$, where $[O_1] = [0, 1, 1]$, and ℓ_I, ℓ_∞ are as in Section 4.2. Let X be any point on ℓ_I, with $[X] = [\mathrm{x}, 0, z]$. Prove that $[X\pi_1] = [\mathrm{x}, -z, 0]$.
(b) Let $\pi_2 = \ell_\infty \circ O_2 \circ \ell_I$, where $[O_2] = [a, 1, 1]$, and let Z be any point on ℓ_∞, with $[Z] = [\mathrm{x}, -z, 0]$. Prove that $[Z\pi_2] = [\mathrm{x} + za, 0, z]$.
(c) Combine parts (a) and (b) to get $[X\pi] = [\mathrm{x} + za, 0, z]$, where $\pi = \pi_1\pi_2$ (a Π_2 on ℓ_I) and $[X] = [\mathrm{x}, 0, z]$.

8. Let ϵ be the elation with axis ℓ_∞, center I (in the notation of Section 4.2), sending O into A, where $[A] = [a, 0, 1]$.
(a) Prove that $O_1\epsilon = O_2$, where $[O_1] = [0, 1, 1]$ and $[O_2] = [a, 1, 1]$. Then, use the result of exercise 7 to conclude that if X is on ℓ_I, with $[X] = [\mathrm{x}, 0, z]$, $[X\epsilon] = [\mathrm{x} + za, 0, z]$.
(b) If X is any point of $\mathcal{P}$, with $[X] = [\mathrm{x}, y, z]$, prove that $[X\epsilon] = [\mathrm{x} + za, y, z]$.

9. (a) Let ϵ_1 be the elation with axis ℓ_∞, center J (in the notation of Section 4.2), sending O into B, where $[B] = [0, b, 1]$. If X is any point of $\mathcal{P}$, with $[X] = [\mathrm{x}, y, z]$, prove that $[X\epsilon_1] = [\mathrm{x}, y + zb, z]$. (Compare with exercise 8.)
(b) Let ϵ_2 be the elation with axis ℓ_∞, center C, sending O into D, where $[D] = [a, b, 1]$ and $[C] = [a, b, 0]$. If $[X] = [\mathrm{x}, y, z]$, prove that $[X\epsilon_2] = [\mathrm{x} + za, y + zb, z]$. Compare ϵ_2 with a translation of $\mathcal{E}_2$.

10. Give an analytic proof of Desargues' theorem in the nondegenerate case depicted in Figure 3.3. (Note that H, A, B, C of that figure are triply noncollinear; assume that the coordinate system in $\mathcal{P}$ has been constructed with $O = H$, $I = A$, $J = B$, $U = C$. Then, $[A'] = [1, 0, a]$, $[B'] = [0, 1, b]$, and $[C'] = [1, 1, 1 + c]$ for some a, b, c, all different from 0.)

11. State the dual of Theorem 4.3.7 and outline a proof of it. Also, dualize the result contained in Equation 4.3.8.

4.4. Equations of Projectivities

We have learned how the coordinate system in $\mathcal{P}$ induces a coordinate system of pairs on any pencil of points. Henceforth, for brevity, we shall speak of a coordinate system on the line k (rather than on the pencil $\mathcal{I}(k)$). Observe that equality, left-multiplication by a number, addition, and left-equivalence are defined for row-pairs in the same way as for row-triples. (Refer to statements (1) (a), (b), (c), (d) of Section 4.1.)

In this section analytic expressions are derived for projectivities between lines in P. We first consider a perspectivity. Let $\pi = k \circ H \circ \ell$; suppose that an induced coordinate system on k is given, determined by A ($\mathbf{A}$), D ($\mathbf{D}$), G, and let $\mathbf{H}$ be a triple for H. Since H, A, $A\pi$ are collinear, and $H \neq A$ or $A\pi$, there is a triple $\mathbf{A}'$ for $A\pi$ and a number c_1 such that $\mathbf{A}' = c_1\mathbf{H} + \mathbf{A}$ (why?). Also, a triple $\mathbf{D}'$ can be found for $D\pi$ such that $[G\pi] = \mathbf{A}' + \mathbf{D}'$. Construct the coordinate system on ℓ determined by $A\pi$ ($\mathbf{A}'$), $D\pi$ ($\mathbf{D}'$), $G\pi$.

Since H, D, $D\pi$ are collinear, and $H \neq D$, there are numbers c_2, f_2, such that $\mathbf{D}' = c_2\mathbf{H} + f_2\mathbf{D}$. Because H, G, $G\pi$ are collinear, with $H \neq G\pi$, and because $[G] = \mathbf{A} + \mathbf{D}$ and $[G\pi] = \mathbf{A}' + \mathbf{D}'$, there are numbers c_3, f_3, such that $\mathbf{A} + \mathbf{D} = c_3\mathbf{H} + f_3(\mathbf{A}' + \mathbf{D}') = c_3\mathbf{H} + f_3(c_1\mathbf{H} + \mathbf{A} + c_2\mathbf{H} + f_2\mathbf{D})$. Thus, $(f_3 - 1)\mathbf{A} + (f_3f_2 - 1)\mathbf{D} + (f_3c_1 + f_3c_2 + c_3)\mathbf{H} = [0, 0, 0]$. Since A, D, H are not collinear, $f_3 - 1 = f_3f_2 - 1 = f_3c_1 + f_3c_2 + c_3 = 0$ (by Exercise 4.3.5). Therefore, $f_3 = 1$; hence $f_2 = 1$, and $\mathbf{D}' = c_2\mathbf{H} + \mathbf{D}$.

Let P be any point on k, with $[P] = u\mathbf{A} + v\mathbf{D}$. From the above, $u\mathbf{A} + v\mathbf{D} = u(\mathbf{A}' - c_1\mathbf{H}) + v(\mathbf{D}' - c_2\mathbf{H}) = (u\mathbf{A}' + v\mathbf{D}') - (uc_1 + vc_2)\mathbf{H}$. The triple $u\mathbf{A}' + v\mathbf{D}'$ represents a point P' on ℓ, and, from the equation in the previous sentence, P, P', H are collinear. Therefore, $P' = (P \cup H) \cap \ell = P\pi$; hence $[P\pi] = u\mathbf{A}' + v\mathbf{D}'$. In other words, in the chosen coordinate system on ℓ, one particular pair $[u_1, v_1]$ for $P\pi$ is given by the equation $[u_1, v_1] = [u, v]$.

Theorem 4.4.1. Let $\pi = k \circ H \circ \ell$, and suppose that an induced coordinate system on k is given. Then:

(a) An induced coordinate system on ℓ can be found such that, relative to it and the coordinate system on k, π is described by the equation $[P\pi] = [u_1, v_1] = [u, v] = [P]$, where P is any point on k.

(b) Relative to the given coordinate system on k and *any* induced coordinate system on ℓ, π is described by the equation $[P\pi] = [u', v'] = u[a_1, d_1] + v[a_2, d_2]$, where $[a_1, d_1]$ and $[a_2, d_2]$ are certain inequivalent pairs, and P is any point on k, with $[P] = [u, v]$.

Proof: (a) This part has been proved in the calculations preceding the theorem.

(b) Part (b) is established by relating a suitable pair $[u', v']$, representing $P\pi$ in a given induced coordinate system on ℓ, to the pair $[u_1, v_1]$, representing $P\pi$ in the coordinate system on ℓ of part (a). By Equation 4.3.8, the relation is $[u', v'] = u_1[a_1, d_1] + v_1[a_2, d_2]$, where $[a_1, d_1]$ and $[a_2, d_2]$ are certain inequivalent pairs. Since $u_1 = u$ and $v_1 = v$, the result follows. ▮

Theorem 4.4.2. (Equations of Projectivities) Let ϕ be a projectivity from any line k to any line m in $\mathcal{P}$, and suppose that induced coordinate systems are given on k and m. Relative to these coordinate systems, ϕ is described by the equation $[P\phi] = u[a_1, d_1] + v[a_2, d_2]$, where $[a_1, d_1]$ and $[a_2, d_2]$ are certain inequivalent pairs, and P is any point on k, with $[P] = [u, v]$.

Proof: Suppose that $\phi = k \circ H_1 \circ \ell_1 \circ H_2 \circ \ell_2 \circ \cdots \circ \ell_{n-1} \circ H_n \circ m$, and set $\ell_0 = k$, $\ell_n = m$. We assume that $n > 1$, because the conclusion follows from part (b) of Theorem 4.4.1 if ϕ is a perspectivity. For each i from 1 to n, let $\pi_i = \ell_{i-1} \circ H_i \circ \ell_i$ and $\phi_i = \pi_1\pi_2 \cdots \pi_i$, so that $\phi_n = \phi$. By part (a) of Theorem 4.4.1, coordinate systems can be successively chosen on $\ell_1, \ell_2, \ldots, \ell_{n-1}$ such that $[P\pi_1] = [u_1, v_1] = [u, v]$, and, for each i from 2 to $n-1$ (if $n > 2$), $[(P\phi_{i-1})\pi_i] = [u_i, v_i] = [u_{i-1}, v_{i-1}] = [P\phi_{i-1}]$. Thus, $[P\phi_{n-1}] = [u_{n-1}, v_{n-1}] = [u, v]$. By part (b) of Theorem 4.4.1, $[P\phi] = [(P\phi_{n-1})\pi_n] = u_{n-1}[a_1, d_1] + v_{n-1}[a_2, d_2] = u[a_1, d_1] + v[a_2, d_2]$. ▮

It should be emphasized that the equation of ϕ in the above theorem relates one special pair for $P\phi$ to the pair $[u, v]$ for P. In general, $[P\phi] = (su)[a_1, d_1] + (sv)[a_2, d_2]$ for any $s \neq 0$, and any pair for $P\phi$ can be obtained in this way. In order to demonstrate the converse of Theorem 4.4.2, we need two lemmas.

Lemma 4.4.3. Let k be a line with induced coordinate system determined by A ($\mathbf{A}$), D ($\mathbf{D}$), G. Let s $\neq 0$ and $t \neq 0$ (in $\mathcal{R}$) be given, and let S and T be the points on k such that $[S] = [1, s]$, $[T] = [t, 1]$. Let P be any point on k, with $[P] = [u, v]$. Then:

(a) If ϕ_1 is the Π_2 on k with central invariant point D, axial invariant point A, sending G into S, $[P\phi_1] = [u, vs]$.

(b) If ϕ_2 is the Π_2 on k with central invariant point A, axial invariant point D, sending G into T, $[P\phi_2] = [ut, v]$.

Proof: (a) Suppose that $\phi_1 = \pi_1\pi_2$, with $\pi_1 = k \circ H_1 \circ \ell$ and $\pi_2 = \ell \circ H_2 \circ k$. The argument of the first part of this section (preceding Theorem 4.4.1) shows that there is a coordinate system on ℓ, determined by $A\pi_1 = A$ ($\mathbf{A}' = \mathbf{A}$), $D\pi_1$ ($\mathbf{D}'$), $G\pi_1$, such that, in this coordinate system, $[P\pi_1] = [u_1, v_1] = [u, v]$ (verify!). Likewise, there is a *second* coordinate system on k, determined by $(A\pi_1)\pi_2 = A$ ($\mathbf{A}'' = \mathbf{A}' = \mathbf{A}$), $(D\pi_1)\pi_2 = D$ ($\mathbf{D}''$), $(G\pi_1)\pi_2 = S$, such that $[(P\pi_1)\pi_2]' = [u', v'] = [u_1, v_1]$, where $[(P\pi_1)\pi_2]'$ indicates a pair for $(P\pi_1)\pi_2$ in this second coordinate system on k. Thus, $[P\phi_1]' = [u, v]$; hence $[P\phi_1] = u\mathbf{A} + v\mathbf{D}''$. Since $\mathbf{D}''$ and $\mathbf{D}$ are equivalent triples, and since $\mathbf{A} + s\mathbf{D}$ and $\mathbf{A} + \mathbf{D}''$ both represent S, $\mathbf{D}'' = s\mathbf{D}$ (proof?). Hence, $[P\phi_1] = u\mathbf{A} + vs\mathbf{D}$, as required.

(b) Choose a *third* coordinate system on k, determined by D ($\mathbf{D}$), A ($\mathbf{A}$), G. Because $[P] = u\mathbf{A} + v\mathbf{D}$, $[P]'' = [v, u]$ in this third coordinate system. In particular, $[T]'' = [1, t]$, so that the hypotheses for part (b) in the third coordinate system are like the hypotheses for part (a) in the first coordinate system (verify!). Therefore, by part (a), $[P\phi_2]'' = [v, ut]$; hence $[P\phi_2] = ut\mathbf{A} + v\mathbf{D}$, as required. ∎

Corollary: In the hypotheses of the above lemma, take $t = s$. Let ϕ_1 and ϕ_2 be as described in the lemma. Then, $[P\phi_1\phi_2] = [us, vs] = s[u\Theta, v\Theta]$, where Θ is the *inner* automorphism (defined in Exercise 3.8.6) of $\mathcal{R}$ given by $x\Theta = s^{-1}xs$ for each x in R.

Proof: Simply calculate the effect of $\phi_1\phi_2$. ∎

The next lemma, still building toward a proof of the converse of Theorem 4.4.2, has an exceedingly beautiful and important corollary.

Lemma 4.4.4. Let k be a line, and suppose that a coordinate system on k is determined by A ($\mathbf{A}$), D ($\mathbf{D}$), G. Let α be a function on $\mathcal{G}(k)$ defined, relative to the given coordinate system on k, by $[P\alpha] = u[a_1, d_1] + v[a_2, d_2]$, where P is any point on k, with $[P] = [u, v]$. In addition, suppose that α fixes A, D, and G. Then, $[P\alpha] = [u\Theta, v\Theta]$, where Θ is an inner automorphism of $\mathcal{R}$. Furthermore, α is a projectivity. (Note that α *is* a function (exercise 3).)

Proof: Since $A\alpha = A$, $[A\alpha] = [a_1, d_1]$ is left-equivalent to $[1, 0]$; therefore, $d_1 = 0$ and $a_1 \neq 0$. Similarly, since $D\alpha = D$, $a_2 = 0$. Because $G\alpha = G$, $[G\alpha] = [a_1, 0] + [0, d_2] = [a_1, d_2]$ is left-equivalent to $[1, 1]$, and $d_2 = a_1$. Thus, $[P\alpha] = [ua_1, va_1] = a_1 [a_1^{-1}ua_1, a_1^{-1}va_1] = a_1[u\Theta, v\Theta]$, where Θ is defined by $x\Theta = a_1^{-1}xa_1$ for each x in $\mathcal{R}$. Hence, also, $[P\alpha] = [u\Theta, v\Theta]$. Finally, in the hypotheses of the corollary of Lemma 4.4.3, take $s = a_1$ to conclude that $[P\alpha] = [P\phi_1\phi_2]$, with ϕ_1, ϕ_2 as in that corollary. Therefore, $P\alpha = P\phi_1\phi_2$ for any P on k; hence $\alpha = \phi_1\phi_2$, a projectivity. ∎

Corollary: The Fundamental Theorem holds in $\mathcal{P}$ if and only if $\mathcal{R}$ is a field.

Proof: Suppose first that $\mathcal{R}$ is a field, and let ϕ be a projectivity on a line k that fixes three distinct points. Construct an induced coordinate system on k having three distinct fixed points of ϕ as base points. Then, ϕ satisfies the hypotheses of the lemma, so that $[P\phi] = [u\Theta, v\Theta]$, with Θ an *inner* automorphism of $\mathcal{R}$. Since $\mathcal{R}$ is a field, Θ is the identity (Exercise 3.8.6). Therefore, $[P\phi] = [P]$ for any P on k; hence ϕ is the identity projectivity.

Conversely, suppose that $\mathcal{R}$ is not a field, and let c and f be numbers of $\mathcal{R}$ such that $cf \neq fc$; then, $c \neq 0$. Choose an induced coordinate system on a line k, and construct ϕ_1 and ϕ_2 as in Lemma 4.4.3, taking $s = t = c$. If P is the point on k such that $[P] = [f, 1]$, then $[P\phi_1\phi_2] = [fc, c]$, which is *not* left-equivalent to $[f, 1]$ (why?). Thus, $\phi_1\phi_2$ is a projectivity on k that fixes at least the three base points of the induced coordinate system, but $\phi_1\phi_2$ does not fix P. Therefore, the Fundamental Theorem does not hold in $\mathcal{P}$. ∎

The final result of this section is the converse of Theorem 4.4.2.

Theorem 4.4.5. (Converse of Theorem 4.4.2) Let k and ℓ be lines with given induced coordinate systems. Suppose that α is a function from $\mathcal{I}(k)$ to $\mathcal{I}(\ell)$ described, relative to the given coordinate systems on k and ℓ, by $[P\alpha] = u[a_1, d_1] + v\,[a_2, d_2]$, where $[a_1, d_1]$ and $[a_2, d_2]$ are inequivalent pairs, neither one $[0, 0]$, and where $[u, v]$ represents the arbitrary point P on k. Then, α is a projectivity.

Proof: Let the coordinate system on k be determined by A (**A**), D (**D**), G. Since $[A\alpha] = [a_1, d_1]$, $[D\alpha] = [a_2, d_2]$, and $[G\alpha] = [a_1, d_1] + [a_2, d_2]$, the restrictions on $[a_1, d_1]$ and $[a_2, d_2]$ ensure that $A\alpha$, $D\alpha$, $G\alpha$ are distinct points on ℓ. Construct (using Theorem 1.7.2) a projectivity ϕ_1, from ℓ to k, such that $(A\alpha)\phi_1 = A$, $(D\alpha)\phi_1 = D$, and $(G\alpha)\phi_1 = G$. By Theorem 4.4.2, $[Q\phi_1] = u'[a_3, d_3] + v'[a_4, d_4]$, where $[Q] =$

$[u', v']$ on ℓ. In particular, since $[P\alpha] = [ua_1 + va_2, ud_1 + vd_2]$, it follows that $[P\alpha\phi_1] = (ua_1 + va_2)[a_3, d_3] + (ud_1 + vd_2)[a_4, d_4] = u[a_1a_3 + d_1a_4, a_1d_3 + d_1d_4] + v[a_2a_3 + d_2a_4, a_2d_3 + d_2d_4]$. Because $\alpha\phi_1$ fixes A, D, and G, Lemma 4.4.4 says that $\alpha\phi_1$ is a projectivity ϕ_2. Thus, $\alpha = \phi_2\phi_1^{-1}$, a projectivity. ▮

Exercise 4.4.A

1. Let ϕ be a projectivity on a line k that fixes the distinct points A and D. Prove that ϕ is a composite of two Π_2's on k with inversely matched invariant points at A and D.

2. Let α be a function defined on the points of $\mathcal{P}$ by $[X\alpha] = [x\Theta, y\Theta, z\Theta]$, where X is an arbitrary point of $\mathcal{P}$, with $[X] = [x, y, z]$, and where Θ is an inner automorphism of $\mathcal{R}$. Prove that α has an extension to a *projective* collineation of $\mathcal{P}$. Use the result of Exercise 4.2.12.

3. Prove that the function α of Lemma 4.4.4 is *well-defined* by the prescription $[P\alpha] = u[a_1, d_1] + v[a_2, d_2]$. That is, prove that *any* choice of a pair for P yields (via this equation) a pair for the same point $(P\alpha)$ on k.

In exercises 4 through 9, k is a line with induced coordinate system determined by A (**A**), D (**D**), G, and P is an arbitrary point on k, with $[P] = [u, v]$.

4. Suppose that $\mathcal{R}$ is a field, and let Q, R, T be the points on k such that $[Q] = [2, 1]$, $[R] = [1, 2]$, $[T] = [1, -1]$. Let ϕ be the unique (by the Fundamental Theorem) projectivity on k such that $Q\phi = R$, $R\phi = T$, and $T\phi = Q$. Write an equation for ϕ.

5. Let ℓ and m be lines with given induced coordinate systems. Let ϕ_1 and ϕ_2 be projectivities from k to ℓ and from ℓ to m, respectively, described by $[P\phi_1] = u[a_1, d_1] + v[a_2, d_2]$ and $[Q\phi_2] = u'[a_3, d_3] + v'[a_4, d_4]$, where Q is any point on ℓ, with $[Q] = [u', v']$. Find an equation for $\phi_1\phi_2$.

Exercise 4.4.B

See the instructions for exercises 6–9 preceding exercise 4.

6. Let ℓ be a line with given induced coordinate system, and suppose that ϕ is a projectivity from k to ℓ such that $[A\phi] = [a', d']$, $[D\phi] = [a'', d'']$, $[G\phi] = [a', d'] + [a'', d'']$. Prove that $[P\phi] = (u\Theta)[a', d'] + (v\Theta)[a'', d'']$, where Θ is some inner automorphism of $\mathcal{R}$.

7. Suppose that $\mathcal{R}$ is a field, and let ϕ be a projectivity on k with equation $[P\phi] = u[a_1, d_1] + v[a_2, d_2]$. Find the (necessary and sufficient) condition for ϕ to be an involution.

8. Assume that $P \neq A$ or D, and let ϕ_1 be the II_2 on k with central invariant point D, axial invariant point A, sending G into P. Use Lemma 4.4.3 (a) to show that $[X\phi_1] = [x, yu^{-1}v]$, where X is any point on k, with $[X] = [x, y]$. From this result and the fact that $\phi_1\phi_2 = \phi_2\phi_1$, where ϕ_2 is the II_2 of Lemma 4.4.3 (b), derive another proof of Lemma 4.4.3 (b).

9. Let s (in $\mathcal{R}$) be given, and let S be the point on k such that $[S] = [s, 1]$. Let ϕ_s be the II_2 on k with central and axial invariant points at A, sending D into S. Prove that $[P\phi_s] = [u + vs, v]$.

10. Suppose that k is a line of $\mathcal{P}$, and that 0, 1, ∞ are distinct points on k. Let $\mathcal{S}$ be the division ring in the set of all points except ∞ on k, constructed as in Section 3.7. Now, give k (as a line of the coordinatized plane $\mathcal{P}$) the induced coordinate system determined by ∞ (**A**), 0 (**D**), 1. Let the function Φ, from $\mathcal{R}$ to $\mathcal{S}$, be defined by $x\Phi = X$, where X is the point of $\mathcal{S}$ such that $[X] = [x, 1]$ in the induced coordinate system on k.

(a) Use Lemma 4.4.3 (a) and the result of exercise 9 to prove that Φ is a coordinatization of $\mathcal{S}$ (Definition 3.8.4).

(b) Conclude that the induced coordinate system on k is identical to the coordinate system on k constructed from $\mathcal{S}$ and the coordinatization Φ of $\mathcal{S}$ as follows: For each x in $\mathcal{R}$, assign to the point $x\Phi$ of $\mathcal{S}$ the class of pairs $s[x, 1]$ for $s \neq 0$; assign to ∞ the class of pairs $s[1, 0]$ for $s \neq 0$. (Compare with Exercise 4.1.9.)

11. Let k be a line with induced coordinate system determined by A (**A**), D (**D**), G. Suppose that ρ is a collineation of $\mathcal{P}$ that fixes A, D, and G. Use the results of exercise 10 and Exercise 3.8.10 to prove that $[P\rho] = [u\Psi, v\Psi]$, where Ψ is some automorphism of $\mathcal{R}$, and where P is an arbitrary point on k, with $[P] = [u, v]$.

4.5. Matrices

In the last section it was established that a projectivity ϕ, between two lines of $\mathcal{P}$, has an equation, relative to given induced coordinate systems on the lines, of the form $[P\phi] = [u', v'] = u[a_1, d_1] + v[a_2, d_2]$. The fact that the effect of ϕ is known when $[a_1, d_1]$ and $[a_2, d_2]$ are known suggests representing ϕ by a *matrix* of these pairs and defining matrix operations in such a way that the complete sense of the above equation for ϕ is captured by the equation $[u', v'] = [u, v]\boldsymbol{\phi}$, where $\boldsymbol{\phi}$ denotes the matrix associated with ϕ.

It is natural to put

$$\boldsymbol{\phi} = \begin{bmatrix} a_1 & d_1 \\ a_2 & d_2 \end{bmatrix}.$$

Then, we define the *product* of $[u, v]$ by $\boldsymbol{\phi}$ (in that order) to be the pair whose ith element ($i = 1, 2$) is the *inner product* of $[u, v]$ with the ith column of $\boldsymbol{\phi}$. A column of $\boldsymbol{\phi}$ may be thought of as a column-pair, and the *inner product* of a row-pair with a column-pair is defined to be the *number* resulting from the addition of terms obtained by multiplying the jth element of the row-pair by the jth element (from the top) of the column-pair (in that order) for $j = 1, 2$. Thus,

$$[u, v]\cdot\begin{bmatrix} a_1 \\ a_2 \end{bmatrix} = ua_1 + va_2\ ;$$

hence

$$[u, v]\begin{bmatrix} a_1 & d_1 \\ a_2 & d_2 \end{bmatrix} = [ua_1 + va_2, ud_1 + vd_2] = u[a_1, d_1] + v[a_2, d_2].$$

The form of the equation of a projectivity has led to the concept of a matrix and to the definition of the product of a pair and a matrix. Our knowledge of projectivities and the representation of points in $\mathcal{P}$ will continue to aid us in the discussion of matrices. However, a projectivity, expressed analytically, is a function on equivalence classes of pairs rather than on pairs, and this fact makes it inconvenient to base the study of matrices solely on their connection with projectivities. Some of the information that we need is most readily acquired by considering matrices as representations of *linear transformations*, a point of view that will now be explored.

Let $\mathcal{R}$ be the division ring associated with $\mathcal{P}$. Denote by $\mathcal{V}_2(\mathcal{R})$ the set of *all* row-pairs of numbers of $\mathcal{R}$ (including $[0, 0]$), together with the operations of addition of pairs and left-multiplication of pairs by numbers of $\mathcal{R}$. In addition to the notation $[x, y]$, members of $\mathcal{V}_2(\mathcal{R})$ will sometimes be indicated by boldface capitals, such as $\mathbf{X}$, $\mathbf{Y}$.

A function λ on $\mathcal{V}_2(\mathcal{R})$ is a *linear transformation* if and only if $(x\mathbf{X} + y\mathbf{Y})\lambda = x(\mathbf{X}\lambda) + y(\mathbf{Y}\lambda)$ for any numbers x, y, and any pairs $\mathbf{X}$, $\mathbf{Y}$. If $\boldsymbol{\beta}$ is any two-by-two matrix with elements in $\mathcal{R}$, the function β, on $\mathcal{V}_2(\mathcal{R})$, defined by $\mathbf{X}\beta = \mathbf{X}\boldsymbol{\beta}$ (the product of $\mathbf{X}$ and the matrix $\boldsymbol{\beta}$) for any pair $\mathbf{X}$, is a linear transformation, as an easy calculation proves. Thus, every two-by-two matrix represents a (unique) linear transformation on $\mathcal{V}_2(\mathcal{R})$. Conversely, suppose that λ is any linear transformation on $\mathcal{V}_2(\mathcal{R})$, and that $[1, 0]\lambda = [a, b]$, $[0, 1]\lambda = [c, d]$. Then, for any pair $[x, y]$,

$$[x, y]\lambda = (x[1, 0] + y[0, 1])\lambda = x([1, 0]\lambda) + y([0, 1]\lambda) = x[a, b] + y[c, d] = [x, y]\begin{bmatrix} a & b \\ c & d \end{bmatrix}.$$

Therefore, λ is represented by a matrix $\boldsymbol{\lambda}$, such that $\mathbf{X}\lambda = \mathbf{X}\boldsymbol{\lambda}$ for any pair $\mathbf{X} = [x, y]$. Furthermore, $\boldsymbol{\lambda}$ is unique, since its first and second rows are $[1, 0]\lambda$ and $[0, 1]\lambda$, respectively.

Suppose that λ_1 and λ_2 are linear transformations on $\mathcal{V}_2(\mathcal{R})$, with

$$\boldsymbol{\lambda}_1 = \begin{bmatrix} a & b \\ c & d \end{bmatrix} \quad \text{and} \quad \boldsymbol{\lambda}_2 = \begin{bmatrix} e & f \\ g & h \end{bmatrix},$$

and let $[x, y]$ be a pair. Then, $[x, y]\lambda_1 = [xa + yc, xb + yd]$, and $([x, y]\lambda_1)\lambda_2 = [xae + yce + xbg + ydg, xaf + ycf + xbh + ydh] = x[ae + bg, af + bh] + y[ce + dg, cf + dh]$. Thus, $\lambda_1\lambda_2$ is a linear transformation, with matrix

$$\begin{bmatrix} ae + bg & af + bh \\ ce + dg & cf + dh \end{bmatrix},$$

and we are led to define the *product* of two matrices as follows:

$$\begin{bmatrix} a & b \\ c & d \end{bmatrix}\begin{bmatrix} e & f \\ g & h \end{bmatrix} = \begin{bmatrix} ae + bg & af + bh \\ ce + dg & cf + dh \end{bmatrix}.$$

Then, the matrix of a composite of two linear transformations is the product of their matrices (and in the same order). Note that the definition of matrix product conforms to the previous definition of the product of a pair and a matrix—the element in the ith row and jth column of the product matrix is the inner product of the ith row of the first matrix and the jth column of the second matrix, for each i and j.

Suppose that $\boldsymbol{\alpha}, \boldsymbol{\beta}, \boldsymbol{\gamma}$ are any two-by-two matrices, and let α, β, γ be the associated linear transformations on $\mathcal{V}_2(\mathcal{R})$. Since α, β, γ are functions, $(\alpha\beta)\gamma = \alpha(\beta\gamma)$. From the last two paragraphs, $\boldsymbol{\alpha\beta}$ is the unique matrix of $\alpha\beta$; hence $(\boldsymbol{\alpha\beta})\boldsymbol{\gamma}$ is the unique matrix of $(\alpha\beta)\gamma$. Similarly, $\boldsymbol{\alpha}(\boldsymbol{\beta\gamma})$ is the matrix of $\alpha(\beta\gamma)$. Therefore, $(\boldsymbol{\alpha\beta})\boldsymbol{\gamma} = \boldsymbol{\alpha}(\boldsymbol{\beta\gamma})$, or matrix multiplication is associative, a result that could also be proved by direct calculation from the definition of matrix product (exercise 4).

If a linear transformation λ is a bijection, then λ^{-1} is also a linear transformation (exercise 1). In this case, $\lambda\lambda^{-1} = \lambda^{-1}\lambda = \iota$, so that

$$\boldsymbol{\lambda}\boldsymbol{\lambda}^{-1} = \boldsymbol{\lambda}^{-1}\boldsymbol{\lambda} = \boldsymbol{\iota} = \begin{bmatrix} 1 & 0 \\ 0 & 1 \end{bmatrix},$$

where $\boldsymbol{\iota}$ is the matrix of the identity function ι on $\mathcal{V}_2(\mathcal{R})$, and $\boldsymbol{\lambda}^{-1}$ (called the *inverse* of the matrix $\boldsymbol{\lambda}$) is the matrix of λ^{-1}. If $\boldsymbol{\beta}$ and $\boldsymbol{\beta}'$ are matrices such that $\boldsymbol{\beta}\boldsymbol{\beta}' = \boldsymbol{\beta}'\boldsymbol{\beta} = \boldsymbol{\iota}$, then $\beta\beta' = \beta'\beta = \iota$ holds for the associated linear transformations β, β'. Therefore, the necessary and sufficient condition that a matrix $\boldsymbol{\beta}$ have an inverse matrix is that β, the associated linear transformation on $\mathcal{V}_2(\mathcal{R})$, be a bijection, and we seek an interpretation of this condition in terms of the elements of $\boldsymbol{\beta}$.

The linear transformation β is one-to-one if and only if $[s, t]\beta = [u, v]\beta$ implies that $[s, t] = [u, v]$, or, equivalently, $([s, t] - [u, v])\beta = [0, 0]$ implies that $[s, t] - [u, v] = [0, 0]$, or, equivalently, $[x, y]\beta = [0, 0]$ implies that $[x, y] = [0, 0]$. If

$$\boldsymbol{\beta} = \begin{bmatrix} a & b \\ c & d \end{bmatrix},$$

then $[x, y]\beta = x[a, b] + y[c, d]$; hence, β is one-to-one if and only if $x[a, b] + y[c, d] = [0, 0]$ implies that $x = y = 0$. Let us say that pairs $\mathbf{X}$ and $\mathbf{Y}$ of $\mathcal{V}_2(\mathcal{R})$ are *linearly independent* if and only if $x\mathbf{X} + y\mathbf{Y} = [0, 0]$ implies that $x = y = 0$. Then, a two-by-two matrix $\boldsymbol{\beta}$ represents a one-to-one linear transformation if and only if its row-pairs are linearly independent. Defining a *nonsingular* matrix to be one whose row-pairs are linearly independent, we obtain the following theorem.

Theorem 4.5.1. A linear transformation β on $\mathcal{V}_2(\mathcal{R})$ is a bijection if and only if its matrix $\boldsymbol{\beta}$ is nonsingular.

Proof: It has already been proved that if $\boldsymbol{\beta}$ is singular (that is, *not* nonsingular), β is not one-to-one, hence it is not a bijection. Assume, then, that $\boldsymbol{\beta}$ is nonsingular. From above, β is one-to-one, and we have only to prove that β is also onto. Let k be a line of $\mathcal{P}$ with an induced coordinate system. Let $[x, y]$ be an arbitrary pair. If $[x, y] = [0, 0]$, then $[0, 0]\beta = [x, y]$; otherwise, $[x, y]$ represents a unique point X on k. Let ϕ be the function on $\mathcal{I}(k)$ defined by $[P\phi] = [u, v]\boldsymbol{\beta}$, where $[P] = [u, v]$ in the coordinate system on k. Because of the nonsingularity of $\boldsymbol{\beta}$, Theorem 4.4.5 ensures that ϕ is a projectivity (exercise 2a).

Thus, ϕ is a bijection on $\mathcal{G}(k)$; hence there is a point S on k, with $[S] = [s, t]$, such that $S\phi = X$. Then, $[s, t]\beta = r[x, y]$ for some $r \neq 0$. Finally, $[r^{-1}s, r^{-1}t]\beta = [x, y]$, so that β is onto. ▮

Corollary: If β is a nonsingular two-by-two matrix, there exists a matrix β^{-1} such that $\beta\beta^{-1} = \beta^{-1}\beta = \iota$. ▮

The results that have been obtained for pairs and two-by-two matrices can be readily extended to triples and three-by-three matrices. Before doing so, we offer three definitions that formalize and generalize some of the important concepts that have appeared in this section.

Definition 4.5.2. Let $\mathcal{R}$ be a division ring. A *left vector space* over $\mathcal{R}$ is a set $\mathcal{V}$ (whose elements are called *vectors*), together with two operations—addition of vectors (indicated by $\mathbf{X} + \mathbf{Y}$) and left-multiplication of vectors by numbers of $\mathcal{R}$ (indicated by $x\mathbf{X}$)—subject to the following postulates.

AV. The elements of $\mathcal{V}$ form a commutative group under the operation $+$. The identity element of this group (denoted by $\mathbf{Z}$) is called the *zero* vector.

SMV. (1) $x\mathbf{X}$ is an element of $\mathcal{V}$,
(2) $x(\mathbf{X} + \mathbf{Y}) = x\mathbf{X} + x\mathbf{Y}$,
(3) $(x + y)\mathbf{X} = x\mathbf{X} + y\mathbf{X}$,
(4) $x(y\mathbf{X}) = (xy)\mathbf{X}$,
(5) $1 \cdot \mathbf{X} = \mathbf{X}$,
for all x, y in $\mathcal{R}$ and all $\mathbf{X}$, $\mathbf{Y}$ in $\mathcal{V}$. ▮

Definition 4.5.3. Let $\mathcal{V}$ and $\mathcal{V}'$ be left vector spaces over $\mathcal{R}$. A function λ, from $\mathcal{V}$ to $\mathcal{V}'$, is a *linear transformation* from $\mathcal{V}$ to $\mathcal{V}'$ if and only if $(x\mathbf{X} + y\mathbf{Y})\lambda = x(\mathbf{X}\lambda) + y(\mathbf{Y}\lambda)$ for any x, y in $\mathcal{R}$ and any $\mathbf{X}$, $\mathbf{Y}$ in $\mathcal{V}$. ▮

Definition 4.5.4. Let $\mathcal{V}$ be a left vector space over $\mathcal{R}$. The vectors $\mathbf{X}_1, \mathbf{X}_2, \ldots, \mathbf{X}_n$ (n an arbitrary positive integer) in $\mathcal{V}$ are *linearly independent* (over $\mathcal{R}$) if and only if $x_1\mathbf{X}_1 + x_2\mathbf{X}_2 + \cdots + x_n\mathbf{X}_n = Z$ (the zero vector) implies that $x_1 = x_2 = \cdots = x_n = 0$. ▮

The ideas of the above definitions have great power and extensive applicability, of which our work can give but modest indication. For our purposes, it is enough to have a working knowledge of the vector spaces $\mathcal{V}_2(\mathcal{R})$ and $\mathcal{V}_3(\mathcal{R})$ (to be treated next), where $\mathcal{R}$ is a division ring associated with a Desarguesian plane $\mathcal{P}$. (In Section 4.8 it will be shown that *every* division ring is associated with some Desarguesian plane, so that the results of Theorems 4.5.1 and 4.5.5 are valid for any division ring $\mathcal{R}$.)

Denote by $\mathcal{V}_3(\mathcal{R})$ the set of *all* row-triples of elements of $\mathcal{R}$ (including [0, 0, 0]), together with the operations of addition of triples and left-multiplication of triples by numbers of $\mathcal{R}$. $\mathcal{V}_3(\mathcal{R})$ is a left vector space over $\mathcal{R}$ (exercise 3) whose theory parallels that of $\mathcal{V}_2(\mathcal{R})$. The details of proof of the results summarized below can easily be supplied (exercise 5) by the reader who has followed the corresponding development for $\mathcal{V}_2(\mathcal{R})$.

(a) The *inner product* of a member of $\mathcal{V}_3(\mathcal{R})$ and a column-triple is defined as follows:

$$[x, y, z] \cdot \begin{bmatrix} k \\ m \\ n \end{bmatrix} = xk + ym + zn\,.$$

If $\mathbf{X}$ is in $\mathcal{V}_3(\mathcal{R})$, and $\boldsymbol{\beta}$ is a three-by-three matrix, $\mathbf{X}\boldsymbol{\beta}$ is defined as the row-triple whose ith member is the inner product of $\mathbf{X}$ and the ith column of $\boldsymbol{\beta}$. Then, the function β on $\mathcal{V}_3(\mathcal{R})$, defined by $\mathbf{X}\beta = \mathbf{X}\boldsymbol{\beta}$, is a linear transformation. Conversely, any linear transformation λ on $\mathcal{V}_3(\mathcal{R})$ is represented by a unique matrix $\boldsymbol{\lambda}$, whose rows are $[1, 0, 0]\lambda$, $[0, 1, 0]\lambda$, and $[0, 0, 1]\lambda$.

(b) The *product* of two three-by-three matrices is the matrix whose entry in row i, column j, is the inner product of the ith row of the first matrix and the jth column of the second matrix. Then, the matrix of the composite of two linear transformations on $\mathcal{V}_3(\mathcal{R})$ is the product of their matrices, and matrix multiplication is associative. Defining a *nonsingular* matrix to be one whose rows are linearly independent, we obtain the following theorem.

Theorem 4.5.5. A linear transformation β on $\mathcal{V}_3(\mathcal{R})$ is a bijection if and only if its matrix $\boldsymbol{\beta}$ is nonsingular.

Proof: An argument entirely similar to that of the paragraph preceding Theorem 4.5.1 shows that β is one-to-one if and only if $\boldsymbol{\beta}$ is nonsingular (exercise 5c). Thus, we have only to prove that β is onto whenever $\boldsymbol{\beta}$ is nonsingular. Accordingly, suppose that $\boldsymbol{\beta}$ is nonsingular, and let $\mathbf{B}_1$, $\mathbf{B}_2$, $\mathbf{B}_3$ be its row-triples (in order, from the top). In the coordinate system in $\mathcal{P}$, $\mathbf{B}_1$, $\mathbf{B}_2$, $\mathbf{B}_3$ represent noncollinear points B_1, B_2, B_3, respectively (exercise 2b). Let $\mathbf{X}$ be an arbitrary triple. If $\mathbf{X} = [0, 0, 0]$, then $[0, 0, 0]\beta = \mathbf{X}$; otherwise, $\mathbf{X}$ represents a point X of $\mathcal{P}$. At least two of B_1, B_2, B_3 are different from X; assume that $X \neq B_1$. (The argument is similar for $X \neq B_2$.) Let $k = X \cup B_1$,

$P = k \cap (B_2 \cup B_3)$, and let $\mathbf{P}$ be a triple for P. Since P is on $B_2 \cup B_3$, $\mathbf{P} = u\mathbf{B}_2 + v\mathbf{B}_3$ for some u, v in $\mathcal{R}$. Because $P \neq B_1$, and X is on $B_1 \cup P$, $\mathbf{X} = s\mathbf{B}_1 + t\mathbf{P} = s\mathbf{B}_1 + (tu)\mathbf{B}_2 + (tv)\mathbf{B}_3$ for some s, t in $\mathcal{R}$. Therefore, $[s, tu, tv]\beta = \mathbf{X}$; hence β is onto. ▌

Corollary: If β is a nonsingular three-by-three matrix, there exists a matrix β^{-1} such that $\beta\beta^{-1} = \beta^{-1}\beta = \iota$. ▌

Exercise 4.5.A

1. Prove that if the linear transformation λ is a bijection, then λ^{-1} is also a linear transformation.

2. (a) Prove that two row-pairs are linearly independent if and only if they are inequivalent and both different from $[0, 0]$.
(b) Prove that three row-triples are linearly independent if and only if they represent (in a coordinate system for $\mathcal{P}$) noncollinear points of $\mathcal{P}$.

3. Prove that $\mathcal{V}_2(\mathcal{R})$ and $\mathcal{V}_3(\mathcal{R})$ are left vector spaces over $\mathcal{R}$. What are the zero vectors of these spaces?

4. Prove by calculation from the definition of matrix product that multiplication of two-by-two matrices is associative.

5. (a) Prove that every three-by-three matrix represents a unique linear transformation on $\mathcal{V}_3(\mathcal{R})$, and that every linear transformation on $\mathcal{V}_3(\mathcal{R})$ is represented by a unique matrix.
(b) Prove that the matrix of the composite of two linear transformations on $\mathcal{V}_3(\mathcal{R})$ is the product of their matrices, and that multiplication of three-by-three matrices is associative.
(c) Prove that a linear transformation on $\mathcal{V}_3(\mathcal{R})$ is one-to-one if and only if its matrix is nonsingular.

6. Prove that there do not exist three linearly independent row-pairs, nor do there exist four linearly independent row-triples.

Exercise 4.5.B

7. Let k, ℓ, m be lines of $\mathcal{P}$ with induced coordinate systems, and let ϕ_1 and ϕ_2 be projectivities from k to ℓ and from ℓ to m, respectively. Suppose that $[\phi_1] = \boldsymbol{\phi}_1$, meaning that $\boldsymbol{\phi}_1$ is one particular matrix for ϕ_1 relative to the given coordinate systems on k and ℓ. Also, suppose that $[\phi_2] = \boldsymbol{\phi}_2$. Prove that $[\phi_1\phi_2] = \boldsymbol{\phi}_1\boldsymbol{\phi}_2$, and that $[\phi_1^{-1}] = \boldsymbol{\phi}_1^{-1}$.

8. Let $\mathcal{C}(\mathcal{R})$ (the *center* of $\mathcal{R}$) be defined as follows: The number s in $\mathcal{R}$ is in $\mathcal{C}(\mathcal{R})$ if and only if $sx = xs$ for every x in $\mathcal{R}$. Let k be a line of $\mathcal{P}$ with an induced coordinate system.

(a) Prove that if s is any nonzero number in $\mathcal{C}(\mathcal{R})$, then the matrix

$$\begin{bmatrix} s & 0 \\ 0 & s \end{bmatrix} (= s\boldsymbol{\iota})$$

is a matrix for the identity projectivity on k.

(b) Conversely, prove that any matrix for the identity projectivity on k has the form given in part (a).

(c) Suppose that ℓ is also a line with an induced coordinate system, and that ϕ is a projectivity from k to ℓ. If $[\phi] = \boldsymbol{\phi}$, prove that $s\boldsymbol{\phi}$ (the matrix obtained by left-multiplication of each element of $\boldsymbol{\phi}$ by s) is likewise a matrix for ϕ for any nonzero s in $\mathcal{C}(\mathcal{R})$, and, conversely, that any matrix for ϕ has this form for some nonzero s in $\mathcal{C}(\mathcal{R})$. (Use the results of exercise 7.)

9. Let k be a line of $\mathcal{P}$ with *two* induced coordinate systems, distinguished by the subscripts 1, 2 in the following.

(a) Use Equation 4.3.8 to show that if P is any point on k, $[P]_2 = [P]_1\boldsymbol{\beta}$, where $\boldsymbol{\beta}$ is a certain nonsingular two-by-two matrix, and $[P]_i$ means a pair for P in coordinate system i.

(b) Suppose that ϕ is a projectivity on k, and that $[\phi]_1 = \boldsymbol{\phi}$. (That is, ϕ is described in the *first* coordinate system on k by the equation $[P\phi]_1 = [P]_1\boldsymbol{\phi}$.) Prove that $[\phi]_2 = \boldsymbol{\beta}^{-1}\boldsymbol{\phi}\boldsymbol{\beta}$.

10. Let the Euclidean plane $\mathcal{E}_2$ be supplied with a Cartesian coordinate system; then, $\mathcal{E}_2$ can be viewed as $\mathcal{V}_2(\mathcal{R})$, where $\mathcal{R}$ is the real number field (why?).

(a) Prove that a linear transformation on $\mathcal{E}_2$ that is a bijection transforms ellipses into ellipses, provided that a circle be considered a special case of an ellipse.

(b) Prove that a linear transformation on $\mathcal{E}_2$ that is a bijection preserves collinearity of points and thus extends to a collineation of $\mathcal{E}_2^*$ that fixes the ideal line (but not necessarily all ideal points).

4.6. Projective Collineations

Let $\boldsymbol{\sigma}$ be a nonsingular three-by-three matrix with elements in $\mathcal{R}$, the division ring associated with $\mathcal{P}$. Let X be an arbitrary point of $\mathcal{P}$, and let $\mathbf{X}$ be a triple for X in the coordinate system in $\mathcal{P}$ constructed in

Section 4.2. Set $\mathbf{Y} = \mathbf{X}\boldsymbol{\sigma}$; since $\mathbf{X} \neq [0, 0, 0]$, and the rows of $\boldsymbol{\sigma}$ are linearly independent, $\mathbf{Y} \neq [0, 0, 0]$. Thus, $\mathbf{Y}$ represents a point Y of $\mathcal{P}$. Furthermore, if X is represented by $r\mathbf{X}$ $(r \neq 0)$ instead of $\mathbf{X}$, then $(r\mathbf{X})\boldsymbol{\sigma} = r\mathbf{Y}$, which still represents Y. Therefore, the equation $[X\sigma] = [X]\boldsymbol{\sigma}$ describes a well-defined function σ on the set of points of $\mathcal{P}$. Moreover, it is easy to see that Theorem 4.5.5 guarantees that σ is a bijection on the set of points of $\mathcal{P}$ (exercise 1).

Suppose that A, B, C are points of $\mathcal{P}$, represented by triples $\mathbf{A}$, $\mathbf{B}$, $\mathbf{C}$, respectively. By Exercise 4.5.2b, A, B, C are collinear if and only if $\mathbf{A}$, $\mathbf{B}$, $\mathbf{C}$ are *not* linearly independent. Since $(x\mathbf{A} + y\mathbf{B} + z\mathbf{C})\boldsymbol{\sigma} = x(\mathbf{A}\boldsymbol{\sigma}) + y(\mathbf{B}\boldsymbol{\sigma}) + z(\mathbf{C}\boldsymbol{\sigma})$, and since $\boldsymbol{\sigma}$ is nonsingular, we see that $\mathbf{A}$, $\mathbf{B}$, $\mathbf{C}$ are linearly independent if and only if $\mathbf{A}\boldsymbol{\sigma}$, $\mathbf{B}\boldsymbol{\sigma}$, $\mathbf{C}\boldsymbol{\sigma}$ are linearly independent. Therefore, A, B, C are collinear if and only if $A\sigma$, $B\sigma$, $C\sigma$ are collinear. Hence, by the extension theorem of Exercise 2.2.10, σ has a unique extension to a collineation of $\mathcal{P}$, which we shall still call σ.

Let k be any line of $\mathcal{P}$, and let an induced coordinate system on k be determined by A $(\mathbf{A})$, D $(\mathbf{D})$, G. On $k\sigma$, construct the induced coordinate system determined by $A\sigma$, $(\mathbf{A}\boldsymbol{\sigma})$, $D\sigma$ $(\mathbf{D}\boldsymbol{\sigma})$, $G\sigma$. If P is any point on k, with $[P] = u\mathbf{A} + v\mathbf{D}$, then $[P\sigma] = u(\mathbf{A}\boldsymbol{\sigma}) + v(\mathbf{D}\boldsymbol{\sigma})$. Thus, the restriction of σ to $\mathcal{I}(k)$ is described by the equation $[P\sigma] = [u', v'] = [u, v]$ and is therefore a projectivity, by Theorem 4.4.5. We have proved the following theorem.

Theorem 4.6.1. If $\boldsymbol{\sigma}$ is a nonsingular three-by-three matrix, the function σ, described by $[X\sigma] = [X]\boldsymbol{\sigma}$ for any point X in $\mathcal{P}$, is (uniquely extendable to) a *projective* collineation of $\mathcal{P}$.

We want to prove that, conversely, every projective collineation of $\mathcal{P}$ is generated by a nonsingular matrix in the manner of the above theorem. First, let η be an arbitrary homology with center O, axis ℓ_∞ (in the notation of Section 4.2), and suppose that $[U\eta] = [a, a, 1]$ $(a \neq 0)$. By Exercise 4.2.7a, $[X\eta] = [x, y, za^{-1}]$, where X is any point of $\mathcal{P}$, with $[X] = [x, y, z]$. Therefore, η is generated by the nonsingular matrix

$$\boldsymbol{\eta} = \begin{bmatrix} 1 & 0 & 0 \\ 0 & 1 & 0 \\ 0 & 0 & a^{-1} \end{bmatrix}.$$

Next, let ϵ be any elation with center ∞, axis ℓ_∞, and suppose that $[O\epsilon] = [b, b, 1]$. By Exercise 4.2.7b, $[X\epsilon] = [x + zb, y + zb, z]$. Therefore, ϵ is generated by the nonsingular matrix

$$\epsilon = \begin{bmatrix} 1 & 0 & 0 \\ 0 & 1 & 0 \\ b & b & 1 \end{bmatrix}.$$

Thus, every homology with center O, axis ℓ_∞, and every elation with center ∞, axis ℓ_∞, is generated by a nonsingular matrix; to establish the corresponding result for all central collineations, we need a lemma.

Lemma 4.6.2. Given any triply noncollinear points P_1, P_2, P_3, P_4 of $\mathcal{P}$, there is a nonsingular matrix $\boldsymbol{\sigma}$ such that $I\sigma = P_1$, $J\sigma = P_2$, $O\sigma = P_3$, and $U\sigma = P_4$, where σ is the projective collineation generated by $\boldsymbol{\sigma}$, and I, J, O, U are the base points of the coordinate system in $\mathcal{P}$.

Proof: For $i = 1, 2, 3, 4$, suppose that $\mathbf{P}_i$ is a triple for P_i. Since P_1, P_2, P_3 are noncollinear, the matrix $\boldsymbol{\rho}$, with rows $\mathbf{P}_1$, $\mathbf{P}_2$, $\mathbf{P}_3$ (in order) is nonsingular. Thus, by Theorem 4.5.5, there exist numbers s_1, s_2, s_3 such that $[s_1, s_2, s_3]\boldsymbol{\rho} = s_1\mathbf{P}_1 + s_2\mathbf{P}_2 + s_3\mathbf{P}_3 = \mathbf{P}_4$. Because P_1, P_2, P_3, P_4 are triply noncollinear, all of s_1, s_2, s_3 are different from 0 (why?). Therefore, the matrix $\boldsymbol{\sigma}$, with rows $s_1\mathbf{P}_1$, $s_2\mathbf{P}_2$, $s_3\mathbf{P}_3$ (in order) is nonsingular, and $[I\sigma] = [1, 0, 0]\boldsymbol{\sigma} = s_1\mathbf{P}_1$, $[J\sigma] = [0, 1, 0]\boldsymbol{\sigma} = s_2\mathbf{P}_2$, $[O\sigma] = [0, 0, 1]\boldsymbol{\sigma} = s_3\mathbf{P}_3$, and $[U\sigma] = [1, 1, 1]\boldsymbol{\sigma} = s_1\mathbf{P}_1 + s_2\mathbf{P}_2 + s_3\mathbf{P}_3 = \mathbf{P}_4$, where σ is the collineation generated by $\boldsymbol{\sigma}$. ∎

Suppose that $\boldsymbol{\rho}$ and $\boldsymbol{\tau}$ are nonsingular three-by-three matrices. Then, $\boldsymbol{\rho\tau}$ is also nonsingular, because the linear transformation on $\mathcal{V}_3(\mathcal{R})$ that it represents is the composite of those represented by $\boldsymbol{\rho}$ and $\boldsymbol{\tau}$, and hence is a bijection. Thus, $\boldsymbol{\rho\tau}$ determines a collineation σ of $\mathcal{P}$ by the prescription $[X\sigma] = [X](\boldsymbol{\rho\tau}) = ([X]\boldsymbol{\rho})\boldsymbol{\tau}$, and, from this equation, it is clear that $\sigma = \rho\tau$, where ρ, τ are the collineations generated by $\boldsymbol{\rho}$ and $\boldsymbol{\tau}$. Similarly, $\boldsymbol{\rho}^{-1}$ is nonsingular, because the linear transformation that it represents is the inverse of that represented by $\boldsymbol{\rho}$, and hence is a bijection. It is also evident that the collineation generated by $\boldsymbol{\rho}^{-1}$ is ρ^{-1} (why?). We can now prove the converse of Theorem 4.6.1.

Theorem 4.6.3. Every projective collineation of $\mathcal{P}$ is generated by a nonsingular matrix.

Proof: First, let η be any homology of $\mathcal{P}$; suppose that η has center H, axis ℓ. Let P_1 and P_2 be distinct points on ℓ, let $P_3 = H$, and let P_4 be any point such that P_1, P_2, P_3, P_4 are triply noncollinear. By Lemma 4.6.2, there is a collineation σ, generated by a nonsingular matrix $\boldsymbol{\sigma}$, such that $I\sigma = P_1$, $J\sigma = P_2$, $O\sigma = P_3$, and $U\sigma = P_4$. Then, $\sigma\eta\sigma^{-1} = \eta'$, a homology with center O, axis ℓ_∞, by the theorem Conjugate of a Central Collineation (3.5.1) (verify!). From the paragraph preceding Lemma 4.6.2, η' is generated by a nonsingular matrix $\boldsymbol{\eta}'$. Since $\eta = \sigma^{-1}\eta'\sigma$, η is generated by the nonsingular matrix $\boldsymbol{\sigma}^{-1}\boldsymbol{\eta}'\boldsymbol{\sigma}$, in view of the paragraph preceding this theorem.

By a very similar argument (exercise 2), every elation of $\mathcal{P}$ can also be shown to be generated by a nonsingular matrix. Then, if τ is any projective collineation, $\tau = \mu_1\mu_2 \cdots \mu_n$, where each μ_i is a central collineation (Corollary 2 to Theorem 3.1.3). If μ_i is generated by the nonsingular matrix $\boldsymbol{\mu}_i$, it follows (by induction) from the remarks preceding this theorem that τ is generated by the nonsingular matrix $\boldsymbol{\mu}_1\boldsymbol{\mu}_2 \cdots \boldsymbol{\mu}_n$. ▮

Two matrices are *equal* if and only if their corresponding elements are equal. Just because two matrices generate the same projective collineation of $\mathcal{P}$, it does not follow that they are equal. In fact, if σ is a collineation generated by a matrix $\boldsymbol{\sigma}$, and if s is any nonzero element in $\mathcal{C}(\mathcal{R})$ (the *center* of $\mathcal{R}$, defined in Exercise 4.5.8), then $\mathrm{s}\boldsymbol{\sigma}$ (obtained by left-multiplication by s of each element of $\boldsymbol{\sigma}$) also generates σ, since $[X](\mathrm{s}\boldsymbol{\sigma}) = (\mathrm{s}[X])\boldsymbol{\sigma}$. Let us prove that every matrix for the identity collineation ι has the form

$$\mathrm{s}\boldsymbol{\iota} = \begin{bmatrix} \mathrm{s} & 0 & 0 \\ 0 & \mathrm{s} & 0 \\ 0 & 0 & \mathrm{s} \end{bmatrix}$$

for some nonzero s in $\mathcal{C}(\mathcal{R})$. Let $\mathbf{A}_1$, $\mathbf{A}_2$, $\mathbf{A}_3$ be row-triples (in order) of an arbitrary matrix $\boldsymbol{\alpha}$ for ι. Since $I\iota = I$, it follows that $\mathbf{A}_1 = \mathrm{s}_1[1, 0, 0]$ for some $\mathrm{s}_1 \neq 0$. Similarly, $\mathbf{A}_2 = \mathrm{s}_2[0, 1, 0]$, and $\mathbf{A}_3 = \mathrm{s}_3[0, 0, 1]$. Because $U\iota = U$, $\mathbf{A}_1 + \mathbf{A}_2 + \mathbf{A}_3 = \mathrm{s}[1, 1, 1]$; hence $\mathrm{s}_1 = \mathrm{s}_2 = \mathrm{s}_3 = \mathrm{s} \neq 0$, and $\boldsymbol{\alpha} = \mathrm{s}\boldsymbol{\iota}$. Finally, let x be any number of $\mathcal{R}$, and let X be the point of $\mathcal{P}$ such that $[X] = [\mathrm{x}, 0, 1]$. Since $X\iota = X$, $[\mathrm{xs}, 0, \mathrm{s}] = r[\mathrm{x}, 0, 1]$ for some $r \neq 0$. Thus, $\mathrm{s} = r$, and $\mathrm{xs} = r\mathrm{x} = \mathrm{sx}$, so that s is in $\mathcal{C}(\mathcal{R})$.

Now, suppose that $\boldsymbol{\sigma}_1$ and $\boldsymbol{\sigma}_2$ are matrices for the same projective collineation σ. Then, $\boldsymbol{\sigma}_1\boldsymbol{\sigma}_2^{-1}$ is a matrix for the identity collineation; hence, $\boldsymbol{\sigma}_1\boldsymbol{\sigma}_2^{-1} = \mathrm{s}\boldsymbol{\iota}$ for some nonzero s in $\mathcal{C}(\mathcal{R})$. Therefore, $\boldsymbol{\sigma}_1 = \mathrm{s}\boldsymbol{\iota}\boldsymbol{\sigma}_2 = \mathrm{s}\boldsymbol{\sigma}_2$, and we have proved that two matrices generate the same projective collineation if and only if one is a multiple of the other by some nonzero number of $\mathcal{C}(\mathcal{R})$.

The connection between projective collineations and matrices will now be exploited to obtain a remarkable theorem (4.6.5) about projectivities. First, we need a lemma that gives a necessary and sufficient condition that a nonsingular matrix generate a *central* collineation.

Lemma 4.6.4. Let $\boldsymbol{\sigma}$ be a nonsingular three-by-three matrix. The collineation σ, generated by $\boldsymbol{\sigma}$, is central if and only if there exist inequivalent triples **A**, **D**, neither one [0, 0, 0], and a nonzero number s in $\mathcal{C}(\mathcal{R})$, such that $\mathbf{A}\boldsymbol{\sigma} = \mathrm{s}\mathbf{A}$ and $\mathbf{D}\boldsymbol{\sigma} = \mathrm{s}\mathbf{D}$.

Proof: Suppose first that **A**, **D**, and s exist as described. Let A and D be the distinct points of $\mathcal{P}$ represented by **A** and **D**, respectively, and let $\ell = A \cup D$. If P is any point on ℓ, $[P] = u\mathbf{A} + v\mathbf{D}$, so that $[P\sigma] = u(\mathbf{A}\boldsymbol{\sigma}) + v(\mathbf{D}\boldsymbol{\sigma}) = (u\mathrm{s})\mathbf{A} + (v\mathrm{s})\mathbf{D} = \mathrm{s}(u\mathbf{A} + v\mathbf{D})$. Therefore, $P\sigma = P$, and σ is central with axis ℓ.

Conversely, suppose that σ is central, and let ℓ be an axis for σ. Let A and D be distinct points on ℓ, represented by triples **A** and **D**, respectively. Since $A\sigma = A$, it follows that $\mathbf{A}\boldsymbol{\sigma} = \mathrm{s}_1\mathbf{A}$ for some $\mathrm{s}_1 \neq 0$; likewise, $\mathbf{D}\boldsymbol{\sigma} = \mathrm{s}_2\mathbf{D}$. If G is the point on ℓ represented by $\mathbf{A} + \mathbf{D}$, $G\sigma = G$; thus $(\mathbf{A} + \mathbf{D})\boldsymbol{\sigma} = \mathrm{s}(\mathbf{A} + \mathbf{D})$. Hence, $\mathrm{s}_1 = \mathrm{s}_2 = \mathrm{s}$ (why?). Finally, if x is any number of $\mathcal{R}$, let X be the point on ℓ represented by $\mathrm{x}\mathbf{A} + \mathbf{D}$. From $X\sigma = X$ follows that $(\mathrm{x}\mathbf{A} + \mathbf{D})\boldsymbol{\sigma} = r(\mathrm{x}\mathbf{A} + \mathbf{D})$ for some $r \neq 0$; hence $(\mathrm{xs})\mathbf{A} + \mathrm{s}\mathbf{D} = (r\mathrm{x})\mathbf{A} + r\mathbf{D}$. Therefore, $\mathrm{s} = r$, and $\mathrm{xs} = r\mathrm{x} = \mathrm{sx}$, proving that s is in $\mathcal{C}(\mathcal{R})$. ∎

Theorem 4.6.5. (Reduction of Projectivities) In a Desarguesian plane $\mathcal{P}$, any projectivity between two distinct lines can be expressed as a composite of two perspectivities.

Proof: Let ϕ be a projectivity from k to $\ell \neq k$. The theorem is true for a 7-point plane (why?); so, we assume that there are at least four points on a line of $\mathcal{P}$. We can then find points A, B on k such that $A \neq B$, and A, B, $A\phi$, $B\phi$ are all different from $k \cap \ell$ (proof?). By Theorem 1.3.3, A, B, $A\phi$, $B\phi$ are triply noncollinear. Construct a coordinate system in $\mathcal{P}$ (as in Section 4.2) with $O = A$, $I = B$, $J = A\phi$, and $U = B\phi$. Let σ be a projective collineation that extends ϕ, and let $\boldsymbol{\sigma}$ be a matrix for σ in the coordinate system just constructed. Then, $[0, 0, 1]\boldsymbol{\sigma} = [0, \mathrm{c}, 0]$, and $[1, 0, 0]\boldsymbol{\sigma} = [d, d, d]$ for some $\mathrm{c} \neq 0$ and some $d \neq 0$ (why?).

Let

$$\boldsymbol{\mu}_1 = \begin{bmatrix} 1 & 0 & 0 \\ 0 & 1 - \mathrm{c} & 1 \\ 0 & \mathrm{c} & 0 \end{bmatrix} \quad \text{and} \quad \boldsymbol{\mu}_2 = \begin{bmatrix} d & d & d \\ 0 & 1 & 0 \\ 0 & 0 & 1 \end{bmatrix}.$$

The matrices $\boldsymbol{\mu}_1$ and $\boldsymbol{\mu}_2$ are nonsingular, and $[1, 0, 0]\boldsymbol{\mu}_1 = [1, 0, 0]$,

$[1, 1, 1]\boldsymbol{\mu}_1 = [1, 1, 1]$, $[0, 0, 1]\boldsymbol{\mu}_2 = [0, 0, 1]$, and $[0, 1, 0]\boldsymbol{\mu}_2 = [0, 1, 0]$. By Lemma 4.6.4, $\boldsymbol{\mu}_1$ generates a central collineation μ_1, with axis $B \cup B\phi$, and $\boldsymbol{\mu}_2$ generates a central collineation μ_2, with axis $A \cup A\phi$. Furthermore, $[0, 0, 1]\boldsymbol{\mu}_1\boldsymbol{\mu}_2\boldsymbol{\sigma}^{-1} = [0, c, 0]\boldsymbol{\mu}_2\boldsymbol{\sigma}^{-1} = [0, c, 0]\boldsymbol{\sigma}^{-1} = [0, 0, 1]$, and $[1, 0, 0]\boldsymbol{\mu}_1\boldsymbol{\mu}_2\boldsymbol{\sigma}^{-1} = [1, 0, 0]\boldsymbol{\mu}_2\boldsymbol{\sigma}^{-1} = [d, d, d]\boldsymbol{\sigma}^{-1} = [1, 0, 0]$. Therefore, by Lemma 4.6.4, $\boldsymbol{\mu}_1\boldsymbol{\mu}_2\boldsymbol{\sigma}^{-1}$ generates a central collineation with axis $A \cup B = k$. Since $\boldsymbol{\mu}_1\boldsymbol{\mu}_2\boldsymbol{\sigma}^{-1}$ generates $\mu_1\mu_2\sigma^{-1}$, the latter is central with axis k. Letting ϕ' be the restriction of $\mu_1\mu_2$ to $\mathcal{I}(k)$, we obtain $\phi'\phi^{-1} = \iota$, the identity projectivity on k (why?). Hence, $\phi' = \phi$, and $\mu_1\mu_2$ also extends ϕ. Since $k\mu_1 = (A \cup B)\mu_1 = A\phi \cup B \neq k$, μ_1 induces a perspectivity π_1 from k to $k\mu_1$, by the theorem Projectivities Induced by Central Collineations (2.5.1). Likewise, because $(k\mu_1)\mu_2 = \ell \neq k\mu_1$, μ_2 induces a perspectivity π_2 from $k\mu_1$ to ℓ. Therefore, $\phi = \pi_1\pi_2$, as required. ∎

Corollary: In a Desarguesian plane, any projective collineation σ is a composite of three (or fewer) central collineations.

Proof: If σ fixes every line, then $\sigma = \iota$, a central collineation. Otherwise, let k be a noninvariant line of σ. Then, σ induces a projectivity ϕ from k to $k\sigma$, and, by the theorem, $\phi = \pi_1\pi_2$, a composite of two perspectivities. Let μ_1 and μ_2 be central collineations that extend π_1 and π_2, respectively (Theorem 3.1.3, Extension of Perspectivities). The collineation $\sigma(\mu_1\mu_2)^{-1}$ fixes all points on k, hence it is a central collineation μ_3. Thus, $\sigma = \mu_3\mu_1\mu_2$, a composite of three central collineations. ∎

In order to answer the question of how lines transform under a collineation generated by a given matrix, we need first to define the product of a matrix and a column-triple. If $\boldsymbol{\sigma}$ is a three-by-three matrix, and $\boldsymbol{k}$ is a column-triple, the product $\boldsymbol{\sigma k}$ is the column-triple whose ith element (from the top) is the inner product of the ith row of $\boldsymbol{\sigma}$ with the column-triple $\boldsymbol{k}$. A simple computation (exercise 4) shows that if $\mathbf{X}$ is a row-triple, the inner product of $\mathbf{X}$ and $\boldsymbol{\sigma k}$ is the same as the inner product of $\mathbf{X}\boldsymbol{\sigma}$ and $\boldsymbol{k}$; that is, $\mathbf{X}\cdot(\boldsymbol{\sigma k}) = (\mathbf{X}\boldsymbol{\sigma})\cdot\boldsymbol{k}$. (Inner product can be regarded as a special case of matrix product, and the equation just written as another manifestation of the associativity of multiplication of matrices.)

Suppose that σ is a projective collineation of $\mathcal{P}$, generated by the matrix $\boldsymbol{\sigma}$. Let k be an arbitrary line of $\mathcal{P}$, and let A and B be distinct points on k; then, $[A]\cdot[k] = [B]\cdot[k] = 0$. Since the column-triples $\boldsymbol{\sigma}^{-1}\boldsymbol{k}$ and $\boldsymbol{\sigma}^{-1}\boldsymbol{k}'$ are right-equivalent whenever the column-triples $\boldsymbol{k}$

and k' are right-equivalent (proof?), there is then a unique line ℓ of $\mathcal{P}$ such that $[\ell] = \boldsymbol{\sigma}^{-1}[k]$. For this line ℓ, $[A\sigma]\cdot[\ell] = ([A]\boldsymbol{\sigma})\cdot(\boldsymbol{\sigma}^{-1}[k]) = ([A]\boldsymbol{\sigma}\boldsymbol{\sigma}^{-1})\cdot[k] = [A]\cdot[k] = 0$. Therefore, $A\sigma$ lies on ℓ, and, similarly, $B\sigma$ lies on ℓ, so that $\ell = A\sigma \cup B\sigma = (A \cup B)\sigma = k\sigma$.

Theorem 4.6.5. If σ is any projective collineation of $\mathcal{P}$, there is a nonsingular three-by-three matrix $\boldsymbol{\sigma}$ such that (relative to a given coordinate system in $\mathcal{P}$) $[X\sigma] = [X]\boldsymbol{\sigma}$, and $[k\sigma] = \boldsymbol{\sigma}^{-1}[k]$, for any point X, and any line k, of $\mathcal{P}$. ∎

Because of the rules of transformation given in the above theorem, $\boldsymbol{\sigma}$ may be called a *point-matrix* of σ, while $\boldsymbol{\sigma}^{-1}$ is a *line-matrix* of σ. In referring to a matrix that generates σ, we shall consistently mean a point-matrix of σ.

Exercise 4.6.A

1. Prove that $[X\sigma] = [X]\boldsymbol{\sigma}$ defines a bijection σ on the points of $\mathcal{P}$ when $\boldsymbol{\sigma}$ is a nonsingular three-by-three matrix.

2. Prove that every elation of $\mathcal{P}$ is generated by a nonsingular matrix. Use the method of the first paragraph of the proof of Theorem 4.6.3.

3. Let a relation $\sim$ be defined on the set of three-by-three matrices over $\mathcal{R}$ as follows: $\boldsymbol{\beta}_2 \sim \boldsymbol{\beta}_1$ if and only if $\boldsymbol{\beta}_2 = s\boldsymbol{\beta}_1$ for some $s \neq 0$ in $\mathcal{C}(\mathcal{R})$. Prove that $\sim$ is an equivalence relation.

4. Let $\mathbf{X}$ be a row-triple, $\boldsymbol{\sigma}$ a three-by-three matrix, and $\boldsymbol{k}$ a column-triple. Prove by calculation that $\mathbf{X}\cdot(\boldsymbol{\sigma}\boldsymbol{k}) = (\mathbf{X}\boldsymbol{\sigma})\cdot\boldsymbol{k}$.

5. Prove that, in a Desarguesian plane, any projectivity *on* a line can be expressed as a composite of three perspectivities.

6. (a) Find a line-matrix for the homology with center O, axis ℓ_∞, sending U into A, where $[A] = [a, a, 1]$ $(a \neq 0)$.
(b) Find a line-matrix for the elation with center ∞, axis ℓ_∞, sending O into B, where $[B] = [b, b, 1]$.

7. Let Φ be an inner automorphism of $\mathcal{R}$, and let $\boldsymbol{\beta}$ be a nonsingular three-by-three matrix. Show that the equation $[X\rho] = [x\Phi, y\Phi, z\Phi]\boldsymbol{\beta}$ (where $[X] = [x, y, z]$) describes a well-defined function ρ on the points of $\mathcal{P}$. Also, prove that ρ has a unique extension to a projective collineation of $\mathcal{P}$. (Refer to Exercise 4.4.2.)

Exercise 4.6.B

8. How many nonsingular three-by-three matrices are there over a field of three elements? Compare with the number of collineations of 13_4.

9. Let σ be a projective collineation of $\mathcal{P}$ that fixes the points O, I, J, and U. Prove that $[X\sigma] = [x\Phi, y\Phi, z\Phi]$, where Φ is some *inner* automorphism of $\mathcal{R}$, and $[X] = [x, y, z]$.

10. Let η be the homology of $\mathcal{P}$ with center ∞, axis ℓ_J (in the notation of Section 4.2), sending U into A, where $[A] = [a, a, 1]$ $(a \neq 0)$. Find a point-matrix for η.

11. Let η be a homology of $\mathcal{P}$ with axis ℓ_∞, center H, where $[H] = [h, k, 1]$. Find a point-matrix for η. (It will contain a parameter because η is not completely specified.) Compare the analytic expression for η with Equation 2.3.4.

12. Let $\mathcal{R}$ be a division ring. Prove that the center of $\mathcal{R}$ is a field.

4.7. Semilinear Transformations

The object of this section is to characterize the group of all collineations of the Desarguesian plane $\mathcal{P}$, as the group of projective collineations has been characterized in the preceding section. As a result of this work, we shall also learn how any two planar coordinate systems of $\mathcal{P}$ are related.

For this and the next paragraph, suppose that ψ is a collineation of $\mathcal{P}$ that fixes each of the points O, I, J, U, in the notation of Section 4.2; then, ψ also fixes ℓ_U, ℓ_∞, and ∞. Let $\mathcal{S}$ be the division ring in the set of points, other than ∞, on ℓ_U (with O and U as additive and multiplicative identities, respectively). Let Ψ be the restriction of ψ to $\mathcal{S}$; by the argument of the first three paragraphs of Section 3.8, Ψ is an automorphism of $\mathcal{S}$. Let Φ be the coordinatization of $\mathcal{S}$ selected in Section 4.2; $\Phi\Psi$ is also a coordinatization of $\mathcal{S}$ (why?). By Theorem 3.8.5, $\Phi\Psi = \Theta\Phi$ for some automorphism Θ of $\mathcal{R}$; hence $\Psi = \Phi^{-1}\Theta\Phi$.

Now, let P be any point not on ℓ_∞, with $[P] = [p, q, r]$. Since $r \neq 0$, $[r^{-1}p, r^{-1}q, 1]$ is also a triple for P. Set $P_1 = (P \cup J) \cap \ell_U$ and $P_2 = (P \cup I) \cap \ell_U$; $P_1 = (r^{-1}p)\Phi$, and $P_2 = (r^{-1}q)\Phi$, by definition of the coordinates of P (Phase 1 of Section 4.2). Therefore (since P_1 is in $\mathcal{S}$), $P_1\psi = P_1\Psi = (r^{-1}p)\Phi\Phi^{-1}\Theta\Phi = (r^{-1}p)\Theta\Phi = [(r\Theta)^{-1}(p\Theta)]\Phi$, and, likewise, $P_2\psi = [(r\Theta)^{-1}(q\Theta)]\Phi$. Because $P_1\psi = (P\psi \cup J) \cap \ell_U$, and $P_2\psi = (P\psi \cup I) \cap \ell_U$, it follows that $[P\psi] = [(r\Theta)^{-1}(p\Theta), (r\Theta)^{-1}(q\Theta), 1]$;

hence, also, $[P\psi] = [p\Theta, q\Theta, r\Theta]$. If T is the point such that $[T] = [p, q, 0]$, then $T = (O \cup P) \cap \ell_\infty$, so that $T\psi = (O \cup P\psi) \cap \ell_\infty$, and $[T\psi] = [p\Theta, q\Theta, 0]$ (Phase 3 of Section 4.2). Thus, for any point X, with $[X] = [x, y, z]$, $[X\psi] = [x\Theta, y\Theta, z\Theta]$ (because $0\Theta = 0$ for any automorphism Θ).

Theorem 4.7.1. If ψ is a collineation of $\mathcal{P}$ that fixes O, I, J, U, then $[X\psi] = [x\Theta, y\Theta, z\Theta]$, where Θ is some automorphism of $\mathcal{R}$, and X is an arbitrary point of $\mathcal{P}$, with $[X] = [x, y, z]$. ▮

Corollary: Let ρ be any collineation of $\mathcal{P}$. Then, ρ is described by the equation $[X\rho] = [x\Theta, y\Theta, z\Theta]\boldsymbol{\sigma}$, where Θ is an automorphism of $\mathcal{R}$, $\boldsymbol{\sigma}$ is a nonsingular three-by-three matrix, and X is an arbitrary point of $\mathcal{P}$, with $[X] = [x, y, z]$.

Proof: Let σ be a *projective* collineation that sends O, I, J, U into $O\rho, I\rho, J\rho, U\rho$, respectively; σ exists by the Quadrangle Mapping Theorem (3.6.1), and it is generated by a nonsingular matrix $\boldsymbol{\sigma}$, by Theorem 4.6.3. Now $\rho\sigma^{-1}$ is a collineation that fixes O, I, J, U. Therefore, $[X\rho\sigma^{-1}] = [x\Theta, y\Theta, z\Theta]$, by the above theorem. Since σ^{-1} is generated by $\boldsymbol{\sigma}^{-1}$, $[X\rho\sigma^{-1}] = [X\rho]\boldsymbol{\sigma}^{-1}$. The last two equations yield $[X\rho] = [x\Theta, y\Theta, z\Theta]\boldsymbol{\sigma}$. ▮

If Θ is any automorphism of $\mathcal{R}$, and $\boldsymbol{\sigma}$ is any three-by-three matrix, the function β on $\mathcal{V}_3(\mathcal{R})$, defined by $[x, y, z]\beta = [x\Theta, y\Theta, z\Theta]\boldsymbol{\sigma}$ is a *semilinear transformation*; β is called nonsingular if and only if $\boldsymbol{\sigma}$ is a nonsingular matrix. The preceding corollary can thus be restated: "Every collineation of $\mathcal{P}$ is generated by a nonsingular semilinear transformation [on $\mathcal{V}_3(\mathcal{R})$]."

A linear transformation on $\mathcal{V}_3(\mathcal{R})$ is a semilinear transformation whose automorphism is the identity. However, the important distinction for projective geometry is that between *inner* and *noninner* automorphisms of $\mathcal{R}$. For, if Θ is inner, defined by $x\Theta = s^{-1}xs$, and if ρ is the collineation described by $[X\rho] = [x\Theta, y\Theta, z\Theta]\boldsymbol{\sigma}$, then $[X\rho] = (s^{-1}[x, y, z])\boldsymbol{\sigma}'$, where $\boldsymbol{\sigma}' = s\boldsymbol{\sigma}$. Hence, also, $[X\rho] = [X]\boldsymbol{\sigma}'$, and ρ is projective. Conversely, if $[X\rho] = [x\Theta, y\Theta, z\Theta]\boldsymbol{\sigma}$, and ρ is projective, then $\rho\sigma^{-1}$ is projective, where σ^{-1} is the (projective) collineation generated by $\boldsymbol{\sigma}^{-1}$. Since $[X\rho\sigma^{-1}] = [x\Theta, y\Theta, z\Theta]$, and since $0\Theta = 0$ and $1\Theta = 1$ for any automorphism Θ (Exercise 3.8.3), $\rho\sigma^{-1}$ fixes O, I, J, U. By Exercise 4.6.9, $[X\rho\sigma^{-1}] = [x\Phi, y\Phi, z\Phi]$ for some *inner* automorphism Φ. Thus, $[x\Theta, y\Theta, z\Theta] = r[x\Phi, y\Phi, z\Phi]$ for some $r \neq 0$ (which, apparently, may depend upon $[x, y, z]$). Let x be an arbitrary number of $\mathcal{R}$, and set $y = z = 1$. Then, $[x\Theta, 1, 1] = r[x\Phi, 1, 1]$, from which it follows that $r = 1$ (at least in this case), and $x\Theta = x\Phi$ (for all x). Therefore, $\Theta = \Phi$, an inner automorphism.

For the sake of brevity of expression, let us agree on the following: If $[X] = [x, y, z] = \mathbf{X}$, then $[X]\Theta = [x\Theta, y\Theta, z\Theta] = [x, y, z]\Theta = \mathbf{X}\Theta$, where Θ is any automorphism of $\mathcal{R}$. To establish the converse of the corollary to Theorem 4.7.1, let β be an arbitrary nonsingular semilinear transformation, with automorphism Θ and matrix $\boldsymbol{\sigma}$. It is simple to verify (exercise 1a) that the equation $[X\rho] = ([X]\Theta)\boldsymbol{\sigma}$ describes a well-defined function ρ on the set of points of $\mathcal{P}$. Moreover, ρ is one-to-one (exercise 1b) and onto (exercise 1c). We want to prove that ρ preserves collinearity. Suppose that X, Y, Z are points of $\mathcal{P}$, represented by triples $\mathbf{X}$, $\mathbf{Y}$, $\mathbf{Z}$, respectively. If X, Y, Z are collinear, then $u\mathbf{X} + v\mathbf{Y} + w\mathbf{Z} = [0, 0, 0]$ for some u, v, w, not all 0. Hence, $(u\Theta)(\mathbf{X}\Theta) + (v\Theta)(\mathbf{Y}\Theta) + (w\Theta)(\mathbf{Z}\Theta) = [0, 0, 0]$, and not all of $u\Theta$, $v\Theta$, $w\Theta$ are 0 (why?). Thus, $(u\Theta)(\mathbf{X}\Theta)\boldsymbol{\sigma} + (v\Theta)(\mathbf{Y}\Theta)\boldsymbol{\sigma} + (w\Theta)(\mathbf{Z}\Theta)\boldsymbol{\sigma} = [0, 0, 0]$, which implies that $X\rho$, $Y\rho$, $Z\rho$ are collinear. We have proved that ρ satisfies the hypotheses of the extension theorem of Exercise 2.2.10, so that it has a unique extension to a collineation of $\mathcal{P}$.

Theorem 4.7.2. (Collineations and Semilinear Transformations) Every collineation of the Desarguesian plane $\mathcal{P}$ is generated by a nonsingular semilinear transformation [on $\mathcal{V}_3(\mathcal{R})$], and, conversely, every nonsingular semilinear transformation generates a collineation of $\mathcal{P}$. If ρ is a collineation of $\mathcal{P}$, with $[X\rho] = ([X]\Theta)\boldsymbol{\sigma}$, then ρ is projective if and only if Θ is an *inner* automorphism. ∎

The coordinate system in $\mathcal{P}$ is determined by the base points O, I, J, U, and the coordinatization Φ of $\mathcal{S}$. Suppose that a *second* coordinate system is constructed by the method of Section 4.2, using any triply noncollinear base points O', I', J', U', and any coordinatization Φ' of $\mathcal{S}'$, where $\mathcal{S}'$ is the division ring in the set of points on ℓ'_U $(= O' \cup U')$ other than ∞' $(= \ell'_U \cap \ell'_\infty$, where $\ell'_\infty = I' \cup J')$, with O' and U' as additive and multiplicative identities, respectively. Let $[X]_1 = [x, y, z]$ and $[X]_2 = [x', y', z']$ mean that $[x, y, z]$ is a triple for X in the *first*, and $[x', y', z']$ a triple for X in the *second* coordinate system in $\mathcal{P}$. We seek the relation between $[X]_1$ and $[X]_2$.

Let ψ be a projective collineation that maps O, I, J, U into O', I', J', U', respectively. Then, $\ell_U\psi = \ell'_U$, $\ell_\infty\psi = \ell'_\infty$, $\infty\psi = \infty'$, and the restriction Ψ of ψ to $\mathcal{S}$ is a bijection from $\mathcal{S}$ to $\mathcal{S}'$. Moreover, by the argument of the first three paragraphs of Section 3.8, Ψ is an isomorphism of the division ring $\mathcal{S}$ onto the division ring $\mathcal{S}'$. Therefore, $\Phi\Psi$ is a coordinatization of $\mathcal{S}'$. Hence, by Theorem 3.8.5, $\Phi\Psi = \Theta\Phi'$ for some automorphism Θ of $\mathcal{R}$, and $\Psi = \Phi^{-1}\Theta\Phi'$.

Let P be any point not on ℓ_∞, with $[P]_1 = [p, q, r]$. Since $r \neq 0$, $[r^{-1}p, r^{-1}q, 1]$ is an equivalent triple for P in the first coordinate system. Set $P_1 = (P \cup J) \cap \ell_U$ and $P_2 = (P \cup I) \cap \ell_U$. Then, $P_1 = (r^{-1}p)\Phi$, and $P_2 = (r^{-1}q)\Phi$, by definition of the coordinates of P in the first coordinate system (Phase 1 of Section 4.2). Hence, because P_1 is in $\mathcal{S}$, $P_1\psi = P_1\Psi = (r^{-1}p)\Phi\Phi^{-1}\Theta\Phi' = (r^{-1}p)\Theta\Phi' = [(r\Theta)^{-1}(p\Theta)]\Phi'$, and, likewise, $P_2\psi = [(r\Theta)^{-1}(q\Theta)]\Phi'$. Since $P\psi$ is not on ℓ'_∞, and since $(P\psi \cup J') \cap \ell'_U = [(P \cup J) \cap \ell_U]\psi = P_1\psi$ and $(P\psi \cup I') \cap \ell'_U = P_2\psi$, it follows that $[P\psi]_2 = [(r\Theta)^{-1}(p\Theta), (r\Theta)^{-1}(q\Theta), 1]$. Hence, also, $[P\psi]_2 = [p\Theta, q\Theta, r\Theta]$. If T is the point such that $[T]_1 = [p, q, 0]$, then $T = (P \cup O) \cap \ell_\infty$, which implies that $T\psi = (P\psi \cup O') \cap \ell'_\infty$, and $[T\psi]_2 = [p\Theta, q\Theta, 0]$.

We have learned that if X is any point of $\mathcal{P}$, with $[X]_1 = [x, y, z]$, then $[X\psi]_2 = [x\Theta, y\Theta, z\Theta] = [X]_1\Theta$. If $\boldsymbol{\psi}$ is a matrix for ψ relative to the *first* coordinate system, so that $[X\psi]_1 = [X]_1\boldsymbol{\psi}$, then $[X]_1 = [X\psi]_1\boldsymbol{\psi}^{-1}$, from which it follows that $[X\psi]_2 = ([X\psi]_1\boldsymbol{\psi}^{-1})\Theta$. Since ψ is onto, $X\psi$ could be *any* point of $\mathcal{P}$. Therefore, $[X]_2 = ([X]_1\boldsymbol{\psi}^{-1})\Theta = ([X]_1\Theta)\boldsymbol{\sigma}$, where $\boldsymbol{\sigma} = \boldsymbol{\psi}^{-1}\Theta$, the matrix obtained by applying the automorphism Θ to each of the elements of $\boldsymbol{\psi}^{-1}$; $\boldsymbol{\sigma}$ is nonsingular because $\boldsymbol{\psi}^{-1}$ is (proof?).

Theorem 4.7.3. Any two coordinate systems of $\mathcal{P}$ (constructed as in Section 4.2) are related by a nonsingular semilinear transformation, and, conversely, any nonsingular semilinear transformation induces a coordinate transformation in $\mathcal{P}$.

Proof: The first half has been proved in the four paragraphs preceding the theorem, since the first and second coordinate systems there could have been any two coordinate systems of $\mathcal{P}$. For the converse, suppose that a (first) coordinate system is given in $\mathcal{P}$, determined by base points O, I, J, U, and a coordinatization Φ of the division ring $\mathcal{S}$ (as in Section 4.2). It is then required to construct a second coordinate system in $\mathcal{P}$ such that $[X]_2 = ([X]_1\Theta)\boldsymbol{\sigma}$, where Θ is a given automorphism of $\mathcal{R}$ and $\boldsymbol{\sigma}$ is a given nonsingular three-by-three matrix.

Let ψ be the projective collineation described by $[X\psi]_1 = [X]_1(\boldsymbol{\sigma}^{-1}\Theta^{-1})$. Let $O' = O\psi$, $I' = I\psi$, $J' = J\psi$, $U' = U\psi$, $\ell'_U = O' \cup U'$, $\ell'_\infty = I' \cup J'$, $\infty' = \ell'_U \cap \ell'_\infty$, and construct the division ring $\mathcal{S}'$ in the set of points on ℓ'_U other than ∞', with O' and U' as additive and multiplicative identities, respectively. The restriction Ψ of ψ to $\mathcal{S}$ is an isomorphism of $\mathcal{S}$ onto $\mathcal{S}'$, as in the first three paragraphs of Section 3.8. Let $\Phi' = \Theta^{-1}\Phi\Psi$; then, Φ' is a coordinatization of $\mathcal{S}'$, and $\Psi = \Phi^{-1}\Theta\Phi'$. Construct a second coordinate system in $\mathcal{P}$ with base points O', I', J', U', and coordinatization Φ' of $\mathcal{S}'$. The argument of the four paragraphs immediately preceding the theorem shows that $[X]_2 = \{[X]_1(\sigma^{-1}\Theta^{-1})^{-1}\}\Theta = \{[X]_1(\sigma\Theta^{-1})\}\Theta = ([X]_1\Theta)\sigma$, as desired. ∎

Thus, both the collineations of $\mathcal{P}$ and the coordinate transformations of $\mathcal{P}$ are generated by nonsingular semilinear transformations. This section ends with a demonstration of the effect of a coordinate transformation upon the analytic expression of a collineation.

Example 4.7.4. Suppose that $\mathcal{P}$ has two coordinate systems, related by $[X]_2 = ([X]_1\Phi)\boldsymbol{\beta}$. Let ρ be a collineation of $\mathcal{P}$, and suppose that $[X\rho]_1 = ([X]_1\Theta)\boldsymbol{\sigma}$ describes ρ in the first coordinate system. We want to find an equation for ρ in the second coordinate system. Now, $[X\rho]_2 = ([X\rho]_1\Phi)\boldsymbol{\beta} = (\{([X]_1\Theta)\boldsymbol{\sigma}\}\Phi)\boldsymbol{\beta} = ([X_1]\Theta\Phi)(\boldsymbol{\sigma}\Phi)\boldsymbol{\beta}$. Since $[X]_1 = ([X]_2\boldsymbol{\beta}^{-1})\Phi^{-1}$, it follows that $[X\rho]_2 = \{([X]_2\boldsymbol{\beta}^{-1})\Phi^{-1}\Theta\Phi\}(\boldsymbol{\sigma}\Phi)\boldsymbol{\beta} = ([X]_2\Phi^{-1}\Theta\Phi)(\boldsymbol{\beta}^{-1}\Phi^{-1}\Theta\Phi)(\boldsymbol{\sigma}\Phi)\boldsymbol{\beta}$, which is the desired equation. Note that, for example, $([X]_2\boldsymbol{\beta}^{-1})\Phi^{-1}$ is not in general the same as $[X]_2(\boldsymbol{\beta}^{-1}\Phi^{-1})$, so that the parentheses are essential in the preceding expressions.

If Θ is the identity automorphism (so that ρ is projective), the above equation reduces to $[X\rho]_2 = [X]_2\boldsymbol{\beta}^{-1}(\boldsymbol{\sigma}\Phi)\boldsymbol{\beta}$; thus, $\boldsymbol{\beta}^{-1}(\boldsymbol{\sigma}\Phi)\boldsymbol{\beta}$ is a matrix for ρ in the second coordinate system. If, additionally, Φ is the identity automorphism (so that the coordinate transformation is *linear*), $\boldsymbol{\beta}^{-1}\boldsymbol{\sigma}\boldsymbol{\beta}$ is a matrix for ρ in the second system. ∎

Exercise 4.7.A

1. (a) Prove that if Θ is any automorphism of $\mathcal{R}$, and $\boldsymbol{\sigma}$ is any nonsingular three-by-three matrix, the equation $[X\rho] = ([X]\Theta)\boldsymbol{\sigma}$ describes a well-defined function ρ on the set of points of $\mathcal{P}$.
(b) Prove that the ρ of part (a) is one-to-one.
(c) Prove that the ρ of part (a) is onto.

2. (a) Prove that every collineation of $\mathcal{P}$ is projective if and only if every automorphism of $\mathcal{R}$ is inner.
(b) Prove that if $\mathcal{R}$ has no automorphism except the identity, then every collineation of $\mathcal{P}$ is projective, *and* the Fundamental Theorem holds in $\mathcal{P}$.

3. Let σ be a nonsingular three-by-three matrix, and let Θ be an automorphism of $\mathcal{R}$. Prove that $(\sigma\Theta)^{-1} = \sigma^{-1}\Theta$.

4. Suppose that ρ_1 and ρ_2 are collineations of $\mathcal{P}$, with $[X\rho_1] = ([X]\Theta_1)\sigma_1$ and $[X\rho_2] = ([X]\Theta_2)\sigma_2$.
   (a) Find an equation for $\rho_1\rho_2$.
   (b) Find an equation for ρ_1^{-1}.

5. Let ρ be a collineation of $\mathcal{P}$, with $[X\rho] = ([X]\Theta)\sigma$. How does ρ transform lines?

Exercise 4.7.B

6. (a) Show that the field of four elements associated with a 21-point plane has exactly two automorphisms. (See Exercises 3.7.11 and 3.8.7b.)
   (b) Prove that a 21-point plane has exactly 120,960 collineations.

7. Let ρ be a collineation of $\mathcal{P}$, and suppose that $[X\rho] = ([X]\Theta_1)\sigma_1$ and $[X\rho] = ([X]\Theta_2)\sigma_2$ are equations that describe ρ in the *same* coordinate system. Prove that $\Theta_2\Theta_1^{-1}$ is an inner automorphism of $\mathcal{R}$, and that $\sigma_2\sigma_1^{-1} = r\iota$ for some $r \neq 0$. Assuming that $x\Theta_2\Theta_1^{-1} = u^{-1}xu$ for each x in $\mathcal{R}$, prove also that $r = (u^{-1}s)\Theta_1$ for some nonzero s in the center of $\mathcal{R}$.

8. In this section, a coordinate system in $\mathcal{P}$ meant a system obtainable by the construction of Section 4.2. An alternative definition is as follows: A coordinate system in $\mathcal{P}$ is any one-to-one, onto assignment of (left-) equivalence classes of row-triples (excluding the class of $[0, 0, 0]$) of elements of $\mathcal{R}$ to the points of $\mathcal{P}$ with the property that $\mathbf{P}_1$, $\mathbf{P}_2$, $\mathbf{P}_3$ are linearly dependent (that is, *not* linearly independent) triples if and only if the points P_1, P_2, P_3, to which they are assigned, are collinear.

Suppose that $\mathcal{P}$ is given two coordinate systems—the *first* by the construction of Section 4.2, the *second* by the assignment of triples according to the above definition. Prove that the equation $[X\alpha]_1 = [X]_2$ describes a well-defined bijection α on the points of $\mathcal{P}$, and that α has an extension to a collineation of $\mathcal{P}$.

9. (a) Continuing exercise 8, prove that the two coordinate systems in $\mathcal{P}$ of that exercise are related by a nonsingular semilinear transformation.
   (b) Deduce that coordinate systems defined as in exercise 8 are

identical to coordinate systems obtainable by the construction of Section 4.2.

4.8. Construction of Desarguesian Planes

It has been shown in Sections 3.7 and 3.8 that a Desarguesian plane determines a (unique) division ring. In this section it is demonstrated that, conversely, any division ring determines a (unique) Desarguesian plane. Let $\mathcal{R}$ be an arbitrary division ring, and construct a plane $\mathcal{P}$ as follows: The *points* of $\mathcal{P}$ are the (left-) equivalence classes of row-triples of elements of $\mathcal{R}$, excluding the class of $[0, 0, 0]$. If P is a point of $\mathcal{P}$, we write $[P] = [p, q, r]$ to indicate that $[p, q, r]$ is one triple of the class P. The *lines* of $\mathcal{P}$ are the (right-) equivalence classes of column-triples of elements of $\mathcal{R}$, excluding the class of

$$\begin{bmatrix} 0 \\ 0 \\ 0 \end{bmatrix}.$$

If k is a line of $\mathcal{P}$, we write

$$[k] = \begin{bmatrix} k \\ m \\ n \end{bmatrix}$$

to indicate that

$$\begin{bmatrix} k \\ m \\ n \end{bmatrix}$$

is one triple of the class k. A point P and a line k, with $[P] = [p, q, r]$ and

$$[k] = \begin{bmatrix} k \\ m \\ n \end{bmatrix},$$

are *incident* if and only if $pk + qm + rn = 0$. (The definition of incidence is seen to be independent of the choice of triples representing P and k.)

If A and D are distinct points of $\mathcal{P}$, with $[A] = [a, b, c]$ and $[D] = [d, e, f]$, a repetition of the argument leading to the solution of Equations 4.3.1 (which depended only upon the properties of a division ring, plus the fact that $[a, b, c]$ and $[d, e, f]$ were inequivalent triples), shows that there is a unique line of $\mathcal{P}$ incident with both A

and D. Thus, Axiom 2 (for projective planes) holds in $\mathcal{P}$, and Axiom 3 is similarly verified, by dualizing the calculations.

Let O, I, J, U be the points of $\mathcal{P}$ represented by $[0, 0, 1]$, $[1, 0, 0]$, $[0, 1, 0]$, and $[1, 1, 1]$, respectively. That these points are triply noncollinear is proved by finding the line joining each pair and showing that the line so found is not incident with either of the two points not used to determine it. For example, the line $I \cup U$ is evidently represented by

$$\begin{bmatrix} 0 \\ 1 \\ -1 \end{bmatrix},$$

and this line is not incident with either O or J. Thus, Axiom 1 holds in $\mathcal{P}$ (exercise 1).

Theorem 4.8.1. The plane $\mathcal{P}$, constructed over the division ring $\mathcal{R}$ by the method given above, is a Desarguesian plane.

Proof: That $\mathcal{P}$ satisfies Axioms 1–3 has been proved in the two paragraphs preceding the theorem. The proof that $\mathcal{P}$ also satisfies Axiom 4 employs Theorem 4.6.1 and Lemma 4.6.2, which were derived from the considerations of Sections 4.3 and 4.4. An examination of Sections 4.3 and 4.4 reveals that the results therein do not depend upon Axiom 4, but only upon Axioms 1–3 and the representation of points and lines by classes of row- and column-triples (of elements of a division ring) in such a way that P is on k if and only if $[P]\cdot[k] = 0$. Therefore, Theorem 4.6.1 and Lemma 4.6.2 are available for our plane $\mathcal{P}$.

Let O, I, J, U be as in the paragraph preceding this theorem, and let $\ell_U = O \cup U$, $\ell_\infty = I \cup J$, and $\infty = \ell_U \cap \ell_\infty$. Then,

$$[\ell_\infty] = \begin{bmatrix} 0 \\ 0 \\ 1 \end{bmatrix},$$

and a point of $\mathcal{P}$ is on ℓ_∞ if and only if the third element of any triple for the point is 0. Also,

$$[\ell_U] = \begin{bmatrix} 1 \\ -1 \\ 0 \end{bmatrix},$$

and a point X, other than ∞, is on ℓ_U if and only if $[X] = [\mathrm{x}, \mathrm{x}, 1]$ for some x in $\mathcal{R}$. Let A be any point on ℓ_U other than O and ∞, with $[A] = [a, a, 1]$ $(a \neq 0)$, and let

$$\eta = \begin{bmatrix} 1 & 0 & 0 \\ 0 & 1 & 0 \\ 0 & 0 & a^{-1} \end{bmatrix}.$$

By Theorem 4.6.1, $\boldsymbol{\eta}$ generates a collineation η of $\mathcal{P}$. It is easy to calculate that η fixes every point on ℓ_∞, and that η also fixes O. Therefore, η is a homology with axis ℓ_∞, center O. Furthermore, η sends U into A.

Now, let $\mathfrak{D} = \{\ell, H, P, P'\}$ be any determining set in $\mathcal{P}$ with ℓ and H not incident. Let R and S be distinct points on ℓ, both different from $(H \cup P) \cap \ell$. By Lemma 4.6.2, there is a collineation σ of $\mathcal{P}$ such that $O\sigma = H$, $I\sigma = R$, $J\sigma = S$, and $U\sigma = P$. Let $B = P'\sigma^{-1}$; then, B is on ℓ_U and is different from O and ∞. Let η be the homology with axis ℓ_∞, center O, sending U into B; η exists by the argument of the preceding paragraph. Since $\{\ell_\infty, O, U, B\}$ is a determining set for η, $\sigma^{-1}\eta\sigma$ is a homology with determining set $\mathfrak{D}$, by the theorem Conjugate of a Central Collineation (3.5.1). We have therefore proved that $\mathcal{P}$ possesses all possible homologies. ∎

Thus, the construction detailed at the beginning of this section produces a (unique) Desarguesian plane $\mathcal{P}$ from an arbitrary division ring $\mathcal{R}$. However, it is not immediately obvious that the division ring associated with $\mathcal{P}$ (in the manner of Sections 3.7 and 3.8) is $\mathcal{R}$. To prove that it is indeed (isomorphic to) $\mathcal{R}$, construct the division ring $\mathcal{S}$ in the set of points on ℓ_U other than ∞, using O and U as the additive and multiplicative identities, respectively. Let Φ be the function from $\mathcal{R}$ to $\mathcal{S}$ defined by $[\mathrm{x}\Phi] = [\mathrm{x}, \mathrm{x}, 1]$. Then, Φ is a bijection, and we want to prove that it is an isomorphism of $\mathcal{R}$ onto $\mathcal{S}$.

If x and y are any numbers of $\mathcal{R}$, $[(\mathrm{x}+y)\Phi] = [\mathrm{x}+y, \mathrm{x}+y, 1]$. Hence, by exercise 9a, $(\mathrm{x}+y)\Phi = X\epsilon_Y$, where $[X] = [\mathrm{x}, \mathrm{x}, 1]$, and ϵ_Y is the elation with center ∞, axis ℓ_∞, sending O into Y, with $[Y] = [y, y, 1]$. In the division ring $\mathcal{S}$, $X\epsilon_Y = X + Y$, so that $(\mathrm{x}+y)\Phi = X + Y = \mathrm{x}\Phi + y\Phi$, and Φ is additive. To show that Φ is multiplicative, let y be any number of $\mathcal{R}$. If $\mathrm{x} = 0$, $(\mathrm{x}y)\Phi = 0\Phi = O = O\cdot(y\Phi) = (\mathrm{x}\Phi)\cdot(y\Phi)$ (in $\mathcal{S}$). If x is any nonzero number of $\mathcal{R}$, $[(\mathrm{x}y)\Phi] = [\mathrm{x}y, \mathrm{x}y, 1] = \mathrm{x}[y, y, \mathrm{x}^{-1}]$; hence, $[(\mathrm{x}y)\Phi] = [y, y, \mathrm{x}^{-1}]$. Thus, by exercise 9b, $(\mathrm{x}y)\Phi = Y\eta_X$, where $[Y] = [y, y, 1]$, and η_X is the homology with center O, axis ℓ_∞, sending U into X, with $[X] = [\mathrm{x}, \mathrm{x}, 1]$. In the division ring $\mathcal{S}$, $Y\eta_X = X\cdot Y$, so that $(\mathrm{x}y)\Phi = X\cdot Y = (\mathrm{x}\Phi)\cdot(y\Phi)$, and Φ is multiplicative. We have therefore proved that Φ is an isomorphism of $\mathcal{R}$ onto $\mathcal{S}$. Since $\mathcal{S}$ is isomorphic to the division ring $\mathcal{R}'$ associated with $\mathcal{P}$ (Theorem 3.8.2), $\mathcal{R}'$ is isomorphic to $\mathcal{R}$.

This section concludes with a construction of a division ring that is not a field. The exhibit is a matrix representation of Hamilton's celebrated quaternions. Let $\mathcal{Q}$ be the set of all two-by-two matrices over the complex numbers with the form

$$\begin{bmatrix} a + bi & c + di \\ -c + di & a - bi \end{bmatrix},$$

where a, b, c, d are real numbers, and $i = \sqrt{-1}$, the imaginary unit. The elements of $\mathcal{Q}$ are called *quaternions*. The sum of two quaternions is defined to be the matrix that results when corresponding components of the two quaternions are added. With this definition, $\mathcal{Q}$ is easily seen to be a commutative group under addition, whose identity element is

$$\begin{bmatrix} 0 & 0 \\ 0 & 0 \end{bmatrix}$$

(exercise 2). The product of two quaternions is defined to be the *matrix* product. With this definition, the quaternions are found to be closed under multiplication (exercise 3a), multiplication is associative, and

$$\begin{bmatrix} 1 & 0 \\ 0 & 1 \end{bmatrix}$$

is the multiplicative identity. Also, the right- and left-distributive laws are readily verified for $\mathcal{Q}$ (exercise 3b).

If not all of a, b, c, d are 0, the quaternion

$$\begin{bmatrix} a + bi & c + di \\ -c + di & a - bi \end{bmatrix}$$

has the multiplicative inverse

$$n^{-1}\begin{bmatrix} a - bi & -c - di \\ c - di & a + bi \end{bmatrix},$$

where $n = a^2 + b^2 + c^2 + d^2 \neq 0$ (exercise 4). Thus, $\mathcal{Q}$ is a division ring, by Definition 3.7.5; but, $\mathcal{Q}$ is not a field, because the quaternions

$$\begin{bmatrix} i & 0 \\ 0 & -i \end{bmatrix} \quad \text{and} \quad \begin{bmatrix} 0 & i \\ i & 0 \end{bmatrix}$$

do not commute (verify!).

Exercise 4.8.A

1. Show that the points O, I, J, U of the plane $\mathcal{P}$ of the first part of this section are triply noncollinear.

2. Prove that the quaternions form a commutative group under addition.

3. (a) Prove that the product of two quaternions is a quaternion.
(b) Verify the right- and left-distributive laws for quaternions.

4. If not all of a, b, c, d are 0, prove that the quaternions

$$\begin{bmatrix} a + bi & c + di \\ -c + di & a - bi \end{bmatrix} \quad \text{and} \quad n^{-1}\begin{bmatrix} a - bi & -c - di \\ c - di & a + bi \end{bmatrix}$$

are multiplicative inverses (of one another), where $n = a^2 + b^2 + c^2 + d^2 \neq 0$.

5. Give an example of a Desarguesian plane in which the Fundamental Theorem does not hold.

Exercise 4.8.B

6. Let $\mathcal{P}_1$ and $\mathcal{P}_2$ be Desarguesian planes, and let $\mathcal{R}_1$ and $\mathcal{R}_2$ be their (respective) associated division rings. Prove that $\mathcal{P}_1$ and $\mathcal{P}_2$ are isomorphic if and only if $\mathcal{R}_1$ and $\mathcal{R}_2$ are isomorphic.

7. Construct an affine plane over the division ring $\mathcal{R}$ by omitting from the plane $\mathcal{P}$ of the first part of this section the classes of row-triples with third members 0 and the class of column-triples equivalent to

$$\begin{bmatrix} 0 \\ 0 \\ 1 \end{bmatrix}$$

(the line ℓ_∞). Show that every point of this affine plane has a *unique* coordinate triple with third member 1.

8. (a) Define the concept of a projective affinity of an affine plane. (*Affinity* is defined in Exercise 3.6.10.)
(b) Show that the projective affinities of the affine plane constructed as in exercise 7 are generated by the nonsingular matrices of the form

$$\begin{bmatrix} a & b & 0 \\ c & d & 0 \\ e & f & g \end{bmatrix}.$$

9. Let $\mathcal{P}$ be the plane constructed over the division ring $\mathcal{R}$ at the beginning of this section.

(a) Let y be any number of $\mathcal{R}$, and set

$$\epsilon = \begin{bmatrix} 1 & 0 & 0 \\ 0 & 1 & 0 \\ y & y & 1 \end{bmatrix}.$$

By Theorem 4.6.1, ϵ generates a collineation ϵ of $\mathcal{P}$. Prove that ϵ fixes every point on ℓ_∞, and that $O\epsilon = Y$, where $[Y] = [y, y, 1]$. If $y \neq 0$, prove that ϵ fixes no point that is not on ℓ_∞. Deduce that ϵ is the elation of $\mathcal{P}$ with axis ℓ_∞, center ∞, sending O into Y. Observe that $[P\epsilon] = [p + y, q + y, r]$, where $[P] = [p, q, r]$.

(b) Let x be any nonzero number of $\mathcal{R}$, and set

$$\eta = \begin{bmatrix} 1 & 0 & 0 \\ 0 & 1 & 0 \\ 0 & 0 & \mathrm{x}^{-1} \end{bmatrix}.$$

By Theorem 4.6.1, η generates a collineation η of $\mathcal{P}$. Prove that η fixes O and every point on ℓ_∞, and that $U\eta = X$, where $[X] = [\mathrm{x}, \mathrm{x}, 1]$. Deduce that η is the homology of $\mathcal{P}$ with axis ℓ_∞, center O, sending U into X. Observe that $[P\eta] = [p, q, r\mathrm{x}^{-1}]$, where $[P] = [p, q, r]$.

10. (a) Prove that any two three-element fields are isomorphic.

(b) Use the result of part (a), together with the results of Exercise 2.8.1 and exercise 6 to obtain another proof that any two 13-point planes are isomorphic.

Chapter 5

PAPPIAN PLANES

5.1. The Fundamental Theorem and Pappus' Theorem

In order to realize the many benefits of the Fundamental Theorem, it is necessary (in view of the corollary to Lemma 4.4.4) to restrict attention to the class of Desarguesian planes whose associated division rings are fields, a class that includes 7_3 (Exercise 3.7.3), 13_4 (Exercise 3.7.4), 21_5 (Exercise 3.7.11), and $\mathcal{E}_2{}^*$ (Example 3.8.3). To effect the restriction in the spirit of this book, an additional axiom is wanted. By Exercise 3.8.2, the multiplicative group of nonzero numbers of $\mathcal{R}$, the division ring associated with the Desarguesian plane $\mathcal{P}$, is commutative if and only if the group of homologies of $\mathcal{P}$ with center H, axis ℓ, is commutative for every choice of (nonincident) H and ℓ. We therefore introduce the following axiom, in which $\mathcal{P}$ is a Desarguesian plane.

Axiom 5. For every choice of a line ℓ and a point H, not on ℓ, in $\mathcal{P}$, the group of homologies of $\mathcal{P}$ with center H, axis ℓ, is commutative.

To denote a projective plane in which *both* Axioms 4 and 5 are valid, the term "Pappian plane" will be used. Since Axiom 5 is self-dual (verify!), the principle of duality retains its validity for Pappian planes. In Axiom 5 we have the instrument for proving the Fundamental Theorem.

Theorem 5.1.1. (The Fundamental Theorem of Projective Geometry) In a Pappian plane $\mathcal{P}$, any projectivity on a line that fixes three distinct points is the identity.

Proof: Exercise 3.8.2 shows that Axiom 5 ensures the commutativity of the multiplicative group of nonzero elements of $\mathcal{R}$, the division ring associated with $\mathcal{P}$. Since $0 \cdot x = x \cdot 0 = 0$ for any x in $\mathcal{R}$, it follows that $\mathcal{R}$ is a field. Therefore, by the corollary to Lemma 4.4.4, the Fundamental Theorem holds in $\mathcal{P}$. ∎

Corollary: In a Pappian plane $\mathcal{P}$, suppose that Q_1, Q_2, Q_3, Q_4 are any triply noncollinear points, and that Q_1', Q_2', Q_3', Q_4' also are any triply noncollinear points. Then, there is exactly one projective collineation σ of $\mathcal{P}$ such that $Q_i\sigma = Q_i'$ for $i = 1, 2, 3, 4$.

Proof: There is at least one such projective collineation σ, by the Quadrangle Mapping Theorem (3.6.1). If σ' also fulfills the conditions, $\sigma'\sigma^{-1}$ is a projective collineation that fixes Q_1, Q_2, Q_3, Q_4; hence $\sigma'\sigma^{-1}$ fixes the diagonal points of the quadrangle $\mathcal{Q}$, with vertices Q_1, Q_2, Q_3, Q_4. The restriction of $\sigma'\sigma^{-1}$ to any side of $\mathcal{Q}$ is a projectivity that fixes three distinct points on that side; thus it fixes all points on that side by the Fundamental Theorem. Therefore, $\sigma'\sigma^{-1}$ is central and has every side of $\mathcal{Q}$ as an axis. Hence $\sigma'\sigma^{-1} = \iota$, or $\sigma' = \sigma$, proving the uniqueness of σ. ∎

Three useful techniques are displayed in the three different proofs of Pappus' theorem, given next.

Theorem 5.1.2. (Pappus' theorem) Let $\mathcal{P}$ be a Pappian plane. If the set $\mathcal{S} = \{k, k', A, B, C, A', B', C', P, Q, R\}$ is a Pappus set (Definition 3.2.3) in $\mathcal{P}$, then P, Q, and R are collinear.

Proof 1 (using two commuting central collineations): Let $H = k \cap k'$ and $\ell = P \cup Q$. Let μ_1 be the central collineation with center H, axis ℓ, sending B into A, and let μ_2 be the central collineation with center H, axis ℓ, sending A into C. If H is on ℓ, μ_1 and μ_2 are elations, and $\mu_1\mu_2 = \mu_2\mu_1$ by the Second Commuting Theorem (3.1.2). If H is not on ℓ, μ_1 and μ_2 are homologies, and $\mu_1\mu_2 = \mu_2\mu_1$ by Axiom 5.

Now, $A'\mu_1 = [(B \cup P) \cap k']\mu_1 = (A \cup P) \cap k' = B'$, and $C'\mu_2 = [(A \cup Q) \cap k']\mu_2 = (C \cup Q) \cap k' = A'$. By the theorem Coaxial Collineations (2.4.4), $\mu = \mu_1\mu_2$ is a central collineation with center H, axis ℓ; from the preceding paragraph, $\mu_1\mu_2 = \mu_2\mu_1$. Therefore, $B\mu = B\mu_1\mu_2 = A\mu_2 = C$, and $C'\mu = C'\mu_2\mu_1 = A'\mu_1 = B'$. Thus, $(B \cup C')\mu = C \cup B'$, so that $R = (B \cup C') \cap (C \cup B')$ is on the axis of μ, which is $\ell = P \cup Q$. (Refer to Figure 5.1.)

Proof 2 (using the Fundamental Theorem): Let $m = A \cup B'$, $n = A \cup C'$, $U = n \cap (C \cup B')$, and $T = m \cap (B \cup C')$. (See Figure

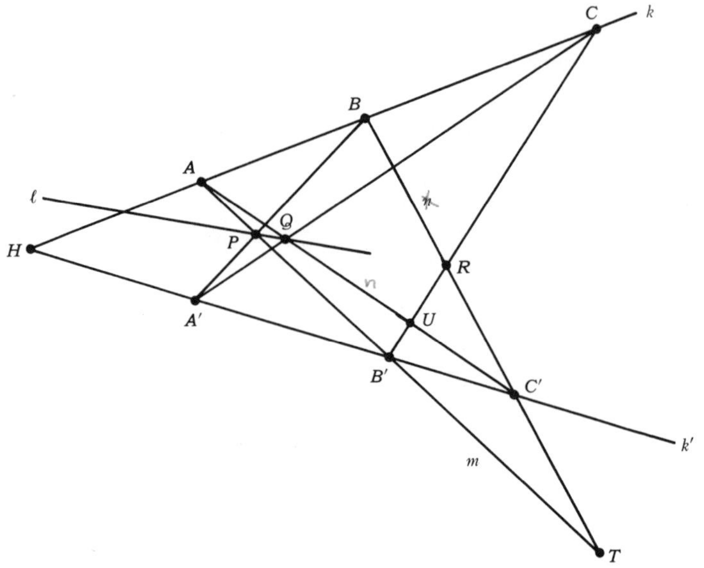

Figure 5.1

5.1.) Let π be the projectivity $m \circ B \circ k' \circ C \circ n$. Then, $A\pi = A$, $P\pi = Q$, $B'\pi = U$, and $T\pi = C'$ (verify!). Since $A\pi = A$, π is a perspectivity, by the Fundamental Theorem. (See Theorem 2.9.1.) The center of this perspectivity is $(B' \cup U) \cap (T \cup C') = R$; hence (because $P\pi = Q$), P, Q, and R are collinear.

Proof 3 (analytic proof): Construct a coordinate system in P such that $[A] = [1, 0, 0]$, $[B] = [0, 1, 0]$, $[A'] = [0, 0, 1]$, and $[B'] = [1, 1, 1]$. Then, $[k \cap k'] = [1, 1, 0]$, $[C] = [c, 1, 0]$ (with $c \neq 0$ or 1), and $[C'] = [1, 1, f + 1]$ (with $f \neq 0$ or -1). Successive calculations yield the following (exercise 2).

$$[A \cup B'] = \begin{bmatrix} 0 \\ 1 \\ -1 \end{bmatrix}, \qquad [B \cup A'] = \begin{bmatrix} 1 \\ 0 \\ 0 \end{bmatrix},$$

$$[P] = [0, 1, 1], \ [A \cup C'] = \begin{bmatrix} 0 \\ f+1 \\ -1 \end{bmatrix}, \qquad [C \cup A'] = \begin{bmatrix} 1 \\ -c \\ 0 \end{bmatrix},$$

$$[Q] = [c, 1, f+1], \qquad [B \cup C'] = \begin{bmatrix} f+1 \\ 0 \\ -1 \end{bmatrix},$$

$$[B' \cup C] = \begin{bmatrix} 1 \\ -c \\ c-1 \end{bmatrix}, \qquad [R] = [1, f - fc^{-1} + 1, f + 1],$$

$$\text{and} \qquad [P \cup Q] = \begin{bmatrix} c^{-1}f \\ 1 \\ -1 \end{bmatrix}.$$

Now, $[R]\cdot[P \cup Q] = c^{-1}f + f - fc^{-1} + 1 - f - 1 = c^{-1}f - fc^{-1} = 0$, since $\mathcal{R}$ is a field. Thus, R is on $P \cup Q$, and P, Q, R are collinear. ▌

The adequacy of Axioms 4 and 5 in effecting the proof of the elegant and characteristic theorem of Pappus is the reason for the designation "Pappian plane" for a projective plane in which these axioms hold. In fact, Pappus' theorem and Axioms 4–5 (together) are equivalent assertions in a projective plane, as we shall learn in Theorem 5.1.5, whose proof depends upon the next lemma.

Lemma 5.1.3. Let $\mathcal{P}$ be a projective plane in which Pappus' theorem is valid. If $\pi = k \circ M \circ \ell \circ N \circ m$ in $\mathcal{P}$, where k, ℓ, m are nonconcurrent lines, *and* if $(k \cap m)\pi = k \cap m$, then π is a perspectivity.

Proof: If $M = N$, the conclusion is trivial; thus, it will be assumed that $M \neq N$. Let $A = k \cap m$, $B = k \cap \ell$, $C = \ell \cap m$, and construct $O = (B \cup N) \cap (C \cup M)$ and $D = (C \cup M) \cap k$. (See Figure 5.2.)

Let $\pi_1 = k \circ O \circ m$. Then, $A\pi_1 = A = A\pi$, $B\pi_1 = (O \cup B) \cap m = (N \cup B) \cap m = B\pi$, and $D\pi_1 = C = D\pi$. We want to show that π is equal to the perspectivity π_1, and, in view of the preceding sentence, it suffices to prove that if X is any point on k different from A, B, D, then $X\pi_1 = X\pi$. For such a point X, set $Y = (M \cup X) \cap \ell$ and $Z = (N \cup Y) \cap m = X\pi$.

Let $\ell' = M \cup N$. Since $A\pi = A$, it follows that A, M, N are collinear. Hence A, M, N are distinct points on ℓ', all of them different from $\ell' \cap \ell$. Also, Y is different from B, C, and $\ell' \cap \ell$, because X is different from B, D, and A, respectively. Pappus' theorem, applied to the Pappus set $\mathcal{S} = \{\ell, \ell', B, C, Y, M, N, A, O, X, Z\}$, shows that O, X, Z are collinear. Therefore, $X\pi_1 = Z = X\pi$, as required. ▌

Corollary: Let $\mathcal{P}$ be a projective plane in which Pappus' theorem is valid. If $\pi = k \circ M \circ \ell \circ N \circ m$, where k, ℓ, m are distinct and concurrent, but M, N, and $k \cap m$ are *not* collinear, then π is a perspectivity.

Proof: The noncollinearity of M, N, and $k \cap m$ implies that $M \neq N$; let $E = (M \cup N) \cap k$, and let ℓ' be a line on E that is different from k and $M \cup N$. Then, ℓ' is not on N; hence $\pi = k \circ M \circ \ell \circ N \circ \ell' \circ N \circ m$.

The projectivity $\phi = k \circ M \circ \ell \circ N \circ \ell'$ fixes $E = k \cap \ell'$, because M, N, E are collinear. Therefore, ϕ satisfies the hypotheses of the theorem (why?), so that $\phi = k \circ M' \circ \ell'$ for some point M'. Thus, $\pi = k \circ M' \circ \ell' \circ N \circ m$, and, since k, ℓ', m are nonconcurrent, and

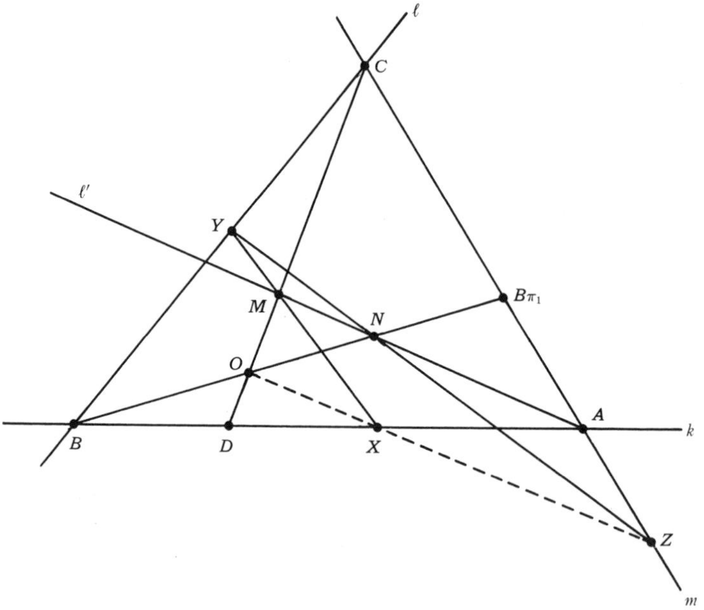

Figure 5.2

$(k \cap m)\pi = k \cap m$ (from the original expression for π), π is a perspectivity, by the theorem. ∎

The above corollary is exactly the special case of the Fundamental Theorem that was used to prove Theorem 2.9.2, as a reference to Theorem 2.9.2 will substantiate. (See also Exercise 2.9.8.) Therefore, if a projective plane (Axioms 1–3) is by some means known to be a plane in which Pappus' theorem holds, then, by the above corollary and Theorem 2.9.2, that plane must also possess all possible homologies. Since the existence of homologies implies Desargues' theorem, we have proved the following theorem.

Theorem 5.1.4. (Hessenberg's theorem) In a projective plane, Pappus' theorem implies Desargues' theorem. ∎

The final result of this section is the equivalence of Axioms 4–5 (together), Pappus' theorem, and the Fundamental Theorem.

Theorem 5.1.5. In a projective plane $\mathcal{P}$, the following assertions are equivalent:

(a) The Fundamental Theorem,

(b) Axioms 4 and 5 (together),

(c) Pappus' theorem.

Proof: If the Fundamental Theorem holds in $\mathcal{P}$, then Axiom 4 is true in $\mathcal{P}$ by Theorem 2.9.2, and Axiom 5 is true in $\mathcal{P}$ by the Corollary to Lemma 4.4.4 (and Exercise 3.8.2). Also, Axioms 4 and 5 imply Pappus' theorem, as has been established in Theorem 5.1.2. It remains to be proved that Pappus' theorem implies the Fundamental Theorem.

Suppose that Pappus' theorem is true in $\mathcal{P}$, and let π be any projectivity between two distinct lines, say k and ℓ, of $\mathcal{P}$ that fixes the point of intersection of these two lines. By the paragraph preceding Theorem 5.1.4, $\mathcal{P}$ is Desarguesian; hence, by the theorem Reduction of Projectivities (4.6.5), $\pi = k \circ M \circ m \circ N \circ \ell$. If k, m, ℓ are non-concurrent, π is a perspectivity by Lemma 5.1.3. If k, m, ℓ are concurrent and distinct, π is a perspectivity by Exercise 3.2.8. Finally, if k, m, ℓ are not distinct, π is obviously a perspectivity. Therefore, the Fundamental Theorem holds in $\mathcal{P}$. (See Theorem 2.9.1.) ▮

By the construction of Section 4.8, we can build a Desarguesian plane whose associated division ring is not a field; by Theorem 5.1.5, Pappus' theorem does not hold in such a plane. Therefore, the converse of Hessenberg's theorem (5.1.4) is not true in general. (It *is* true, however, for finite projective planes because of Wedderburn's theorem that a finite division ring is a field. See [16], pp. 318–325.) The equivalence of Pappus' theorem and the commutativity of multiplication in the division ring associated with a Desarguesian plane was a discovery of David Hilbert.

Exercise 5.1.A

1. In a Pappian plane, let η_1 be a homology with center H, axis ℓ, sending P into P' and Q into Q', where H, P, Q are distinct and collinear, with neither P nor Q on ℓ. Let η_2 be the homology with center H, axis ℓ, sending P into Q. Prove that $P'\eta_2 = Q'$.

2. Verify the calculations in Proof 3 of Pappus' theorem.

3. (a) Use the method of Proof 3 of Pappus' theorem to give another proof of the Restricted Pappus Property (Example 3.2.4) for Desarguesian planes.
(b) Use the method of Proof 3 of Pappus' theorem to give another proof of the Special Pappus Property (Exercise 3.2.7) for Desarguesian planes.

4. Show how Proof 3 of Pappus' theorem can be modified to prove that, in a Desarguesian plane, Pappus' theorem implies Axiom 5.

5. Prove that if a projectivity on a line k of a Pappian plane has a fixed point, then it is a Π_2 on k.

6. Prove that in a Pappian plane of characteristic different from two, a projectivity on a line that is an involution has either no fixed point or exactly two distinct fixed points. (Use the result of exercise 5.)

Exercise 5.1.B

7. Let η be a homology of a Pappian plane, with center H, axis ℓ. Prove that if k is any line on H, η induces a Π_2 on k with axial invariant point H and central invariant point $k \cap \ell$.

8. Let M, O, U be distinct, collinear points in a Pappian plane, and suppose that $\mathcal{Q}(U, A, M; C, B, O)$. Prove that $\mathcal{Q}'(U, B, M; C, A, O)$.

9. In a Pappian plane, prove that $\mathcal{Q}(A, B, C; D, E, F)$ implies $\mathcal{Q}'(D, E, F; A, B, C)$.

10. In a Pappian plane, let π be a projectivity from a line k to a line $m \neq k$. Prove that there is a line ℓ (called the *axis of homology* of π) such that $(X \cup Y\pi) \cap (Y \cup X\pi)$ is on ℓ for every choice of X, Y on k, with $X \neq Y$, $X \neq Y\pi$, and $Y \neq X\pi$.

11. In a Pappian plane, let O, O' be distinct points, k, ℓ, m distinct lines on O, all different from $O \cup O'$, and k', ℓ', m' distinct lines on O', all different from $O \cup O'$. Let $A_1 = k \cap \ell'$, $A_2 = \ell \cap m'$, $A_3 = m \cap k'$, $B_1 = k' \cap \ell$, $B_2 = \ell' \cap m$, and $B_3 = m' \cap k$. Prove that triangles $A_1A_2A_3$ and $B_1B_2B_3$ are perspective from a point, with the vertices corresponding in the order named. (Note that the conditions are that triangles $A_1A_2A_3$ and $B_3B_1B_2$ are perspective from O, while triangles $A_1A_2A_3$ and $B_2B_3B_1$ are perspective from O'. Thus, in a Pappian plane, if two triangles are doubly perspective, they are triply perspective.)

12. Let k be a line in a Pappian plane, and suppose that π is a projectivity on k that exchanges the distinct points P, Q on k. Prove that π is an involution.

13. (a) Let $\mathcal{P}$ be a Pappian plane, and let σ be a projective collineation of $\mathcal{P}$ that has at least four distinct invariant points. Prove that σ is central.
(b) Let ρ be a collineation of a 13-point plane that has at least three distinct invariant points. Prove that ρ is central.

14. Let $\mathcal{P}$ be a Pappian plane, and let σ be a projective collineation of $\mathcal{P}$ that is an involution.
(a) Prove that σ is central.
(b) If the characteristic of $\mathcal{P}$ is different from 2, prove that σ is a harmonic homology.
(c) If the characteristic of $\mathcal{P}$ is 2, prove that σ is an elation.

5.2. Cross Ratio

Two figures in a projective plane are *projectively equivalent* if there is a projective collineation of the plane that transforms one figure into the other. Let $\mathcal{P}$ be an arbitrary Pappian plane. Then, any two ordered sets of three distinct, collinear points in $\mathcal{P}$ are projectively equivalent, by the First Existence Theorem for Projectivities (1.7.2) and Corollary 1 of the theorem Extension of Perspectivities (3.1.3). If there are more than four points on a line of $\mathcal{P}$, the corresponding statement for ordered sets of four distinct, collinear points in $\mathcal{P}$ is not true. For, by the Fundamental Theorem, the image under a projectivity (and, hence, under a projective collineation) of the fourth point of such a set is determined once the images of the first three points have been specified. Thus, different ordered sets of four collinear points may have what can be thought of as different relative positions on their respective lines. In this section, we establish a numerical measure, called *cross ratio*, of the relative position of four points on a line. First, we need to learn how to assign *nonhomogeneous* coordinates to points on a line of $\mathcal{P}$.

Suppose that a coordinate system has been constructed (as in Section 4.2) in the Pappian plane $\mathcal{P}$. Let k be a line of $\mathcal{P}$ with an induced coordinate system (as in Section 4.3) whose first, second, and third base points are A, D, G, respectively. By Exercise 4.3.4, the specification of A, D, G determines the induced coordinate system on k to within an *inner* automorphism of $\mathcal{R}$ (the division ring associated with $\mathcal{P}$). Since $\mathcal{R}$ is a field (Axiom 5), any inner automorphism of $\mathcal{R}$ is the identity; therefore, the base points A, D, G determine the coordinate system on k. In this coordinate system, every point on k except A has a unique coordinate pair whose second member is 1. If to the point P on k, where $[P] = [p, 1]$, we assign the single number p, then every point on k except A receives a unique coordinate from $\mathcal{R}$. Let us assign to A the symbol ∞ (*not* a number of $\mathcal{R}$) as its coordinate. Thus, the specification of A, D, G determines an induced coordinate system in which an arbitrary point P on k is uniquely represented both by an equivalence class of pairs (the homogeneous coordinates of P) and by a single coordinate (a number of $\mathcal{R}$ or the symbol ∞), called the nonhomogeneous coordinate of P, or, for short (since it cannot be confused with homogeneous coordinates, which are pairs), the coordinate of P. Observe also that each number of $\mathcal{R}$, as well as the symbol ∞, is the coordinate of a unique point on k in this induced coordinate system. In particular, ∞, 0, and 1 are the coordinates of A, D, G, respectively. (Compare with Exercises 4.1.9 and 4.4.10.)

If P ($\neq A$) is on k, with $[P] = [u, v]$ ($v \neq 0$), then, also, $[P] = [v^{-1}u, 1]$, so that $v^{-1}u$ is the coordinate of P. Since $\mathcal{R}$ is a field, $v^{-1}u = uv^{-1}$, and we agree to write $v^{-1}u = u/v$, as we do for real numbers. Thus, expressions of the form u/v ($v \neq 0$) define numbers of $\mathcal{R}$, and these expressions are easily seen to have the customary properties of fractional expressions because of the commutativity of multiplication in $\mathcal{R}$. Since ∞ is the coordinate of A, and since $[A] = [r, 0]$ ($r \neq 0$), we also agree to write (formally) $r/0 = \infty$ for any $r \neq 0$. (In saying that $r/0 = \infty$, we are not implying that division by 0 is possible in $\mathcal{R}$, but merely that ∞ is the coordinate of the point represented by the pair $[r, 0]$.) We are now ready to define cross ratio.

Definition 5.2.1. Let k be a line of the Pappian plane $\mathcal{P}$, and suppose that an induced coordinate system on k is determined by A, D, G. Let W, X, Y, Z be any points on k such that W, X, Y are distinct. By Theorem 1.7.2 and the Fundamental Theorem, there is a unique projectivity ψ on k that sends W, X, Y into A, D, G, respectively. Then, in the given coordinate system on k, the *cross ratio* of W, X, Y, Z (in that order), designated by the symbol $\mathcal{R}(W, X; Y, Z)$, is the coordinate of $Z\psi$. ∎

The next theorem establishes the projective invariance of cross ratio, and its first corollary shows that the value of a cross ratio, which appears to depend upon the choice of an induced coordinate system in which to compute it, is in fact independent of that choice, as we would want it to be.

Theorem 5.2.2. (Invariance of Cross Ratio) Let k, k' be any lines of the Pappian plane $\mathcal{P}$, and suppose that induced coordinate systems are determined on k and k' by A, D, G (on k) and A', D', G' (on k'). Let ϕ be any projectivity from k to k', and suppose that W, X, Y, Z are any points on k such that W, X, Y are distinct. Then, $\mathcal{R}(W\phi, X\phi; Y\phi, Z\phi) = \mathcal{R}(W, X; Y, Z)$, where the two cross ratios are calculated in the induced coordinate systems on k', k, respectively.

Proof: Let ψ be the projectivity on k that sends W, X, Y into A, D, G, respectively, and let ψ' be the projectivity on k' that sends $W\phi$, $X\phi$, $Y\phi$ into A', D', G', respectively. Then, $\psi^{-1}\phi\psi'$ is the projectivity from k to k' that sends A, D, G into A', D', G', respectively. Relative to the given induced coordinate systems on k, k', the equation $[P\pi]' = [P]$ describes (by Theorem 4.4.5) a projectivity π from k to k'. (Here, $[P\pi]'$ means a pair for $P\pi$ in the coordinate system on k', while $[P]$ means a pair for P in the coordinate system on k.) Since $A\pi = A'$, $D\pi = D'$, and $G\pi = G'$ (verify!), $\pi = \psi^{-1}\phi\psi'$, by the Fundamental Theorem. Therefore, $\psi\pi = \phi\psi'$, and $[Z\psi\pi]' = [Z\phi\psi']'$. Since $[Z\psi\pi]' = [Z\psi]$ (by the definition of π), we see that $[Z\phi\psi']' = [Z\psi]$. It follows that the coordinate of $(Z\phi)\psi'$ (on k') is the same as the coordinate of $Z\psi$ (on k). By the definition of cross ratio, these coordinates are $\mathcal{R}(W\phi, X\phi; Y\phi, Z\phi)$ and $\mathcal{R}(W, X; Y, Z)$, respectively, and the theorem is proved. ∎

Corollary 1: In a Pappian plane, if W, X, Y, Z are points on a line k such that W, X, Y are distinct, then $\mathcal{R}(W, X; Y, Z)$ is independent of the choice of an induced coordinate system on k in which to compute it.

Proof: In the above theorem, let $k' = k$, let the coordinate systems on k, k' be any two induced coordinate systems on k, and let ϕ be the identity projectivity on k; this corollary then follows at once. ∎

Corollary 2: In a Pappian plane, cross ratio is invariant under projective collineations.

Proof: If σ is a projective collineation of the plane, the restriction of σ to $\mathcal{G}(k)$ is a projectivity from k to $k' = k\sigma$. By the above theorem, $\mathcal{R}(W\sigma, X\sigma; Y\sigma, Z\sigma) = \mathcal{R}(W, X; Y, Z)$. ∎

Corollary 3: Cross ratio is invariant under linear coordinate transformations in the Pappian plane $\mathcal{P}$.

Proof: Let a linear coordinate transformation in $\mathcal{P}$ be described by $[P]_2 = [P]_1\boldsymbol{\beta}$, where $\boldsymbol{\beta}$ is a nonsingular three-by-three matrix, and $[P]_i$ $(i = 1, 2)$ represents a triple for P in the ith coordinate system in $\mathcal{P}$. Let σ be the projective collineation of P described (relative to the first coordinate system in $\mathcal{P}$) by $[P\sigma]_1 = [P]_1\boldsymbol{\beta}$. Then, $[P\sigma]_1 = [P]_2$. Let W, X, Y, Z be points on a line k such that W, X, Y are distinct. Finally, let $\mathcal{R}_i(W, X; Y, Z)$ $(i = 1, 2)$ denote the cross ratio of W, X, Y, Z calculated in a coordinate system on k induced by the ith coordinate system in $\mathcal{P}$. For a given i, $\mathcal{R}_i(W, X; Y, Z)$ is independent of the induced coordinate system on k, by Corollary 1; we have to prove that it also does not depend upon i.

In the *second* coordinate system in $\mathcal{P}$, let W, X, Y determine an induced coordinate system on k, and suppose that $\mathbf{W}$, $\mathbf{X}$, $\mathbf{Y}$ are triples for W, X, Y, respectively, such that $\mathbf{Y} = \mathbf{W} + \mathbf{X}$. Then, for some e, f, $[Z]_2 = \mathrm{e}\mathbf{W} + f\mathbf{X}$; hence $[\mathrm{e}, f]$ is a pair for Z in the chosen coordinate system on k. Since W, X, Y are the base points of this coordinate system, $\mathcal{R}_2(W, X; Y, Z)$ is simply the coordinate of Z (why?), which is e/f.

In the *first* coordinate system in $\mathcal{P}$, let $W\sigma$, $X\sigma$, $Y\sigma$ determine an induced coordinate system on $k\sigma$. Since $[P\sigma]_1 = [P]_2$ for any P, $[W\sigma]_1 = \mathbf{W}$, $[X\sigma]_1 = \mathbf{X}$, $[Y\sigma]_1 = \mathbf{Y}$, and $[Z\sigma]_1 = \mathrm{e}\mathbf{W} + f\mathbf{X}$. Because $\mathbf{Y} = \mathbf{W} + \mathbf{X}$, $[\mathrm{e}, f]$ is a pair for $Z\sigma$ in this coordinate system on $k\sigma$; hence $\mathcal{R}_1(W\sigma, X\sigma; Y\sigma, Z\sigma) = \mathrm{e}/f = \mathcal{R}_2(W, X; Y, Z)$. By Corollary 2, $\mathcal{R}_1(W\sigma, X\sigma; Y\sigma, Z\sigma) = \mathcal{R}_1(W, X; Y, Z)$. Therefore, $\mathcal{R}_2(W, X; Y, Z) = \mathcal{R}_1(W, X; Y, Z)$, as required. ∎

In Corollary 1 above, the two coordinate systems on k are assumed to be induced by a single coordinate system in $\mathcal{P}$, though, in view of Corollary 3, they could as well be induced by different coordinate systems in $\mathcal{P}$ that are related by a linear transformation. Corollaries 2 and 3 above concern collineations and coordinate transformations generated by linear transformations. More generally, a collineation or a coordinate transformation that is generated by a semilinear transformation affects cross ratio by an automorphism of $\mathcal{R}$ (exercise 8).

It will be useful to have a formula expressing the cross ratio of four collinear points in terms of homogeneous coordinates of those points. Suppose that an induced coordinate system is given on the line k, and that $[W] = [w_1, w_2]$, $[X] = [x_1, x_2]$, $[Y] = [y_1, y_2]$, and $[Z] = [z_1, z_2]$ in this coordinate system. We need first to write an equation for the projectivity ψ (on k) that sends W, X, Y into A, D, G (the base points of the coordinate system on k), respectively. It is not difficult to calculate (exercise 9), and even easier to verify, the following equation for ψ.

5.2.3. $[P\psi] = [P]\begin{bmatrix} sx_2 & tw_2 \\ sx_1 & -tw_1 \end{bmatrix}$,

where $s = y_1w_2 - y_2w_1$, and $t = y_1x_2 - y_2x_1$. Then, $[Z\psi] = [s(z_1x_2 - z_2x_1), t(z_1w_2 - z_2w_1)]$, and

$$\mathcal{R}(W, X; Y, Z) = \frac{s(z_1x_2 - z_2x_1)}{t(z_1w_2 - z_2w_1)} = \frac{(y_1w_2 - y_2w_1)(z_1x_2 - z_2x_1)}{(y_1x_2 - y_2x_1)(z_1w_2 - z_2w_1)}.$$

The formula just derived makes sense when *any* three of W, X, Y, Z are different, and we therefore use it to *define* cross ratio in all such cases, thus extending Definition 5.2.1. We then have the following theorem.

Theorem 5.2.4. Let k be a line of the Pappian plane $\mathcal{P}$, and suppose that an induced coordinate system is given on k. Let W, X, Y, Z be any points on k such that at least three are distinct, and suppose that $[W] = [w_1, w_2]$, $[X] = [x_1, x_2]$, $[Y] = [y_1, y_2]$, and $[Z] = [z_1, z_2]$ in the given coordinate system on k. Then, the cross ratio of W, X, Y, Z (in that order) is given by

5.2.5. $$\mathcal{R}(W, X; Y, Z) = \frac{(y_1w_2 - y_2w_1)(z_1x_2 - z_2x_1)}{(y_1x_2 - y_2x_1)(z_1w_2 - z_2w_1)}.$$ ∎

It should be clear that the cross ratio of four points can be expressed in terms of the nonhomogeneous coordinates of those points, and that equations of projectivities between lines can also be written in nonhomogeneous coordinates. (See exercise 10. Also, observe how nonhomogeneous coordinates are effectively employed in the study of affine planes in the next section.) In closing this section, we list several additional properties of cross ratio. Proofs of these properties, easily effected with the machinery developed above, are relegated to the exercises. In the statements of these properties, $\mathcal{P}$ is a Pappian plane, $\mathcal{R}$ its associated field, and the *characteristic* of $\mathcal{R}$ means the characteristic of $\mathcal{P}$. (The fundamental property of the characteristic of $\mathcal{R}$ is stated in Exercise 3.8.5a.)

(a) If $\mathcal{R}(W, X; Y, Z)$ is defined in $\mathcal{P}$, then $\mathcal{R}(W, X; Y, Z) = \mathcal{R}(X, W; Z, Y) = \mathcal{R}(Y, Z; W, X) = \mathcal{R}(Z, Y; X, W)$ (exercise 1a). Therefore, the 24 cross ratios resulting from the 24 arrangements of W, X, Y, Z may be partitioned into six sets of four each such that the four cross ratios within any one set are equal (exercise 1b).

(b) If $\mathcal{R}(W, X; Y, Z) = r$, the 24 arrangements of W, X, Y, Z

yield the cross ratios r, $1-r$, $1/r$, $1-(1/r)$, $1/(1-r)$, and $r/(r-1)$, with proper interpretation in case $r = 0$ or ∞ (exercise 3). The number of *different* values of these six expressions can be one, two, three, or six (exercises 2, 11, and 12).

(c) If the characteristic of $\mathcal{R}$ is not 2, then $\mathcal{R}(W, X; Y, Z) = -1$ is equivalent to $\mathcal{H}(W, X; Y, Z)$ (exercise 4). (See exercise 5 for the case in which $\mathcal{R}$ has characteristic 2.)

(d) If W, X, Y are distinct points on a line k of $\mathcal{P}$, and if r is any number of $\mathcal{R}$, or the symbol ∞, there is a unique point Z on k such that $\mathcal{R}(W, X; Y, Z) = r$ (exercise 7).

Exercise 5.2.A

All exercises pertain to a Pappian plane.

1. Let W, X, Y, Z be collinear, with at least three of them distinct.
(a) Prove that $\mathcal{R}(W, X; Y, Z) = \mathcal{R}(X, W; Z, Y) = \mathcal{R}(Y, Z; W, X) = \mathcal{R}(Z, Y; X, W)$.
(b) List the 24 arrangements of W, X, Y, Z, and partition them into six sets of four each such that the cross ratios of the arrangements in any one set are equal.

2. Let $\mathcal{R}(W, X; Y, Z) = r$. Prove that $r = \infty$, 0, or 1 if and only if some two of W, X, Y, Z coincide.

3. If $\mathcal{R}(W, X; Y, Z) = r$, prove that the 24 arrangements of W, X, Y, Z yield the cross ratios r, $1-r$, $1/r$, $1-(1/r)$, $1/(1-r)$, and $r/(r-1)$. Explain how these expressions are to be interpreted in case $r = 0$ or ∞.

4. Suppose that the characteristic of $\mathcal{R}$ is not 2. Prove that $\mathcal{R}(W, X; Y, Z) = -1$ if and only if $\mathcal{H}(W, X; Y, Z)$.

5. Suppose that the characteristic of $\mathcal{R}$ is 2, so that $-1 = 1$ in $\mathcal{R}$.
(a) If $\mathcal{H}(W, X; Y, Z)$, prove that $\mathcal{R}(W, X; Y, Z) = -1$.
(b) If $\mathcal{R}(W, X; Y, Z) = -1$, prove that either $\mathcal{H}(W, X; Y, Z)$ or $\mathcal{H}(Y, Z; W, X)$.

6. Suppose that $\mathcal{R}(W, X; Y, Z) = \mathcal{R}(W', X'; Y', Z')$, where W, X, Y, Z lie on a line k of $\mathcal{P}$, and W', X', Y', Z' are on a line k' of $\mathcal{P}$. Prove that there is a projectivity π, from k to k', that sends W, X, Y, Z into W', X', Y', Z', respectively.

7. Let W, X, Y be distinct points on a line k of $\mathcal{P}$, and suppose that

r is any number of $\mathcal{R}$, or the symbol ∞. Prove that there is a unique point Z on k such that $\mathcal{R}(W, X; Y, Z) = r$.

Exercise 5.2.B

All exercises pertain to a Pappian plane.

8. (a) Let $[P\rho] = ([P]\Theta)\sigma$ describe a collineation of $\mathcal{P}$. Prove that $\mathcal{R}(W\rho, X\rho; Y\rho, Z\rho) = [\mathcal{R}(W, X; Y, Z)]\Theta$, where we agree that $(\infty)\Theta = \infty$.

(b) Let $[P]_2 = ([P]_1\Theta)\sigma$ describe a coordinate transformation in $\mathcal{P}$. Suppose that $\mathcal{R}_1(W, X; Y, Z) = r$, and $\mathcal{R}_2(W, X; Y, Z) = r'$, where $R_i(W, X; Y, Z)$ $(i = 1, 2)$ denotes the cross ratio calculated in the ith coordinate system in $\mathcal{P}$. Prove that $r' = r\Theta$, where we agree that$(\infty)\Theta = \infty$.

9. Derive Equation 5.2.3 for the projectivity ψ sending W, X, Y into A, D, G, respectively. (In Equation 5.2.3, $s = y_1w_2 - y_2w_1$, and $t = y_1x_2 - y_2x_1$.)

10. (a) Write a formula for the cross ratio of W, X, Y, Z in terms of the nonhomogeneous coordinates of these points. Explain how this formula is to be interpreted in the cases that arise when one or two of the coordinates is ∞.

(b) Show how the equation of a projectivity between lines of $\mathcal{P}$ can be expressed in nonhomogeneous coordinates. Give the interpretations in the awkward cases that arise.

11. Prove that the following list covers all the cases in which not all the values of the expressions in exercise 3 are different:

(a) $r = \infty$, 0, or 1, and the three distinct values of the six expressions are ∞, 0, and 1.

(b) $r = -1$, 2, or 1/2, and the characteristic of $\mathcal{R}$ is not 2. If the characteristic of $\mathcal{R}$ is not 3 either, the three distinct values of the six expressions are -1, 2, and 1/2. If the characteristic of $\mathcal{R}$ is 3, then $-1 = 2 = 1/2$, and the expressions all have the same value.

(c) $r^2 - r + 1 = 0$. (This equation is discussed in exercise 12.)

12. Consider the equation $x^2 - x + 1 = 0$ in the field $\mathcal{R}$.

(a) Prove that if r is a solution of this equation, then $r^3 = -1$.

(b) If the characteristic of $\mathcal{R}$ is 3, prove that -1 is the only solution.

(c) If the characteristic of $\mathcal{R}$ is not 3, prove that the equation has either no solution or two distinct solutions in $\mathcal{R}$.

(d) Show that there is no solution in the field associated with 7_3.
(e) Show that there are two solutions in the field associated with 21_5.
(f) If $\mathcal{R}$ has characteristic 2, and if the equation has a solution in $\mathcal{R}$, prove that $\mathcal{R}$ has a subfield isomorphic to the field associated with 21_5.

13. Let $\mathcal{S} = \mathcal{R} \cup \{\infty\}$, where $\mathcal{R}$ is a field. Let α_i ($i = 1, 2, 3, 4, 5, 6$) be the functions on $\mathcal{S}$ defined as follows: $x\alpha_1 = x$, $x\alpha_2 = 1 - x$, $x\alpha_3 = 1/x$, $x\alpha_4 = 1 - (1/x)$, $x\alpha_5 = 1/(1 - x)$, and $x\alpha_6 = x/(x - 1)$, with suitable interpretations of the values of these expressions when $x = 0$ or ∞. (See exercise 3.)
(a) Prove that the α_i form a group under composition.
(b) Write a composition (multiplication) table for this group.
(c) Prove that this group is isomorphic to the group of permutations on a three-element set.

5.3. Applications to Affine Geometry

In this section, $\mathcal{A}$ denotes an arbitrary affine plane (defined in Section 1.5) whose projective extension $\mathcal{P}$ (defined in Exercise 1.5.6) is Pappian. (For example, $\mathcal{E}_2$ is such an affine plane, because $\mathcal{E}_2^*$ is Pappian.) We shall use our knowledge of the plane $\mathcal{P}$ to derive some results for $\mathcal{A}$. We commence with a glossary.

(1) The *ideal line* is that line of $\mathcal{P}$ that is not in $\mathcal{A}$. If k is a line of $\mathcal{A}$, the *ideal point* on k is that point of $\mathcal{P}$ in which k (considered as a line of $\mathcal{P}$) intersects the ideal line.

(2) *Coordinate system* in $\mathcal{A}$: Construct a coordinate system in $\mathcal{P}$ by the method of Section 4.2, taking the points I and J to lie on the ideal line, which is therefore cast in the role of ℓ_∞. Every point of $\mathcal{A}$ has a unique coordinate triple with third member 1; if X is a point of $\mathcal{A}$, with $[X] = [x, y, 1]$, assign to X the coordinate *pair* $[x, y]$. Since, in a given coordinate system, the pair assigned to a point of $\mathcal{A}$ is unique, we shall write $X = [x, y]$ rather than the strictly correct $[X] = [x, y]$. Lines of $\mathcal{A}$ are still represented by equivalence classes of column-triples. If k is a line of $\mathcal{A}$, with

$$[k] = \begin{bmatrix} k \\ m \\ n \end{bmatrix},$$

then $X = [x, y]$ and k are incident if and only if $xk + ym + n = 0$ (why?).

(3) *Representation of points on a line* of $\mathcal{A}$: Suppose that k is a line of $\mathcal{A}$, and that $D = [d, e]$ and $G = [g, h]$ are distinct points (of $\mathcal{A}$) on k. If $P = [p, q]$ is any point (of $\mathcal{A}$) on k, we know from Theorem 4.3.7 that $[p, q, 1] = u[g, h, 1] + v[d, e, 1]$ for unique numbers u, v of $\mathcal{R}$ (the field associated with $\mathcal{P}$). Comparing the third members of the pairs on the two sides of this equation, we see that $1 = u + v$, or $v = 1 - u$. Hence, $[p, q] = u[g, h] + (1 - u)\,[d, e]$. Conversely, for any number u of $\mathcal{R}$, $u[g, h] + (1 - u)\,[d, e]$ is a pair for a point (of $\mathcal{A}$) on k, by Theorem 4.3.7.

(4) *Induced coordinate system on a line* of $\mathcal{A}$: Suppose that k is a line of $\mathcal{A}$. Let A be the ideal point on k, and let D and G be any distinct points of $\mathcal{A}$ on k. Then, A, D, G determine an induced coordinate system on k (as a line of $\mathcal{P}$) in which A, D, G have the nonhomogeneous coordinates ∞, 0, 1, respectively. (See the discussion in the second and third paragraphs of Section 5.2.) Each point of $\mathcal{A}$ on k has a (nonhomogeneous) coordinate that is different from ∞, hence is a number of $\mathcal{R}$. If $D = [d, e]$, $G = [g, h]$, and $[p, q] = u[g, h] + (1 - u)[d, e]$, then $P = [p, q]$ is (from (3) above) on k and has the (nonhomogeneous) coordinate u in the induced coordinate system on k (exercise 3).

(5) *Ratio of division*: Let k be a line of $\mathcal{A}$, and let B, C, P be points of $\mathcal{A}$ on k such that at least two of B, C, P are different. Let A be the ideal point on k, and suppose that an induced coordinate system, as described in (4) above, has been chosen on k (with A as first base point). If B, C, P have (nonhomogeneous) coordinates b, c, p, respectively, then $[B] = [b, 1]$, $[C] = [c, 1]$, $[P] = [p, 1]$, and $[A] = [1, 0]$, where $[X]$ (with X on k) here denotes a pair for X in the induced (homogeneous) coordinate system on k. The formula for cross ratio (Equation 5.2.5) yields

$$-\mathcal{R}(B, C; P, A) = \frac{(p\cdot 1 - 1\cdot b)(1\cdot 1 - 0\cdot c)}{-(p\cdot 1 - 1\cdot c)(1\cdot 1 - 0\cdot b)} = \frac{p - b}{c - p}.$$

In Euclidean geometry, when $B \neq C$ and $P \neq C$, the number $(p - b)/(c - p)$ is the *ratio of division* of the segment BC by the point P. Let us introduce the symbol $(B, C/P)$, which we shall call the *ratio of division* of BC by P, to stand for $(p - b)/(c - p) = -\mathcal{R}(B, C; P, A)$ (where A is the ideal point on k). From this definition of $(B, C/P)$, it follows immediately that $(C, B/P) = 1/(B, C/P)$ (with the interpretation that $1/0 = \infty$, and $1/\infty = 0$). Also, it is easy to see (exercise 4) that if $B \neq C$, and if r is any number of $\mathcal{R}$ except -1, there is a (unique) point P on k such that $(B, C/P) = r$.

(6) An *affinity* of $\mathcal{A}$ is the restriction to $\mathcal{A}$ of a collineation of $\mathcal{P}$ that fixes the ideal line. (Compare with Exercise 3.6.10.) A *projective* affinity of $\mathcal{A}$ is the restriction to $\mathcal{A}$ of a *projective* collineation of $\mathcal{P}$ that fixes the ideal line. In particular, a *translation* and a *central dilatation* of $\mathcal{A}$ are the respective restrictions to $\mathcal{A}$ of an elation and a homology of $\mathcal{P}$ that have the ideal line as axis.

Suppose that a coordinate system has been constructed in $\mathcal{P}$, using the ideal line as ℓ_∞, thus giving rise to a coordinate system in $\mathcal{A}$ (as explained in (2) above). Let us write equations for translations and central dilatations of $\mathcal{A}$ relative to this coordinate system.

First, let τ be a translation of $\mathcal{A}$, and suppose that $O\tau = \mathcal{E}$, where $O = [0, 0]$ and $E = [e, f]$ (in $\mathcal{A}$). If ϵ is the (unique by the Extension Theorem (2.2.2)) elation of $\mathcal{P}$ that extends τ, then, also, $O\epsilon = E$. In the coordinate system in $\mathcal{P}$, $[O] = [0, 0, 1]$ and $[E] = [e, f, 1]$. Since the axis of ϵ is the ideal line (ℓ_∞), Exercise 4.3.9b shows that ϵ is described by the equation $[X\epsilon] = [x + ze, y + zf, z]$, where $[X] = [x, y, z]$ (in $\mathcal{P}$). If $X = [x, y]$ is in $\mathcal{A}$, we get $X\tau = [x + e, y + f] = [x, y] + [e, f]$. (Compare with Equation 1.1.5.)

Next, let δ be a central dilatation of $\mathcal{A}$, and let η be the (unique) homology of $\mathcal{P}$ that extends δ. Suppose that the center of η is H; since H is in $\mathcal{A}$, we shall also call it the center of δ. (Of course, if δ is the identity, its center could be taken as any point of $\mathcal{A}$.) Assume that $H = [h, k]$, and let $U = [h + 1, k]$. Then, $U\delta = r[h + 1, k] + (1 - r)[h, k] = [h + r, k]$ for some $r \neq 0$ (why?). From the facts that η fixes every ideal point, fixes H, and sends U into $U\delta$, the following matrix for η can be calculated (exercise 8), and its verification (recalling that $\mathcal{R}$ is a field) is very easy.

5.3.1. $$[\eta] = \begin{bmatrix} r & 0 & 0 \\ 0 & r & 0 \\ (1 - r)h & (1 - r)k & 1 \end{bmatrix}.$$

Therefore, $[X\eta] = [xr + z(1 - r)h,\ yr + z(1 - r)k,\ z]$, where $[X] = [x, y, z]$ (in $\mathcal{P}$). If $X = [x, y]$ is a point of $\mathcal{A}$, we get $X\delta = [xr + (1 - r)h, yr + (1 - r)k] = r[x, y] + (1 - r)[h, k]$. (Compare with Equation 2.3.4.)

Suppose that δ is a central dilatation of $\mathcal{A}$ with center $H = [h, k]$, and that $X = [x, y]$ is any point of $\mathcal{A}$ different from H. Let $k = X \cup H$, and construct the induced coordinate system on k (as explained in (4) above), taking A as the ideal point on k, $D = H$, and $G = X$. From the last paragraph, $X\delta = r[x, y] + (1 - r)[h, k]$ for some $r \neq 0$. Therefore, in the induced coordinate system on k, H, X, and $X\delta$ have the (nonhomogeneous) coordinates 0, 1, and r, respectively (exercise 3). Thus, from (5) above we get the following equation (valid for any $X \neq H$ in $\mathcal{A}$).

5.3.2. $$-(X\delta, X/H) = \frac{-(0 - r)}{1 - 0} = r\,.$$

The number r is called the *ratio* of δ.

Since translations and central dilatations of $\mathcal{A}$ extend to elations and homologies, respectively, of $\mathcal{P}$ with the ideal line as axis, the theorem Coaxial Collineations (2.4.4) provides a good deal of information about composites of these affinities. For instance, the composite of two translations of $\mathcal{A}$ is a translation, and the composite of a translation and a central dilatation of $\mathcal{A}$ is a central dilatation (why?). To learn what happens when two central dilatations are composed, let δ_i ($i = 1, 2$) be the central dilatation of $\mathcal{A}$ with center $H_i = [h_i, k_i]$ and ratio r_i. Two applications of the equation of a central dilatation (derived above) yield the following equation for $\delta_1\delta_2$.

5.3.3. $$[x, y]\delta_1\delta_2 = r_2r_1[x, y] + r_2(1 - r_1)[h_1, k_1] + (1 - r_2)[h_2, k_2]\,.$$

Equation 5.3.3 and Theorem 2.4.4 are the keys to the next theorem.

Theorem 5.3.4. Let $\mathcal{A}$ be an affine plane whose projective extension $\mathcal{P}$ is Pappian. Let δ_i ($i = 1, 2$) be the central dilatation of $\mathcal{A}$ with center $H_i = [h_i, k_i]$ and ratio r_i, and assume that $H_1 \neq H_2$. Then:

(a) If $r_2r_1 \neq 1$, $\delta_1\delta_2$ is a central dilatation with ratio r_2r_1 and center on the line $H_1 \cup H_2$.

(b) If $r_2r_1 = 1$, $\delta_1\delta_2$ is a translation τ. If ϵ is the elation of $\mathcal{P}$ that extends τ, the center of ϵ is the ideal point on $H_1 \cup H_2$.

Proof: (a) Let $H_3 = [h_3, k_3]$ be the point given by

$$[h_3, k_3] = \frac{1}{1 - r_2r_1}\{r_2(1 - r_1)[h_1, k_1] + (1 - r_2)[h_2, k_2]\}\,.$$

Equation 5.3.3 then becomes $[x, y]\delta_1\delta_2 = r_2r_1[x, y] + (1 - r_2r_1)[h_3, k_3]$, proving that $\delta_1\delta_2$ is the central dilatation with center H_3 and ratio r_2r_1. That H_3 is on $H_1 \cup H_2$ follows easily from the theorem Coaxial Collineations (2.4.4).

(b) Again using Equation 5.3.3, and the assumption that $r_2r_1 = 1$, we have $[x, y]\delta_1\delta_2 = [x, y] + (1 - r_2)[h_2 - h_1, k_2 - k_1]$. Thus, $\delta_1\delta_2$ is a translation τ. That the center of ϵ (the elation extending τ) is the ideal point on $H_1 \cup H_2$ follows easily from Theorem 2.4.4. ∎

We end this section with a proof of a famous theorem attributed to Menelaus. (Some additional results of affine geometry may be found in the exercises.)

Theorem 5.3.5. (Menelaus' theorem) Let $\mathcal{A}$ be an affine plane whose projective extension $\mathcal{P}$ is Pappian. Suppose that ABC is a triangle in $\mathcal{A}$, and let P, Q, R be points on the sides $A \cup B$, $B \cup C$, $C \cup A$, respectively, all different from any of A, B, C. Then, P, Q, R are collinear if and only if

5.3.6. $(A, B/P) \cdot (B, C/Q) \cdot (C, A/R) = -1$.

Proof: Suppose first that P, Q, R are collinear (Figure 5.3), and construct (using Axiom 4) central dilatations of $\mathcal{A}$ as follows:

δ_1 has center P and sends A into B, so that (by Equation 5.3.2) its ratio is $r_1 = -(B, A/P)$.

δ_2 has center Q and sends B into C, so that its ratio is $r_2 = -(C, B/Q)$.

If μ is the central collineation of $\mathcal{P}$ that extends $\delta_1\delta_2$, the center of μ is on $P \cup Q$ by Theorem 5.3.4. Since $A\delta_1\delta_2 = C$, the center of μ must

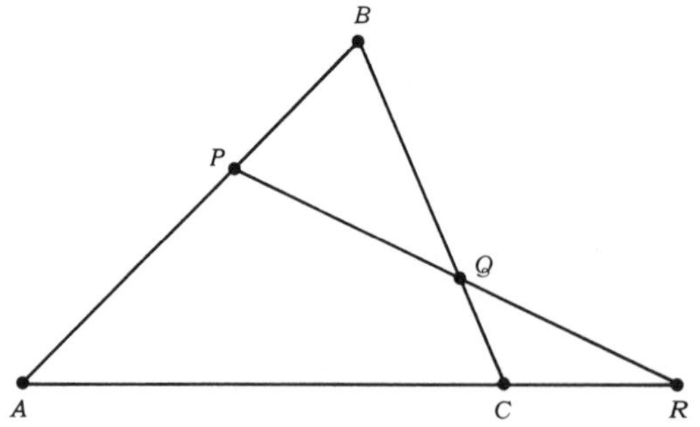

Figure 5.3

be $(A \cup C) \cap (P \cup Q) = R$. Because R is in $\mathfrak{A}$, μ is a homology. Hence $\delta = \delta_1\delta_2$ is a central dilatation, with center R and ratio $r = -(C, A/R)$ (since $A\delta = C$). By Theorem 5.3.4, the ratio of δ is also r_2r_1. Therefore, $\{-(C, B/Q)\} \cdot \{-(B, A/P)\} = -(C, A/R)$. Observing that $(B, A/P) = 1/(A, B/P)$, and $(C, B/Q) = 1/(B, C/Q)$, we easily get Equation 5.3.6.

Conversely, suppose that Equation 5.3.6 is satisfied, and let δ_1, δ_2 be as above. Then, Equation 5.3.6 implies that $r_2r_1 = -(C, A/R)$ (why?). Since $C \neq A$, $(C, A/R) \neq -1$ (why?); hence $r_2r_1 \neq 1$. It follows from Theorem 5.3.4 that $\delta = \delta_1\delta_2$ is a central dilatation with ratio $-(C, A/R)$ and center on $P \cup Q$. Because $A\delta = A\delta_1\delta_2 = C$, the center of δ is also on $A \cup C$. Hence, $P \cup Q$ and $A \cup C$ intersect in a point R' of $\mathfrak{A}$. Then, R' is the center of δ, and the ratio of δ is also given by $-(C, A/R')$. Thus, $(C, A/R') = (C, A/R) \neq -1$; hence, by exercise 4, $R' = R$. Therefore, P, Q, R are collinear. ∎

Exercise 5.3.A

For all the exercises, $\mathfrak{A}$ is an affine plane whose projective extension $\mathfrak{P}$ is Pappian.

1. Prove that a coordinate system in $\mathfrak{A}$ is determined to within an automorphism of $\mathfrak{R}$ by the specification of the three noncollinear points to be represented by the pairs $[0, 0]$, $[1, 0]$, and $[0, 1]$.

2. Let k_i $(i = 1, 2)$ be a line of $\mathfrak{A}$, with

$$[k_i] = \begin{bmatrix} k_i \\ m_i \\ n_i \end{bmatrix},$$

and assume that $k_1 \neq k_2$. Prove that k_1 and k_2 are parallel (do not intersect in $\mathfrak{A}$) if and only if $k_1m_2 - k_2m_1 = 0$.

3. Let k be a line of $\mathfrak{A}$, and suppose that an induced coordinate system on k is determined by the base points A, D, G, where A is the ideal point on k, $D = [d, e]$, and $G = [g, h]$. If $[p, q] = u[g, h] + (1 - u)[d, e]$, prove that the point $P = [p, q]$ has (nonhomogeneous) coordinate u in this induced coordinate system.

4. Let B, C be distinct points on a line k in $\mathfrak{A}$, and let r be any number of $\mathfrak{R}$ except -1. Prove that there is a unique point P on k such that $(B, C/P) = r$.

5. Assume that the characteristic of $\mathcal{R}$ is not 2.

(a) Let $B = [-2, 1]$ and $C = [1, 2]$. Find the point P such that $(B, C/P) = 3$.

(b) Let δ be the central dilatation of $\mathcal{A}$ with center $[0, 1]$, sending $[2, 1]$ into $[-1, 1]$. Write an equation for δ.

(c) Let δ_1 be the central dilatation of $\mathcal{A}$ with center $[0, 0]$ and ratio $1/2$, and let δ_2 be the central dilatation of $\mathcal{A}$ with center $[1, -2]$ and ratio 2. Find equations for $\delta_1\delta_2$ and $\delta_2\delta_1$.

6. Let k be a line of $\mathcal{A}$, and let μ be either a translation or a central dilatation of $\mathcal{A}$. Prove that either $k\mu = k$, or $k\mu$ is parallel to k.

7. Let B, C, P be points on a line k of $\mathcal{A}$, and assume that at least two of B, C, P are different. Let σ be any projective affinity of $\mathcal{A}$. Prove that $(B\sigma, C\sigma/P\sigma) = (B, C/P)$.

Exercise 5.3.B

See the instructions preceding exercise 1.

8. Let η be the homology of $\mathcal{P}$ with axis the ideal line, center $H = [h, k]$ (in $\mathcal{A}$), sending $[h + 1, k]$ into $[h + r, k]$ $(r \neq 0)$. Calculate a point-matrix for η, and compare with Equation 5.3.1.

9. Prove Ceva's theorem: Let ABC be a triangle in $\mathcal{A}$, and let P, Q, R be points on the sides $A \cup B$, $B \cup C$, $C \cup A$, respectively, all different from any of A, B, C. Then, if the lines $A \cup Q$, $B \cup R$, $C \cup P$ are concurrent, the equation $(A, B/P) \cdot (B, C/Q) \cdot (C, A/R) = 1$ holds. Conversely, if this equation holds, the lines $A \cup Q$, $B \cup R$, $C \cup P$ are either concurrent or mutually parallel.

10. Assume that the characteristic of $\mathcal{R}$ is not 2, so that $1 \neq -1$. Let B, C be distinct points on a line k of $\mathcal{A}$. By exercise 4, there is a unique point P on k such that $(B, C/P) = 1$. This point P is called the *midpoint* of BC (by analogy with Euclidean geometry).

(a) Define the *medians* of a triangle in $\mathcal{A}$.

(b) Prove that the medians of any triangle in $\mathcal{A}$ are concurrent.

11. Let $A = [a, b]$, $C = [c, d]$, and $E = [e, f]$ be vertices of a triangle in $\mathcal{A}$. Show that for any point $X = [x, y]$, there are unique numbers r, s of $\mathcal{R}$ such that $[x, y] = r[a, b] + s[c, d] + (1 - r - s)[e, f]$. (The numbers r, s, and $1 - r - s$ are called the *barycentric coordinates* of X with respect to triangle ACE.)

5.4. A Projective Definition of Conic

In Euclidean geometry, a conic section is the set of points of intersection of a circular cone with a plane not through the vertex of the cone. Our first aim in this section is to find a property of Euclidean conic sections that can be formulated in purely projective terms. We shall then take that property as the basis of the definition of conic in an arbitrary Pappian plane.

Let $\mathcal{K}$ be a circular cone in $\mathcal{E}_3$, generated by the collection of all lines through a point O that intersect a circle $\mathcal{C}_1$, where O is not in the plane $\mathcal{P}_1$ that contains $\mathcal{C}_1$. Let $\mathcal{P}$ be any plane of $\mathcal{E}_3$ that does not contain O; then, $\mathcal{P}$ intersects the cone $\mathcal{K}$ in a conic section $\mathcal{C}$. Extend $\mathcal{E}_3$ to $\mathcal{E}_3^*$, and let $\mathcal{K}^*$ be the extension of $\mathcal{K}$ (all the points of $\mathcal{K}$ plus the ideal points on the lines that generate $\mathcal{K}$), $\mathcal{P}_1^*$ the extension of $\mathcal{P}_1$, $\mathcal{P}^*$ the extension of $\mathcal{P}$, and $\mathcal{C}^*$ the intersection of $\mathcal{P}^*$ with $\mathcal{K}^*$. (Note that the intersection of $\mathcal{P}_1^*$ with $\mathcal{K}^*$ is still the circle $\mathcal{C}_1$.) It is natural to call $\mathcal{C}^*$ a conic section in the extended plane $\mathcal{P}^*$, and, from this picture of $\mathcal{C}^*$, it is apparent that $\mathcal{C}^*$ is the image of the circle $\mathcal{C}_1$ under the perspectivity ϕ from $\mathcal{P}_1^*$ to $\mathcal{P}^*$, with center O.

There is an isometry ψ of $\mathcal{E}_3$ (a composite of a translation and a rotation in three-space) that carries $\mathcal{P}_1$ onto $\mathcal{P}$; $\mathcal{C}_1\psi$ (the image of $\mathcal{C}_1$ under ψ) is a circle $\mathcal{C}_2$ in $\mathcal{P}$. The restriction of ψ to $\mathcal{P}_1$ is an (affine) isomorphism α of $\mathcal{P}_1$ onto $\mathcal{P}$, and α can be extended to an isomorphism θ of $\mathcal{P}_1^*$ onto $\mathcal{P}^*$. Therefore, $\mathcal{C}^*$ is the image of the circle $\mathcal{C}_2$ (in $\mathcal{P}$) under the mapping $\theta^{-1}\phi$, which is a collineation of $\mathcal{P}^*$. Replacing $\mathcal{P}^*$ by (the isomorphic plane) $\mathcal{E}_2^*$, we thus have the following view of conic sections in $\mathcal{E}_2^*$: A conic section in $\mathcal{E}_2^*$ is any image of a circle (of $\mathcal{E}_2$) under a collineation of $\mathcal{E}_2^*$. While we have not rigorously established the correctness of this view, we have given sufficient intuitive justification for it. The advantage of this conception of conic sections in $\mathcal{E}_2^*$ is that it permits us to restrict our attention to a circle (in $\mathcal{E}_2$) in our attempt to find a satisfactory projective definition of conic.

Let $\mathcal{C}$ be a circle in $\mathcal{E}_2$, and let A and B be diametrically opposite points of $\mathcal{C}$. Let ℓ_A and ℓ_B be the tangent lines to $\mathcal{C}$ at A and B, respectively, let C be the point that bisects one of the semicircular arcs determined by A and B, and let $m = B \cup C$ and $n = A \cup C$. (See Figure 5.4.) Extend $\mathcal{E}_2$ to $\mathcal{E}_2^*$, and let $O = \ell_A \cap \ell_B$ (an ideal point). Construct the projectivity $\pi = A \circ m \circ O \circ n \circ B$. If k is an arbitrary line on A, $k\pi$ is found by constructing $P = k \cap m$, joining P to O with the line $P \cup O$, finding the point $P' = (P \cup O) \cap n$, and, finally, joining P' to B; the line $P' \cup B$ is $k\pi$. As special cases, $n\pi = m$, $\ell_A\pi = A \cup B$, and $(A \cup B)\pi = \ell_B$. In each of these cases, the point of intersection of the line on A with its image under π lies on $\mathcal{C}$. Setting $Q = k \cap k\pi$, we want to prove that Q is on $\mathcal{C}$ for every choice of the line k on A.

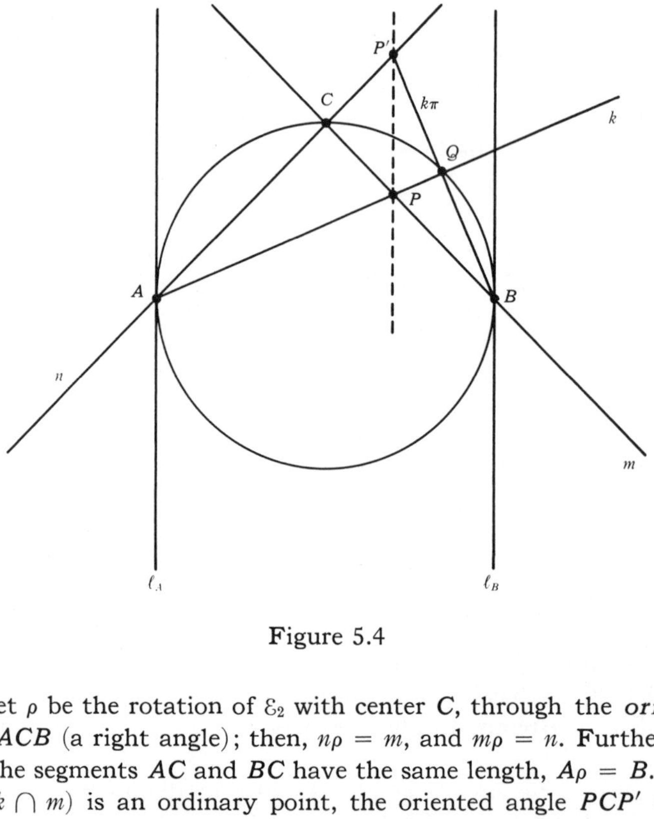

Figure 5.4

Let ρ be the rotation of $\mathcal{E}_2$ with center C, through the *oriented* angle ACB (a right angle); then, $n\rho = m$, and $m\rho = n$. Furthermore, since the segments AC and BC have the same length, $A\rho = B$. When $P\ (= k \cap m)$ is an ordinary point, the oriented angle PCP' (where $P' = (P \cup O) \cap n$) is equal to the oriented angle ACB (exercise 1a), and the segments PC and $P'C$ have the same length (exercise 1b). It follows (when P is ordinary) that $P\rho = P'$; hence $(A \cup P)\rho = B \cup P'$, implying that k and $k\pi$ are perpendicular. If P were an ideal point, k would be parallel (in $\mathcal{E}_2$) to m, and $k\pi$ would therefore be parallel to n (proof?). In this case, too, the lines k and $k\pi$ are perpendicular. Thus, the angle at Q between k and $k\pi$ is always a right angle, so that Q lies on $\mathcal{C}$ for every choice of k on A. It follows easily that the circle $\mathcal{C}$ is precisely the set of points of intersection of pairs of corresponding lines under the projectivity π, which is not a perspectivity, since $(A \cup B)\pi \neq A \cup B$.

Our discussion of conic sections in $\mathcal{E}_2^*$ suggests an appropriate definition of conic for arbitrary Pappian planes.

Definition 5.4.1. In a Pappian plane $\mathcal{P}$, let A and B be any distinct points, and let π be any projectivity from A to B that is not a perspectivity. The *point-conic* determined by A, B, and π is the set of all points of the form $k \cap k\pi$, where k is an arbitrary line on A. ▌

The above definition is meaningful in any projective plane, but little can be proved about conics without the full power of the Fundamental Theorem, and that is the reason for the restriction to Pappian planes. A point-conic is so named because it is a set of points; the dual notion is that of *line-conic*, for which the reader should supply a definition.

Definition 5.4.1 has one apparent defect—the special role played by the points A and B in determining the conic $\mathcal{C}$. By exercise 2, A and B are points of $\mathcal{C}$, but it is not obvious that *any* two distinct points of $\mathcal{C}$, together with a suitable projectivity between those points, determine the same conic $\mathcal{C}$. In order to prove that a point-conic *is* determined by any two of its points and a certain projectivity between those points, we need the next theorem, which gives a necessary and sufficient condition that a point of the plane lie on a point-conic $\mathcal{C}$. The theorem bears some resemblance to Pappus' theorem, to which it is, in fact, closely related.

Theorem 5.4.2. In a Pappian plane, let $\mathcal{C}$ be a point-conic determined by distinct points A and C and a projectivity (not a perspectivity) π from A to C. Let B, D, E be points of $\mathcal{C}$ such that A, B, C, D, E are all different. If F is any point of the plane different from all of A, B, C, D, E, then F is a point of $\mathcal{C}$ if and only if the points $P = (A \cup B) \cap (D \cup E)$, $Q = (B \cup C) \cap (E \cup F)$, and $R = (C \cup D) \cap (F \cup A)$ are collinear.

Proof: Let $m = D \cup E$, $n = E \cup F$, $T = (C \cup D) \cap n$, and $S = (A \cup F) \cap m$. (Refer to Figure 5.5.)

(a) Suppose that F is on $\mathcal{C}$. Let $\delta_1 = m \circ A$ and $\delta_2 = C \circ n$, and consider the projectivity $\pi' = \delta_1 \pi \delta_2$; $P\pi' = (P \cup A)\pi\delta_2 = (B \cup C)\delta_2 =$

Q, and, similarly, $D\pi' = T$, $E\pi' = E$, and $S\pi' = F$. Since $E\pi' = E$, π' is a perspectivity, by the Fundamental Theorem. Its center must be $(D \cup T) \cap (S \cup F) = R$, so that P, Q $(= P\pi')$, and R are collinear.

(b) Suppose that the points P, Q, R are collinear, and define $\pi_1 = A \circ m \circ R$, $\pi_2 = R \circ n \circ C$, and $\pi' = \pi_1\pi_2$. Then, $(A \cup B)\pi' = \{[(A \cup B) \cap m] \cup R\}\pi_2 = (P \cup R)\pi_2 = [(P \cup R) \cap n] \cup C = Q \cup C = C \cup B$. Similarly, $(A \cup D)\pi' = C \cup D$, $(A \cup E)\pi' = C \cup E$, and $(A \cup F)\pi' = C \cup F$. Since π' agrees with π on $A \cup B$, $A \cup D$, and $A \cup E$, $\pi' = \pi$, by the dual of the Fundamental Theorem. Therefore, $(A \cup F)\pi = C \cup F$, proving that F is on $\mathcal{C}$. ∎

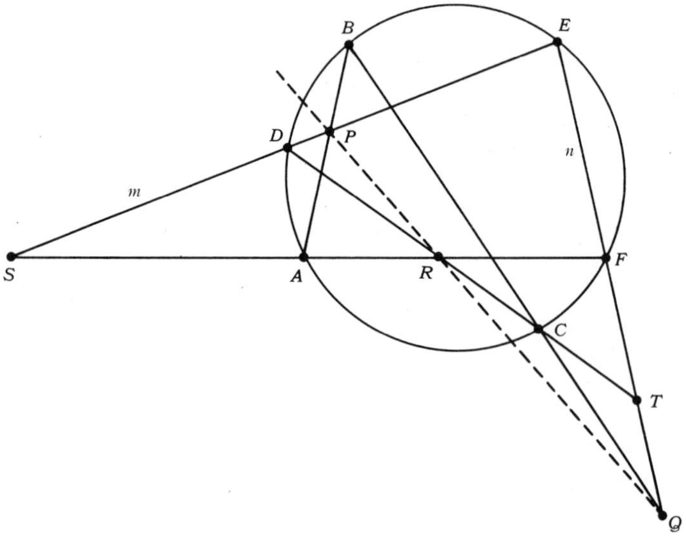

Figure 5.5

The above theorem has content if (and only if) a point-conic in the plane $\mathcal{P}$ contains at least six distinct points. It is an easy consequence of Definition 5.4.1 that every conic in $\mathcal{P}$ has the same number of points as the number of lines on a point in $\mathcal{P}$ (exercise 3a). Hence, Theorem 5.4.2 provides useful information for every Pappian plane except the 7-, 13-, and 21-point planes.

The conic $\mathcal{C}$ of Theorem 5.4.2 is determined by A, C, and π. In view of the dual of the Fundamental Theorem, π is determined by the fact that B, D, and E are points of intersection of three lines on A with their respective images under π. Therefore, $\mathcal{C}$ is determined by the points A, B, C, D, E, with the understanding that A and C carry the projectively related pencils. Likewise, a unique conic $\mathcal{C}'$ is determined by E, D, C, B, A, with the understanding that E and C carry the projectively related pencils. The preceding theorem applied to $\mathcal{C}'$ states that F is on $\mathcal{C}'$ if and only if $P' = (E \cup D) \cap (B \cup A)$, $Q' = (D \cup C) \cap (A \cup F)$, and $R' = (C \cup B) \cap (F \cup E)$ are collinear. Since P', Q', R' are the points P, R, Q, respectively, that are defined in the statement of Theorem 5.4.2, it follows that F is on $\mathcal{C}'$ if and only if it is on $\mathcal{C}$.

Thus, $\mathcal{C}$ and $\mathcal{C}'$ are the same, so that $\mathcal{C}$ is also determined by E, C, and a projectivity π' from E to C. Since E could have been *any* point of $\mathcal{C}$ other than A and C, we see that any other point of $\mathcal{C}$ can be substituted for A (with appropriate change of the projectivity) without altering $\mathcal{C}$. But the conic determined by A, C, and π is clearly the same as the conic determined by C, A, and π^{-1}. Therefore, a repetition of the above argument shows that any other point of $\mathcal{C}$ can be substituted for C without affecting the point-conic so determined. By a two-step substitution, any two distinct points of $\mathcal{C}$ could be substituted for A and C in the determination of $\mathcal{C}$. Thus, the next theorem has been proved for any Pappian plane in which there are at least six lines on a point, and the theorem is easily established by a separate argument (exercise 4) for the 7-, 13-, and 21-point planes.

Theorem 5.4.3. (Steiner's theorem) In a Pappian plane, a point-conic $\mathcal{C}$ is determined by any two of its (distinct) points, together with a suitable projectivity between those points. ▌

Corollary 1: In a Pappian plane $\mathcal{P}$, let A, B, C, D, E be any triply noncollinear points. Then, there is one and only one point-conic $\mathcal{C}$ in $\mathcal{P}$ that contains all five points.

Proof: By Steiner's theorem, if there exists a point-conic containing all five points, it is determined by projectively related pencils on A and B. Let $\mathcal{C}$ be the conic determined by A, B, and the projectivity π, from A to B, that sends $A \cup C$, $A \cup D$, $A \cup E$ into $B \cup C$, $B \cup D$, $B \cup E$, respectively. Then, $\mathcal{C}$ contains the five given points and is unique because π is unique. ▌

Corollary 2: In a Pappian plane, let A be any point of a point-conic $\mathcal{C}$. Then, there is precisely one line ℓ_A on A that does not have a second point of intersection (besides A) with $\mathcal{C}$.

Proof: Let B be another point of $\mathcal{C}$. By Steiner's theorem, $\mathcal{C}$ is determined by A, B, and a projectivity π from A to B. Since π is a bijection, and since $A \cup B$ is a line on B, there is a unique line ℓ_A on A such that $\ell_A\pi = A \cup B$. By the definition of point-conic, the only point (besides A) on ℓ_A that lies on $\mathcal{C}$ is the point $\ell_A \cap \ell_A\pi$; but, $\ell_A \cap \ell_A\pi = A$, implying that ℓ_A intersects $\mathcal{C}$ only in the point A. If k is any line on A other than ℓ_A, then $k\pi \neq A \cup B$; hence $k \cap k\pi \neq A$. Therefore, k has a second point of intersection with $\mathcal{C}$. ∎

Contained implicitly in the proof of the last corollary is the fact that a line cannot intersect a point-conic in more than two distinct points (exercise 5). The line ℓ_A of Corollary 2 above seems to depend upon the choice of the point B. However, since ℓ_A turns out to be the only line on A that intersects $\mathcal{C}$ in just one point, it is independent of B. The line ℓ_A is important enough to receive a special name.

Definition 5.4.4. Let $\mathcal{C}$ be a point-conic in a Pappian plane, and let A be a point of $\mathcal{C}$. The unique line ℓ_A that intersects $\mathcal{C}$ only in the point A is the *tangent* line to $\mathcal{C}$ at A. ∎

At this point, the reader should formulate the duals of the definitions, theorems, and corollaries of this section. In dualizing Definition 5.4.1, the name *line-conic* may be used for the figure obtained. Also, the term *point of contact* may be used for the point on a line of a line-conic that is incident with no other line of that conic.

Exercise 5.4.A

1. Refer to the situation depicted in Figure 5.4. Suppose that P is an ordinary point.

(a) Prove that the oriented angle PCP' is equal to the oriented angle ACB.

(b) Prove that the lengths of the segments PC and $P'C$ are equal.

2. In a Pappian plane, let $\mathcal{C}$ be a point-conic determined by A, B, and a projectivity π. Prove that A and B are points of $\mathcal{C}$.

3. (a) Prove that the cardinal number of points of a point-conic in a Pappian plane $\mathcal{P}$ is equal to the cardinal number of lines on a point of $\mathcal{P}$.

(b) In a 7-point plane, prove that any three noncollinear points constitute a point-conic.
(c) In a 13-point plane, prove that any four triply noncollinear points constitute a point-conic.

4. (a) Prove Steiner's theorem for a 7-point plane.
(b) Prove Steiner's theorem for a 13-point plane.
(c) Prove Steiner's theorem for a 21-point plane.

5. (a) Let $\mathcal{C}$ be a point-conic in a Pappian plane. Prove that no three distinct points of $\mathcal{C}$ are collinear.
(b) State and prove the dual of the statement of part (a).

6. Let $\mathcal{C}$ be a point-conic in a Pappian plane, determined by A, B, and π (from A to B). Prove that $(A \cup B)\pi$ is the tangent line to $\mathcal{C}$ at B.

7. Show how Theorem 5.4.2 gives a construction for points on a point-conic $\mathcal{C}$ determined by the triply noncollinear points A, B, C, D, E in a Pappian plane.

Exercise 5.4.B

8. In a Pappian plane, let A, C, D, E, F be distinct points of a conic $\mathcal{C}$, and let ℓ_C be the tangent line to $\mathcal{C}$ at C. Prove that the points $P = (A \cup C) \cap (D \cup E)$, $Q = (E \cup F) \cap \ell_C$, and $R = (C \cup D) \cap (F \cup A)$ are collinear.

9. In a Pappian plane, let A, C, D, E be distinct points of a conic $\mathcal{C}$, and let ℓ_A and ℓ_C be the tangent lines to $\mathcal{C}$ at A and C, respectively. Prove that $P = (A \cup C) \cap (D \cup E)$, $Q = (E \cup A) \cap \ell_C$, and $R = (C \cup D) \cap \ell_A$ are collinear.

10. Prove that a point-conic in a Pappian plane is determined by any four of its (distinct) points and the tangent line to the conic at one of those points.

11. Prove that a point-conic in a Pappian plane is determined by any three of its (distinct) points and the tangent lines to the conic at two of those points.

12. In the 31-point plane whose incidence table you have saved from Exercise 1.4.4, the points P_0, P_4, P_6, P_9, P_{16} are triply noncollinear and therefore determine a unique point-conic $\mathcal{C}$. (Every 31-point plane is Pappian.) Find the sixth point of $\mathcal{C}$, and also find all the tangent lines to $\mathcal{C}$. Save this information.

13. How many different point-conics are there in a 31-point plane? (Every 31-point plane is Pappian.)

5.5. Pascal's Theorem

The combination of Theorem 5.4.2 and Steiner's theorem yields an easy proof of a classic and beautiful theorem discovered (for Euclidean conics) by Pascal. To simplify the statement of Pascal's theorem, let us agree that by the *simple hexagon ABCDEF* we shall mean the figure consisting of the distinct points A, B, C, D, E, F, together with the lines $A \cup B$, $B \cup C$, $C \cup D$, $D \cup E$, $E \cup F$, and $F \cup A$. For the simple hexagon $ABCDEF$, $A \cup B$ and $D \cup E$ are *opposite sides*, $B \cup C$ and $E \cup F$ are opposite sides, and $C \cup D$ and $F \cup A$ are opposite sides.

Theorem 5.5.1. (Pascal's theorem) In a Pappian plane, if a simple hexagon is inscribed in a point-conic $\mathcal{C}$, the points of intersection of pairs of opposite sides are collinear.

Proof: Let the hexagon be $ABCDEF$. By Steiner's theorem, $\mathcal{C}$ is determined by A, C, and a certain projectivity from A to C. The result now follows from Theorem 5.4.2. ∎

The line on which the points of intersection of pairs of opposite sides (of the hexagon of Pascal's theorem) lie is the *Pascal line* of the hexagon. (See Figure 5.5.) The points A, B, C, D, E, F on $\mathcal{C}$ determine (through their various reorderings) 60 different simple hexagons (exercise 1) and, hence, 60 (not necessarily all different) Pascal lines. For a fuller discussion of these matters, see [18]. (This reference also contains an elegant development of the metric properties of the Euclidean conic sections.)

Let us turn our attention to the problem of writing an equation for a point-conic $\mathcal{C}$ in a Pappian plane $\mathcal{P}$. Let A, B, C be distinct points of $\mathcal{C}$, and let ℓ_A, ℓ_B be the tangent lines to $\mathcal{C}$ at A and B, respectively. (By Exercise 5.4.11, $\mathcal{C}$ is determined by A, B, C, ℓ_A, ℓ_B.) Set $J = \ell_A \cap \ell_B$; then, A, B, C, J are triply noncollinear (exercise 2). Construct a coordinate system in $\mathcal{P}$ (as in Section 4.2) in which

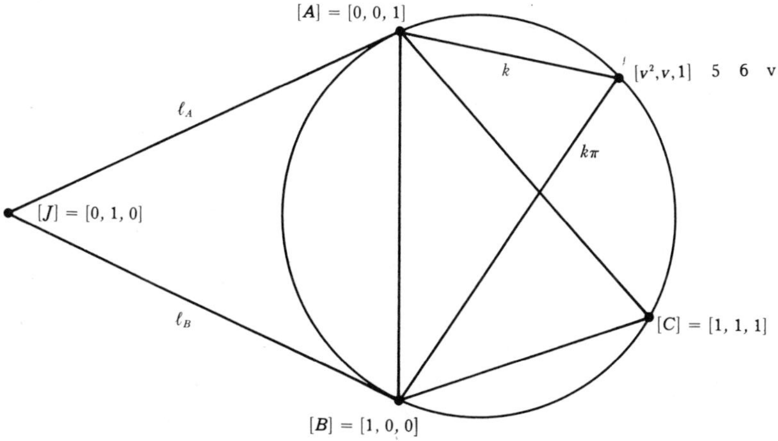

Figure 5.6

$[A] = [0, 0, 1]$, $[B] = [1, 0, 0]$, $[C] = [1, 1, 1]$, and $[J] = [0, 1, 0]$. (See **Figure 5.6**.) Simple calculations show that

$$[A \cup B] = \begin{bmatrix} 0 \\ 1 \\ 0 \end{bmatrix}, \qquad [A \cup C] = \begin{bmatrix} 1 \\ -1 \\ 0 \end{bmatrix}, \qquad [\ell_A] = \begin{bmatrix} 1 \\ 0 \\ 0 \end{bmatrix},$$

$$[\ell_B] = \begin{bmatrix} 0 \\ 0 \\ 1 \end{bmatrix}, \qquad \text{and} \qquad [B \cup C] = \begin{bmatrix} 0 \\ 1 \\ -1 \end{bmatrix}.$$

On the (set of lines on the) point A, establish the induced coordinate system (the dual of an induced coordinate system on a line, explained in Section 4.3) with base lines $A \cup B$, $A \cup C$, and triples

$$\begin{bmatrix} 0 \\ 1 \\ 0 \end{bmatrix} \quad \text{and} \quad \begin{bmatrix} 1 \\ -1 \\ 0 \end{bmatrix},$$

respectively, for them. Since

$$[\ell_A] = \begin{bmatrix} 1 \\ 0 \\ 0 \end{bmatrix} = \begin{bmatrix} 0 \\ 1 \\ 0 \end{bmatrix} + \begin{bmatrix} 1 \\ -1 \\ 0 \end{bmatrix},$$

we see that

$$[A \cup B] = \begin{bmatrix} 1 \\ 0 \end{bmatrix}, \qquad [A \cup C] = \begin{bmatrix} 0 \\ 1 \end{bmatrix}, \qquad \text{and} \qquad [\ell_A] = \begin{bmatrix} 1 \\ 1 \end{bmatrix}$$

in this coordinate system on A. Similarly, establish the induced coordinate system on B with base lines ℓ_B, $B \cup C$, and triples

$$\begin{bmatrix} 0 \\ 0 \\ 1 \end{bmatrix} \quad \text{and} \quad \begin{bmatrix} 0 \\ 1 \\ -1 \end{bmatrix},$$

respectively, for them. Then,

$$[\ell_B] = \begin{bmatrix} 1 \\ 0 \end{bmatrix}, \qquad [B \cup C] = \begin{bmatrix} 0 \\ 1 \end{bmatrix}, \qquad \text{and} \qquad [B \cup A] = \begin{bmatrix} 1 \\ 1 \end{bmatrix}$$

in this coordinate system on B (why?).

The conic $\mathcal{C}$ is determined by A, B, and π, where π is the projectivity from A to B that sends $A \cup B$ into ℓ_B (by Exercise 5.4.6), $A \cup C$ into $B \cup C$ (because C is on $\mathcal{C}$), and ℓ_A into $B \cup A$ (by the proof of Corollary 2 of Steiner's theorem). Relative to the chosen coordinate systems on A and B, π has (by the dual of Theorem 4.4.2) an equation of the form

$$[k\pi] = \begin{bmatrix} a & b \\ c & d \end{bmatrix} [k],$$

where $[k]$ denotes a pair (in the coordinate system on A) for the arbitrary line k on A, and $[k\pi]$ denotes a pair (in the coordinate system on B) for $k\pi$. Using the pairs for $A \cup B$, $A \cup C$, ℓ_A (on A), and ℓ_B, $B \cup C$, $B \cup A$ (on B) calculated in the preceding paragraph, and noting that π is uniquely determined by the statements $(A \cup B)\pi = \ell_B$, $(A \cup C)\pi = B \cup C$, and $\ell_A\pi = B \cup A$, we see that

$$\begin{bmatrix} a & b \\ c & d \end{bmatrix} = \begin{bmatrix} 1 & 0 \\ 0 & 1 \end{bmatrix}$$

is a suitable matrix for π; hence $[k\pi] = [k]$ is an equation (in pairs) for π relative to the chosen coordinate systems on A and B.

Now, let k be any line on A other than $A \cup B$. Then, in the induced coordinate system on A,

$$[k] = \begin{bmatrix} u \\ 1 \end{bmatrix}$$

for some u in $\mathcal{R}$ (why?). It follows that

$$[k\pi] = \begin{bmatrix} u \\ 1 \end{bmatrix}$$

in the induced coordinate system on B. Therefore, *triples* for k and $k\pi$ are given by

$$[k] = \begin{bmatrix} 0 \\ 1 \\ 0 \end{bmatrix} u + \begin{bmatrix} 1 \\ -1 \\ 0 \end{bmatrix} = \begin{bmatrix} 1 \\ u - 1 \\ 0 \end{bmatrix},$$

and

$$[k\pi] = \begin{bmatrix} 0 \\ 0 \\ 1 \end{bmatrix} u + \begin{bmatrix} 0 \\ 1 \\ -1 \end{bmatrix} = \begin{bmatrix} 0 \\ 1 \\ u - 1 \end{bmatrix}.$$

Thus, $[k \cap k\pi] = [(1 - u)^2, 1 - u, 1]$ (verify!). Setting $v = 1 - u$, we have $[k \cap k\pi] = [v^2, v, 1]$ for some v in $\mathcal{R}$. Hence, every point of $\mathcal{C}$ except B has a triple of the form $[v^2, v, 1]$ for some v in $\mathcal{R}$, and, conversely, every triple of this form is a triple for some point of $\mathcal{C}$, as is seen by repeating the above argument, taking k to be the line defined by

$$[k] = \begin{bmatrix} 1 \\ -v \\ 0 \end{bmatrix}.$$

Since $[B] = [1, 0, 0]$, we see that the coordinates of every point of $\mathcal{C}$ satisfy the homogeneous quadratic equation $y^2 = xz$. (The homogeneity of this equation guarantees that if one triple for a certain point satisfies the equation, every triple for that point satisfies the equation.) Conversely, suppose that $[P] = [p, q, r]$, and that $q^2 = pr$. If $r = 0$, then $q = 0$, so that $p \neq 0$, and $[P] = [1, 0, 0]$. Hence $P = B$, which is on $\mathcal{C}$. If $r \neq 0$,

$$[P] = \left[\frac{p}{r}, \frac{q}{r}, 1\right], \qquad \text{and} \qquad \left(\frac{q}{r}\right)^2 = \left(\frac{p}{r}\right) \cdot 1 .$$

Let $\frac{q}{r} = v$, so that $[P] = [v^2, v, 1]$, and, from above, P is a point of $\mathcal{C}$.

Theorem 5.5.2. If $\mathcal{C}$ is a point-conic in a Pappian plane $\mathcal{P}$, a coordinate system can be constructed for $\mathcal{P}$ in which $\mathcal{C}$ has the equation $y^2 = xz$. Then, the point V of $\mathcal{P}$ is a point of $\mathcal{C}$ if and only if either $[V] = [1, 0, 0]$ or $[V] = [v^2, v, 1]$ for some v in $\mathcal{R}$. Furthermore, the tangent lines to $\mathcal{C}$ have coordinate triples as follows: If B is the point of $\mathcal{C}$ such that $[B] = [1, 0, 0]$, then

$$[\ell_B] = \begin{bmatrix} 0 \\ 0 \\ 1 \end{bmatrix};$$

if V is any other point of $\mathcal{C}$, with $[V] = [v^2, v, 1]$, then

$$[\ell_V] = \begin{bmatrix} 1 \\ -2v \\ v^2 \end{bmatrix}.$$

Proof: All the statements except the last (concerning ℓ_V) have been proved in the discussion preceding the theorem. To prove the last statement, let V be any point of $\mathcal{C}$ except B, with $[V] = [v^2, v, 1]$. Since the line ℓ_V intersects $\mathcal{C}$ only in V, it does not lie on B; hence,

$$[\ell_V] = \begin{bmatrix} 1 \\ s \\ t \end{bmatrix}$$

for some s, t in $\mathcal{R}$. Because V is on ℓ_V, $v^2 + vs + t = 0$. Let $w = -(v + s)$; then, $w^2 + ws + t = v^2 + 2vs + s^2 - vs - s^2 + t = v^2 + vs + t = 0$. Therefore, the point W such that $[W] = [w^2, w, 1]$ lies on ℓ_V and is also a point of $\mathcal{C}$. Since ℓ_V intersects $\mathcal{C}$ only in V, $W = V$; hence $w = v$. It follows that $s = -2v$, and $t = v^2$ (why?). Therefore,

$$[\ell_V] = \begin{bmatrix} 1 \\ -2v \\ v^2 \end{bmatrix},$$

as required. ▮

The analytic machinery developed above makes possible an easy proof of the next theorem, which is concerned with the possible concurrency of tangent lines to a point-conic.

Theorem 5.5.3. Let $\mathcal{C}$ be a point-conic in a Pappian plane $\mathcal{P}$.

(a) If the characteristic of $\mathcal{P}$ is 2, the tangent lines to $\mathcal{C}$ are concurrent.

(b) If the characteristic of $\mathcal{P}$ is not 2, the tangent lines to $\mathcal{C}$ are triply nonconcurrent.

Proof: Let A, B, C be *any* distinct points of $\mathcal{C}$, and let ℓ_A, ℓ_B, ℓ_C be the tangent lines to $\mathcal{C}$ at A, B, C, respectively. Set $J = \ell_A \cap \ell_B$, and construct a coordinate system in $\mathcal{P}$ such that $[A] = [0, 0, 1]$, $[B] = [1, 0, 0]$, $[C] = [1, 1, 1]$, and $[J] = [0, 1, 0]$. In this coordinate system, $\mathcal{C}$ has equation $y^2 = xz$, and, by Theorem 5.5.2,

$$[\ell_C] = \begin{bmatrix} 1 \\ -2 \\ 1 \end{bmatrix}.$$

(a) In this case, $2 = 0$ in $\mathcal{R}$. (Compare with Exercise 3.8.5a.) Thus,

$$[\ell_C] = \begin{bmatrix} 1 \\ 0 \\ 1 \end{bmatrix},$$

and ℓ_C lies on $J = \ell_A \cap \ell_B$. Since C could have been any point of $\mathcal{C}$ other than A and B, the tangent lines to $\mathcal{C}$ are concurrent at J.

(b) In this case, $2 \neq 0$ in $\mathcal{R}$ (why?). Therefore,

$$[0, 1, 0] \cdot \begin{bmatrix} 1 \\ -2 \\ 1 \end{bmatrix} = -2 \neq 0,$$

and ℓ_C does not lie on J. Thus, ℓ_A, ℓ_B, ℓ_C are not concurrent. Since A, B, C could have been any distinct points of $\mathcal{C}$, the tangent lines to $\mathcal{C}$ are triply nonconcurrent. ∎

Exercise 5.5.A

1. Let A, B, C, D, E, F be distinct points of a point-conic $\mathcal{C}$ in a Pappian plane. Show that these points are the vertices of 60 different simple hexagons.

2. Let A, B, C be distinct points of a point-conic $\mathcal{C}$ in a Pappian plane, and let ℓ_A, ℓ_B be the tangent lines to $\mathcal{C}$ at A and B, respectively. Prove that A, B, C, and $\ell_A \cap \ell_B$ are triply noncollinear.

3. By Exercise 5.4.3a and Corollary 1 of Steiner's theorem, any five triply noncollinear points of a 21-point plane constitute a point-conic. Using the incidence table for 21_5 (Figure 1.10), construct a point-conic $\mathcal{C}$ in 21_5. Find the tangent lines to $\mathcal{C}$, and verify that they are concurrent.

4. Let A, B, C be distinct points of a point-conic $\mathcal{C}$ in a Pappian plane, and let ℓ_A, ℓ_B, ℓ_C be the tangent lines to $\mathcal{C}$ at A, B, C, respectively. Set $P = (A \cup B) \cap \ell_C$, $Q = (B \cup C) \cap \ell_A$, and $R = (C \cup A) \cap \ell_B$. Use the analytic method developed in this section to prove that P, Q, R are collinear.

5. Prove the following converse of Pascal's theorem: In a Pappian plane, if a simple hexagon has the properties that its vertices are triply noncollinear, and the three points of intersection of pairs of its opposite sides are collinear, then there is a point-conic that contains its vertices.

6. Let $\mathcal{C}$ be a point-conic in a Pappian plane $\mathcal{P}$, and let ρ be any collineation of $\mathcal{P}$. Prove that $\mathcal{C}\rho$ (the image of $\mathcal{C}$ under ρ) is a point-conic. Also, if ℓ_A is the tangent line to $\mathcal{C}$ at A, prove that $\ell_A\rho$ is the tangent line to $\mathcal{C}\rho$ at $A\rho$.

Exercise 5.5.B

7. Let $\mathcal{C}$ be a point-conic in a Pappian plane, and let A, B, ℓ_A, ℓ_B be any distinct points of $\mathcal{C}$ and the tangent lines to $\mathcal{C}$ at these points, respectively. Let $P = \ell_A \cap \ell_B$, and let C be any third point of $\mathcal{C}$ (other than A and B). Set $k = P \cup C$, $Q = (A \cup B) \cap k$, and let D be the other point in which k intersects $\mathcal{C}$. (If k is the tangent line to $\mathcal{C}$ at C, put $D = C$.) Prove that $\mathcal{H}(P, Q; C, D)$.

8. Let $\mathcal{C}_1$ and $\mathcal{C}_2$ be any point-conics in a Pappian plane $\mathcal{P}$. Prove that there is a projective collineation σ of $\mathcal{P}$ that transforms $\mathcal{C}_1$ into $\mathcal{C}_2$.

9. In a Pappian plane $\mathcal{P}$, let $\mathcal{C}$ be a point-conic, and let P be a point not on $\mathcal{C}$. Call P an *interior* point of $\mathcal{C}$ if no tangent line to $\mathcal{C}$ lies on P, and call P an *exterior* point of $\mathcal{C}$ in the contrary case.

(a) If $\mathcal{P}$ is finite and has characteristic 2, prove that every point not on $\mathcal{C}$ is exterior to $\mathcal{C}$.

(b) If $\mathcal{P}$ is finite and has characteristic different from 2, prove that $\mathcal{C}$ has interior points.

(c) If $\mathcal{C}$ has interior points, prove that every point-conic in $\mathcal{P}$ has interior points. (Use the result of exercise 8.)

10. Let $\mathcal{A}$ be an affine plane whose projective extension $\mathcal{P}$ is Pappian, and let $\mathcal{C}$ be a point-conic in $\mathcal{P}$. Let $\mathcal{C}'$ be the set of points of $\mathcal{C}$ that are in $\mathcal{A}$; then, $\mathcal{C}'$ is called a point-conic in $\mathcal{A}$. Further, $\mathcal{C}'$ is called a *parabola*, a *hyperbola*, or an *ellipse* in $\mathcal{A}$ if the ideal line is tangent to $\mathcal{C}$, intersects $\mathcal{C}$ in two distinct points, or fails to intersect $\mathcal{C}$, respectively.

(a) If $\mathcal{C}'$ is a parabola in $\mathcal{A}$, show that there is a coordinate system for $\mathcal{A}$ in which $\mathcal{C}'$ has equation $y^2 = x$.

(b) If $\mathcal{C}'$ is a hyperbola in $\mathcal{A}$, show that there is a coordinate system for $\mathcal{A}$ in which $\mathcal{C}'$ has equation $xy = 1$.

11. Let $\mathcal{C}$ be the point-conic whose construction was requested in Exercise 5.4.12. Use the information saved from that exercise to:

(a) verify that the tangent lines to $\mathcal{C}$ are triply nonconcurrent;

(b) verify Pascal's theorem for a certain simple hexagon inscribed in $\mathcal{C}$.

5.6. Brianchon's Theorem

We commence this section with a needed lemma.

Lemma 5.6.1. Let $\mathcal{C}$ be a point-conic in a Pappian plane. Let A, B, C, D be distinct points of $\mathcal{C}$, and let ℓ_A, ℓ_B, ℓ_C, ℓ_D be the tangent lines to $\mathcal{C}$ at A, B, C, D, respectively. Then, the points $P = \ell_A \cap \ell_B$, $Q = \ell_C \cap \ell_D$, $\mathcal{R} = (A \cup C) \cap (B \cup D)$, and $S = (A \cup D) \cap (B \cup C)$ are collinear.

Proof: Let $m = B \cup D$, $n = A \cup D$, $T = m \cap \ell_A$, and $U = n \cap \ell_B$. (See Figure 5.7.) The conic $\mathcal{C}$ is determined by A, B, and a projectivity π from A to B. Let $\delta_1 = m \circ A$ and $\delta_2 = B \circ n$. Consider the projectivity $\pi' = \delta_1\pi\delta_2$; $T\pi' = (T \cup A)\pi\delta_2 = (A \cup B)\delta_2 = (A \cup B) \cap n = A$. Similarly, $B\pi' = U$, $D\pi' = D$, and $R\pi' = S$. Since D is fixed by π', π' is a perspectivity, by the Fundamental Theorem. The center of π' must be $(T \cup A) \cap (B \cup U) = \ell_A \cap \ell_B = P$. Therefore, P, R, and S $(= R\pi')$ are collinear. If the roles of A and C are exchanged, and the roles of B and D are exchanged, a similar argument shows that Q, R, and S are collinear (exercise 1). Since $R \neq S$ (why?), the two results combined imply that P, Q, R, and S are collinear. ▌

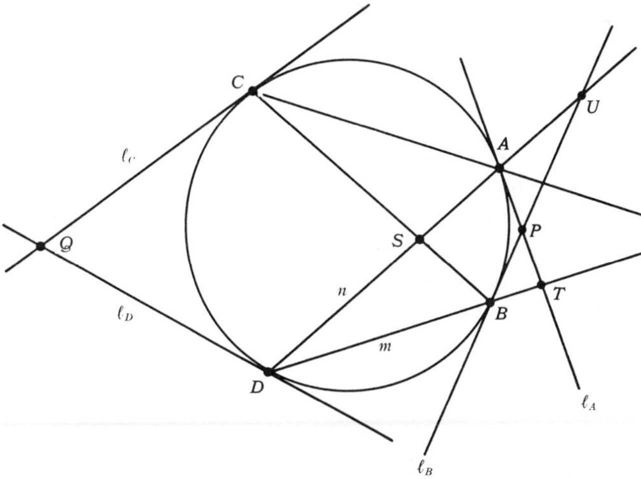

Figure 5.7

Suppose that $\mathcal{C}$ is a point-conic in a Pappian plane $\mathcal{P}$. If the characteristic of $\mathcal{P}$ is 2, the tangent lines to $\mathcal{C}$ certainly do not constitute a line-conic, because they are concurrent by Theorem 5.5.3. However, if the characteristic of $\mathcal{P}$ is not 2, the tangent lines to $\mathcal{C}$ are at least triply nonconcurrent (also by Theorem 5.5.3), and it is a natural conjecture that they do constitute a line-conic in this case.

Theorem 5.6.2. In a Pappian plane of characteristic different from 2, the tangent lines to any point-conic $\mathcal{C}$ constitute a line-conic.

Proof: It is sufficient to establish a projectivity ϕ between two distinct tangent lines to $\mathcal{C}$ such that ϕ is not a perspectivity, and the set of lines of the form $X \cup X\phi$ (with X in the domain of ϕ) is precisely the set of tangent lines to $\mathcal{C}$. Let A, B, C be distinct points of $\mathcal{C}$, and let ℓ_A, ℓ_B, ℓ_C be the tangent lines to $\mathcal{C}$ at A, B, C, respectively. Let $M = \ell_B \cap \ell_C$, $N = \ell_A \cap \ell_C$, $U = \ell_A \cap \ell_B$, and $k = A \cup B$. (See Figure 5.8.) Since the characteristic of $\mathcal{P}$ is not 2, M, N, and U are distinct, by Theorem 5.5.3; hence, M is not on ℓ_A, and N is not on ℓ_B. Also, neither M nor N is on k (why?). Therefore, we can define a projectivity ϕ, from ℓ_A to ℓ_B, by the expression $\phi = \ell_A \circ M \circ k \circ N \circ \ell_B$. Then, $A\phi = \{[(A \cup M) \cap k] \cup N\} \cap \ell_B = (A \cup N) \cap \ell_B = \ell_A \cap \ell_B = U$. Similarly, $U\phi = B$, and $N\phi = M$. Hence, ϕ is not a perspectivity (since $U\phi \neq U$), $A \cup A\phi = \ell_A$, $U \cup U\phi = \ell_B$, and $N \cup N\phi = \ell_C$. It remains to be proved that if P is any point of $\mathcal{C}$ other than A, B, and C, then $\ell_P = X \cup X\phi$ for some X on ℓ_A, and, conversely, if X is any point on ℓ_A other than A, U, and N, then $X \cup X\phi$ is a tangent line to $\mathcal{C}$.

Accordingly, let P be any point of $\mathcal{C}$ except A, B, C, and let ℓ_P be the tangent line to $\mathcal{C}$ at P. Let $X = \ell_P \cap \ell_A$, $Y = \ell_P \cap \ell_B$, and $Q = (P \cup C) \cap k$. (Refer to Figure 5.8.) Lemma 5.6.1, applied to B, C, A, P (in the roles of A, B, C, D, respectively, of the lemma), shows that M, X, and Q are collinear. The same lemma, applied to A, C, B, P (in the roles of A, B, C, D, respectively, of the lemma), proves that N, Y, and Q are collinear. It follows that $X\phi = \{[(X \cup M) \cap k] \cup N\} \cap \ell_B = (Q \cup N) \cap \ell_B = Y$. Therefore, $\ell_P = X \cup Y = X \cup X\phi$.

Conversely, let X be any point on ℓ_A except A, U, N, let $Q = (X \cup M) \cap k$, and let P be the point other than C in which the line $Q \cup C$ intersects $\mathcal{C}$. ($Q \cup C$ is not tangent to $\mathcal{C}$, since $X \neq N$.) Lemma 5.6.1, applied to B, C, A, P (in the roles of A, B, C, D, respectively, of the lemma), shows that M, $\ell_P \cap \ell_A$, and Q are collinear. It follows that $\ell_P \cap \ell_A = X$ (why?). Let $Y = \ell_P \cap \ell_B$; then, Lemma 5.6.1, applied to A, C, B, P (in the roles of A, B, C, D, respectively, of the lemma), proves that N, Y, and Q are collinear. Therefore, as in the preceding paragraph, $X\phi = Y$; hence $X \cup X\phi = \ell_P$, which is a tangent line to $\mathcal{C}$. ∎

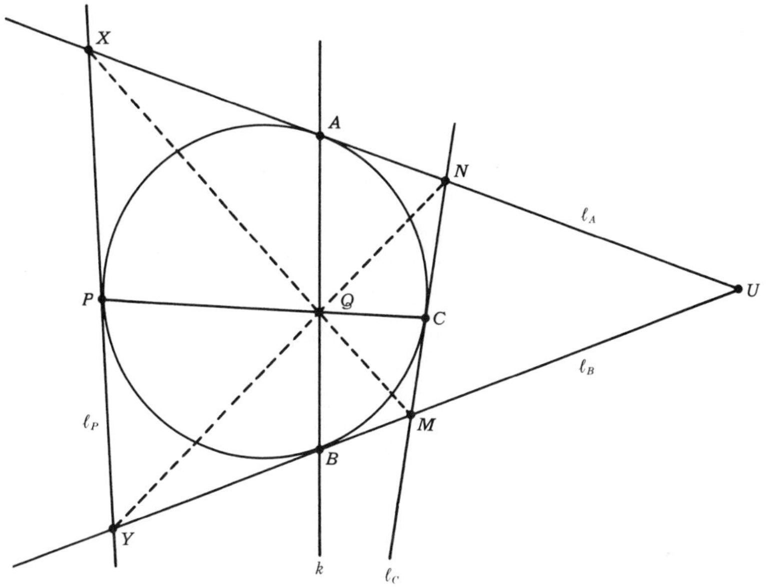

Figure 5.8

Corollary 1: Let $\mathcal{P}$ be a Pappian plane of characteristic different from 2.

(a) The points of contact of any line-conic in $\mathcal{P}$ constitute a point-conic.

(b) If $\mathcal{C}$ is any point-conic in $\mathcal{P}$, $\mathcal{C}'$ the line-conic consisting of the tangent lines to $\mathcal{C}$, and $\mathcal{C}''$ the point-conic consisting of the points of contact of $\mathcal{C}'$, then $\mathcal{C}'' = \mathcal{C}$.

Proof: Statement (a) follows from the theorem and the principle of duality. To prove (b), let P be any point of $\mathcal{C}$. Then, P is on precisely one line ℓ_P of $\mathcal{C}'$, by Corollary 2 of Steiner's theorem (5.4.3). Thus, P is the point of contact on ℓ_P, when ℓ_P is considered as a line of $\mathcal{C}'$. Therefore, P is a point of $\mathcal{C}''$. Conversely, if Q is any point of $\mathcal{C}''$, then Q is on precisely one line, say $\ell_{Q'}$, of $\mathcal{C}'$. If $\ell_{Q'}$ is tangent to $\mathcal{C}$ at Q' (a point of $\mathcal{C}$), then Q' is the point of contact on $\ell_{Q'}$, as has already been shown. It follows that $Q' = Q$, since the point of contact on $\ell_{Q'}$

is unique by the dual of Corollary 2 of Steiner's theorem; thus, Q is a point of $\mathcal{C}$. We have proved that every point of $\mathcal{C}$ is a point of $\mathcal{C}''$, and conversely. Therefore, $\mathcal{C}'' = \mathcal{C}$. ▌

Corollary 2: Let $\mathcal{C}$ be a point-conic in a Pappian plane $\mathcal{P}$ of characteristic different from 2, and let P be any point of $\mathcal{P}$ that is not on $\mathcal{C}$. Then, either P lies on no tangent line to $\mathcal{C}$, or P lies on precisely two distinct tangent lines to $\mathcal{C}$.

Proof: Let $\mathcal{C}'$ be the line-conic consisting of the tangent lines to $\mathcal{C}$. Since P is not on $\mathcal{C}$, it is not a point of contact for any line of $\mathcal{C}'$, by Corollary 1 above. Therefore, either P is on no line of $\mathcal{C}'$, or P is on at least two distinct lines of $\mathcal{C}'$. Since no three lines of $\mathcal{C}'$ are concurrent (by Theorem 5.5.3), P cannot lie on more than two distinct lines of $\mathcal{C}'$, and the result follows. ▌

The theorem of Brianchon, to be proved next, closely resembles the dual of Pascal's theorem (which the reader should formulate). However, Brianchon's theorem concerns a point-conic, while the dual of Pascal's theorem concerns a line-conic. Moreover, Brianchon's theorem has content only for Pappian planes of characteristic different from 2.

Theorem 5.6.3. (Brianchon's theorem) In a Pappian plane of characteristic different from 2, if the sides of a simple hexagon are distinct tangent lines to a point-conic $\mathcal{C}$, the lines joining pairs of opposite vertices of the hexagon are concurrent.

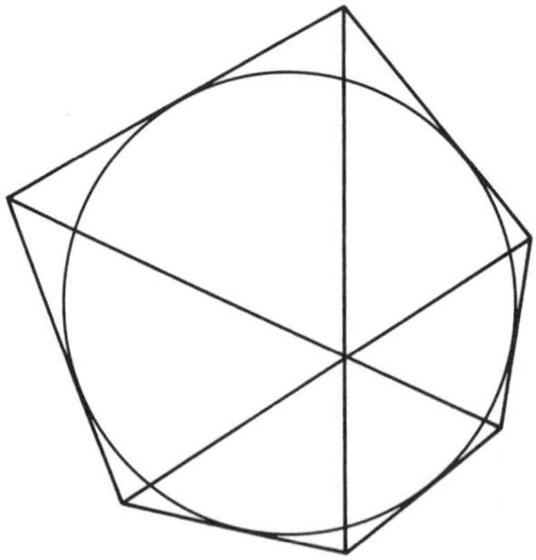

Figure 5.9

Proof: The tangent lines to $\mathcal{C}$ constitute a line-conic $\mathcal{C}'$, by Theorem 5.6.2. The sides of the hexagon are thus lines of $\mathcal{C}'$, and the theorem follows from the dual of Pascal's theorem. (Figure 5.9 illustrates Brianchon's theorem.) ∎

Exercise 5.6.A

1. Prove that Q, R, S of Lemma 5.6.1 are collinear by repeating the argument of that lemma with A and C exchanged and with B and D exchanged.

2. Suppose that $\mathcal{C}$ is a point-conic in a Pappian plane $\mathcal{P}$ of characteristic 2. Prove that there is a point of $\mathcal{P}$ that is not on $\mathcal{C}$ and that is incident with precisely one tangent line to $\mathcal{C}$.

3. Let $\mathcal{P}$ be a Pappian plane of characteristic different from 2, and suppose that a coordinate system has been constructed in $\mathcal{P}$. Let $\mathcal{C}$ be the point-conic in $\mathcal{P}$ with equation $y^2 = xz$ in this coordinate system. Let P be the point of $\mathcal{P}$ such that $[P] = [3, -2, 1]$. Find coordinate triples for the tangent lines to $\mathcal{C}$ that lie on P.

4. Let $\mathcal{C}$ be a point-conic in a Pappian plane $\mathcal{P}$ of characteristic different from 2, and let $\mathcal{T}$ be a triangle in $\mathcal{P}$ whose sides are tangent lines to $\mathcal{C}$. Prove that the lines joining the vertices of $\mathcal{T}$ to the points of contact on the opposite sides are concurrent. (Use the dual of the result in Exercise 5.5.4.)

5. In a Pappian plane of characteristic different from 2, suppose that M, N, U are vertices of a triangle whose sides, $N \cup U = \ell_A$, $M \cup U = \ell_B$, and $M \cup N = \ell_C$, are tangent lines to the point-conic $\mathcal{C}$ at A, B, C, respectively. Let $D = (A \cup C) \cap \ell_B$. Prove that $\mathcal{H}(B, D; M, U)$. (Use the result of exercise 4.)

Exercise 5.6.B

6. Let k, m, n be nonconcurrent lines in a Pappian plane $\mathcal{P}$ of characteristic different from 2. Suppose that A is a point on k different from $k \cap m$ and $k \cap n$, and that B is a point on m different from $m \cap k$ and $m \cap n$. Prove that there is a (unique) point-conic of $\mathcal{P}$ that contains A and B and that has k, m, n as tangent lines.

7. Give an analytic proof of Lemma 5.6.1.

8. Prove that every point-conic in $\mathcal{E}_2^*$ has interior points. (Interior point is defined in Exercise 5.5.9.)

9. Let $\mathcal{C}$ be a point-conic in $\mathcal{E}_2^*$, and let P be an interior point of $\mathcal{C}$. (See Exercise 5.5.9 and exercise 8.) Prove that every line of $\mathcal{E}_2^*$ that lies on P intersects $\mathcal{C}$ in two distinct points.

10. Let $\mathcal{C}$ be the point-conic whose construction was requested in Exercise 5.4.12. Use the information saved from that exercise to verify Brianchon's theorem for a certain simple hexagon in a 31-point plane.

5.7. Projectivities on a Conic

The fact that there is a natural one-to-one correspondence between the points of a point-conic $\mathcal{C}$ (in a Pappian plane) and the lines on any point of $\mathcal{C}$ leads us to make the following definition.

Definition 5.7.1. Let $\mathcal{C}$ be a point-conic in a Pappian plane, and let P be a point of $\mathcal{C}$. The function δ, from the set of points of $\mathcal{C}$ to the set of lines on P, defined by $X\delta = X \cup P$ if X is a point of $\mathcal{C}$ different from P, and $P\delta = \ell_P$, the tangent line to $\mathcal{C}$ at P, is a *generalized elementary correspondence*, and we write $\delta = \mathcal{C} \circ P$. ▮

The properties of point-conics guarantee that the function $\delta = \mathcal{C} \circ P$ is a bijection; the inverse of this function, written $\delta^{-1} = P \circ \mathcal{C}$, is also called a generalized elementary correspondence. (See exercise 1.) The generalized elementary correspondences $\delta_1 = P \circ \mathcal{C}$ and $\delta_2 = \mathcal{C} \circ Q$ can clearly be composed in the order given, and we write $\delta_1\delta_2 = P \circ \mathcal{C} \circ Q$. The next theorem is an immediate consequence of our definitions and Steiner's theorem (5.4.3).

Theorem 5.7.2. Let $\mathcal{C}$ be a point-conic in a Pappian plane, and let P, Q be points of $\mathcal{C}$. Then, the function $P \circ \mathcal{C} \circ Q$ is a projectivity.

Proof: If $P = Q$, then $P \circ \mathcal{C} \circ Q$ is the identity function on $\mathcal{J}(P)$. If $P \neq Q$, then $P \circ \mathcal{C} \circ Q = \pi$, the projectivity from P to Q that, together with P and Q, determines the conic $\mathcal{C}$. ▮

Corollary: If $\mathcal{C}$ is a point-conic in a Pappian plane, the function $k \circ P \circ \mathcal{C} \circ Q \circ \ell$, where k is not on P, ℓ is not on Q, and P and Q are points of $\mathcal{C}$, is a projectivity from k to ℓ. ▮

We now apply the idea of a generalized elementary correspondence to the proofs of two charming theorems.

Theorem 5.7.3. In a Pappian plane, let $\mathcal{T}_1$ and $\mathcal{T}_2$ be triangles with no common vertex and no common side. If the six vertices of these triangles are points of a point-conic $\mathcal{C}$, then the six sides of the triangles are lines of a line-conic, and conversely.

Proof: Let the vertices of $\mathfrak{T}_1$ be P, Q, R, and let the vertices of $\mathfrak{T}_2$ be S, T, U. Locate the additional points $V = (Q \cup R) \cap (S \cup U)$, $W = (Q \cup R) \cap (S \cup T)$, $X = (P \cup R) \cap (T \cup U)$, and $Y = (P \cup Q) \cap (T \cup U)$. (See Figure 5.10.) Let $m = R \cup Q$, $n = U \cup T$, and consider the projectivity ϕ, from m to n, given by $\phi = m \circ S \circ \mathcal{C} \circ P \circ n$. It is readily verified that $Q\phi = Y$, $V\phi = U$, $W\phi = T$, and $R\phi = X$. Since $Q \cup Q\phi$, $V \cup V\phi$, $W \cup W\phi$, and $R \cup R\phi$ are not concurrent (proof?), ϕ is *not* a perspectivity. Therefore, m, n, and ϕ determine a line-conic that contains the lines m, n, $Q \cup Y$, $V \cup U$, $W \cup T$, and $R \cup X$. We have thus proved the direct statement of the theorem; because the converse is the dual of the direct statement, it follows by the principle of duality. Observe that if the characteristic of $\mathcal{P}$ is not 2, the conclusion (of the direct statement) may also be phrased, "the six sides of the triangles are tangent lines to a point-conic." ▮

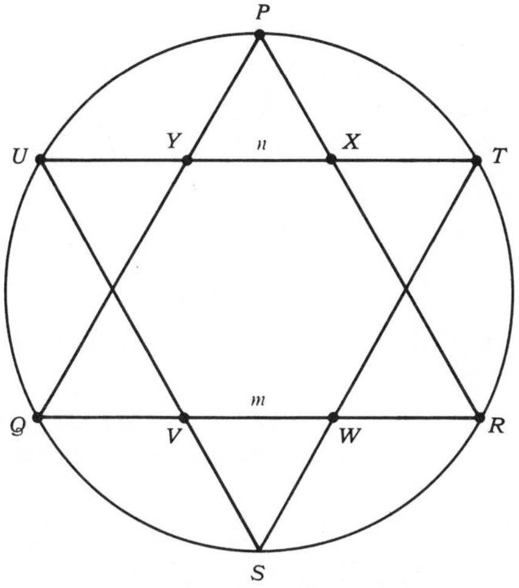

Figure 5.10

Theorem 5.7.4. (Desargues' Involution Theorem) Let $\mathcal{Q}$ be a complete quadrangle in a Pappian plane $\mathcal{P}$, and let ℓ be a line of $\mathcal{P}$ that lies on no vertex of $\mathcal{Q}$ and that does not lie on all three diagonal points of $\mathcal{Q}$ (if $\mathcal{P}$ happens to have characteristic 2). Then, of the point-conics that contain the vertices of $\mathcal{Q}$, those that intersect ℓ do so in pairs of points that correspond under a certain involutory projectivity on ℓ.

Proof: Refer to Figure 5.11, where P, Q, R, S are the vertices of $\mathcal{Q}$, ℓ is the given line, and T and U are the (not necessarily different) points in which a certain (arbitrarily selected) point-conic $\mathcal{C}$, containing P, Q, R, S, intersects ℓ. Since ℓ does not lie on all the diagonal points of $\mathcal{Q}$, we may suppose that the vertices of $\mathcal{Q}$ have been labeled in such a way that the diagonal point $(P \cup S) \cap (Q \cup R)$ is not on ℓ. Then, the points $A = (P \cup S) \cap \ell$ and $D = (Q \cup R) \cap \ell$ are different. Let $B = (Q \cup S) \cap \ell$ and $E = (P \cup R) \cap \ell$. By the Second Existence Theorem for Projectivities (1.7.3), there is a (unique, by the Fundamental Theorem) projectivity π on ℓ such that $A\pi = D$, $D\pi = A$, $B\pi = E$, and $E\pi = B$. By Exercise 5.1.12, π is an involution, since it exchanges the distinct points A and D. (Observe that the definition of the involutory projectivity π on ℓ is independent of the choice of the point-conic $\mathcal{C}$.)

Let $\phi = \ell \circ P \circ \mathcal{C} \circ Q \circ \ell$, a projectivity on ℓ by the corollary to Theorem 5.7.2. (The definition of ϕ depends upon the choice of $\mathcal{C}$.) Then, $A\phi = B$, $E\phi = D$, $T\phi = T$, and $U\phi = U$.

Suppose first that $\mathcal{C}$ intersects ℓ in two distinct points, T and U, as shown in Figure 5.11. By Theorem 1.7.3, there is a projectivity ψ on ℓ such that $B\psi = D$, $D\psi = B$, $T\psi = U$, and $U\psi = T$. Then, $A\phi\psi = B\psi = D$, $E\phi\psi = B$, $T\phi\psi = U$, and $U\phi\psi = T$. Since $\phi\psi$ exchanges the distinct points T and U, it is an involution, by Exercise 5.1.12. Therefore, $\phi\psi$ exchanges A with D and B with E; hence $\phi\psi = \pi$ (why?). It follows that $T\pi = T\phi\psi = U$, and $U\pi = U\phi\psi = T$, so that T and U are a pair of corresponding points under the involution π.

Next, suppose that $\mathcal{C}$ intersects ℓ in only one point, so that $T = U$. Because B, D, T are distinct, and B, D, $T\pi$ are distinct (why?), there is (also by Theorem 1.7.3) a projectivity ψ' on ℓ such that $B\psi' = D$, $D\psi' = B$, $T\psi' = T\pi$, and $(T\pi)\psi' = T$. Then, $A\pi\psi' = D\psi' = B = A\phi$, $E\pi\psi' = E\phi$, and $T\pi\psi' = T\phi$, where ϕ is the projectivity defined two paragraphs back. Since A, E, T are distinct, $\pi\psi' = \phi$; hence $\psi' = \pi^2\psi' = \pi\phi$, because π is an involution. Thus, $(T\pi)\phi = T\psi' = T\pi$, or $T\pi$ is a fixed point of ϕ. Because $\phi = \ell \circ P \circ \mathcal{C} \circ Q \circ \ell$, the projectivity $P \circ \mathcal{C} \circ Q$ must send $T\pi \cup P$ into $Q \cup T\pi$. Because P, Q, and $P \circ \mathcal{C} \circ Q$ determine $\mathcal{C}$, it follows that $T\pi$ is a point of $\mathcal{C}$. Therefore, $T\pi = T$, for we are assuming here that $\mathcal{C}$ intersects ℓ only in the point T.

Thus, we have shown that if $\mathcal{C}$ meets ℓ in two distinct points, these points are exchanged by the involution π, while if $\mathcal{C}$ meets ℓ in only one point, that point is a self-corresponding (fixed) point under π. Since a self-corresponding point may be regarded as a special case of a pair of corresponding points, the theorem is proved. ▮

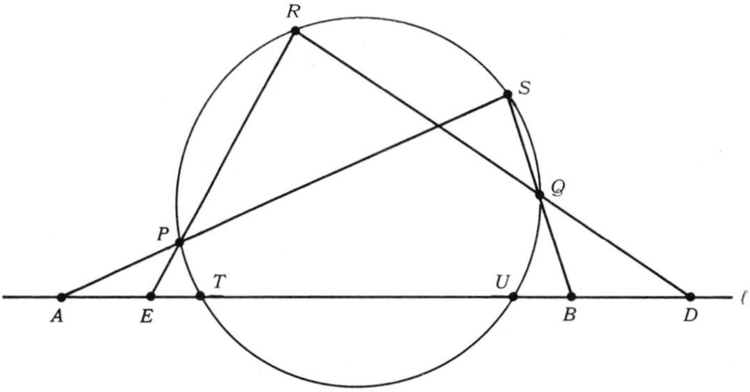

Figure 5.11

In closing this section, we present a definition of a useful class of bijections on a conic, obtained by composing projectivities with generalized elementary correspondences. Properties of these bijections are explored in the exercises.

Definition 5.7.5. Let $\mathcal{C}$ be a point-conic in a Pappian plane, and let P and Q be any points of $\mathcal{C}$. Let $\delta = \mathcal{C} \circ P$, $\epsilon = Q \circ \mathcal{C}$, and suppose that π is any projectivity from P to Q. Then, the function $\kappa = \delta\pi\epsilon$ is a *generalized projectivity* on $\mathcal{C}$. ▮

Exercise 5.7.A

1. Let $\mathcal{C}$ be a point-conic in a Pappian plane, let P, Q be any distinct points of $\mathcal{C}$, and let $\delta = \mathcal{C} \circ P$.

(a) Prove that δ is a bijection.

(b) State what δ^{-1} does to each line on P.

(c) If $\pi = P \circ \mathcal{C} \circ Q$, what are $\ell_P\pi$ and $(P \cup Q)\pi$, where ℓ_P is the tangent line to $\mathcal{C}$ at P?

2. Let $\mathcal{Q}$ be a complete quadrangle in a Pappian plane of characteristic 2, and let ℓ be the line on the diagonal points of $\mathcal{Q}$. If $\mathcal{C}$ is any point-conic that contains the vertices of $\mathcal{Q}$ and intersects ℓ, prove that $\mathcal{C}$ intersects ℓ in only one point.

3. Verify the conclusion in exercise 2 for a certain quadrangle $\mathcal{Q}$ in $\mathfrak{Z}_5$ and the line ℓ on its diagonal points.

4. Let $\mathcal{C}$ be a point-conic in a Pappian plane, and let κ and κ' be any generalized projectivities on $\mathcal{C}$.

(a) Prove that κ^{-1} is a generalized projectivity on $\mathcal{C}$.

(b) Prove that $\kappa\kappa'$ is a generalized projectivity on $\mathcal{C}$.

5. Let $\mathcal{C}$ be a point-conic in a Pappian plane $\mathcal{P}$, and suppose that σ is a projective collineation of $\mathcal{P}$ that maps $\mathcal{C}$ onto $\mathcal{C}$. Prove that the restriction of σ to the points of $\mathcal{C}$ is a generalized projectivity on $\mathcal{C}$.

Exercise 5.7.B

6. Let $\mathcal{C}$ be any point-conic in a Pappian plane. Suppose that A, B, C are any distinct points of $\mathcal{C}$, and that A', B', C' also are any distinct points of $\mathcal{C}$.

(a) If κ is a generalized projectivity on $\mathcal{C}$ that fixes A, B, and C, prove that κ is the identity function on $\mathcal{C}$.

(b) Prove that there is one and only one generalized projectivity on $\mathcal{C}$ that sends A into A', B into B', and C into C'.

7. Let $\mathcal{C}$ be a point-conic in a Pappian plane, and let κ be any generalized projectivity, other than the identity, on $\mathcal{C}$. Prove that there is a line ℓ (called the *axis* of κ) such that $(X \cup Y\kappa) \cap (Y \cup X\kappa)$ is on ℓ for every two distinct points X, Y of $\mathcal{C}$, where $X \cup Y\kappa$ is to be interpreted as the tangent line to $\mathcal{C}$ at X if $X = Y\kappa$, and similarly for $Y \cup X\kappa$.

8. Let κ be a generalized projectivity on a point-conic $\mathcal{C}$ in a Pappian plane. Prove that the invariant points (if there are any) of κ are precisely the points of intersection of the axis of κ (defined in exercise 7) with $\mathcal{C}$.

9. Let κ be a generalized projectivity on a point-conic $\mathcal{C}$ in a Pappian plane $\mathcal{P}$. Suppose that κ exchanges the distinct points A, A' of $\mathcal{C}$, and that κ also exchanges the distinct points B, B' of $\mathcal{C}$, where $B \neq A$ or A'.

(a) Prove that κ is an involution. (Use the results of exercises 4 and 6.)

(b) Prove that the axis of κ (defined in exercise 7) is the line on the points $(A \cup B') \cap (A' \cup B)$ and $(A \cup B) \cap (A' \cup B')$.

(c) Prove that there is a (unique) point O (called the *center* of κ) such that the line $X \cup X\kappa$ lies on O for every point X of $\mathcal{C}$ that is not fixed by κ.

10. Let $\mathcal{C}$ be a point-conic in a Pappian plane $\mathcal{P}$ of characteristic different from 2. Suppose that κ is a generalized projectivity on $\mathcal{C}$, that κ is an involution, and that at least four distinct points of $\mathcal{C}$ are not fixed by κ. Let ℓ be the axis (defined in exercise 7), and O the center (defined in exercise 9c), of κ.

(a) If X is any point of $\mathcal{C}$ that is not fixed by κ, prove that $\mathcal{H}(O, M; X, X\kappa)$, where $M = (O \cup X) \cap \ell$.

(b) Prove that κ can be extended to a harmonic homology of $\mathcal{P}$.

(c) Deduce that if F is a fixed point of κ, then ℓ_F (the tangent line to $\mathcal{C}$ at F) lies on O.

5.8. Pole and Polar

Throughout this section, $\mathcal{P}$ is an arbitrary Pappian plane of characteristic different from 2, $\mathcal{C}$ is an arbitrary point-conic in $\mathcal{P}$, and $\mathcal{C}'$ is the line-conic consisting of the tangent lines to $\mathcal{C}$ (Theorem 5.6.2). Furthermore, $\mathcal{K}$ will denote the union of $\mathcal{C}$ and $\mathcal{C}'$, and we call $\mathcal{K}$ a *complete conic;* observe that $\mathcal{K}$ is determined by either $\mathcal{C}$ or $\mathcal{C}'$. A line of $\mathcal{P}$ that intersects $\mathcal{C}$ in two distinct points is a *secant* of $\mathcal{C}$. An *interior* point of $\mathcal{C}$ is a point of $\mathcal{P}$ that lies on no tangent line to $\mathcal{C}$, while an *exterior* point of $\mathcal{C}$ is a point of $\mathcal{P}$ that is not on $\mathcal{C}$, and that lies on some tangent line to $\mathcal{C}$. (By Corollary 2 of Theorem 5.6.2, an exterior point of $\mathcal{C}$ lies on precisely two tangent lines to $\mathcal{C}$. Also, note that every point of $\mathcal{P}$ is either a point of $\mathcal{C}$, an interior point of $\mathcal{C}$, or an exterior point of $\mathcal{C}$.) We are going to show how the complete conic $\mathcal{K}$ induces an involution on $\mathcal{P}$ that sends points into lines and lines into points.

Theorem 5.8.1. With $\mathcal{P}$, $\mathcal{C}$ having the meanings stated above, let P be any point of $\mathcal{P}$ that is not on $\mathcal{C}$, and let k be an arbitrary secant of $\mathcal{C}$ that is on P. Suppose that k intersects $\mathcal{C}$ in the distinct points C and D. Let Q be the (unique) point on k such that $\mathcal{H}(P, Q; C, D)$. Then:

(a) If P is an exterior point of $\mathcal{C}$, Q lies on the line $\ell_P = A \cup B$, where A and B are the points of contact of the two tangent lines to $\mathcal{C}$ that lie on P.

(b) If P is an interior point of $\mathcal{C}$, there is a unique line ℓ_P such that Q is on ℓ_P for all positions of k.

Proof: (a) This part follows directly from the result in Exercise 5.5.7. (See Figure 5.12.)

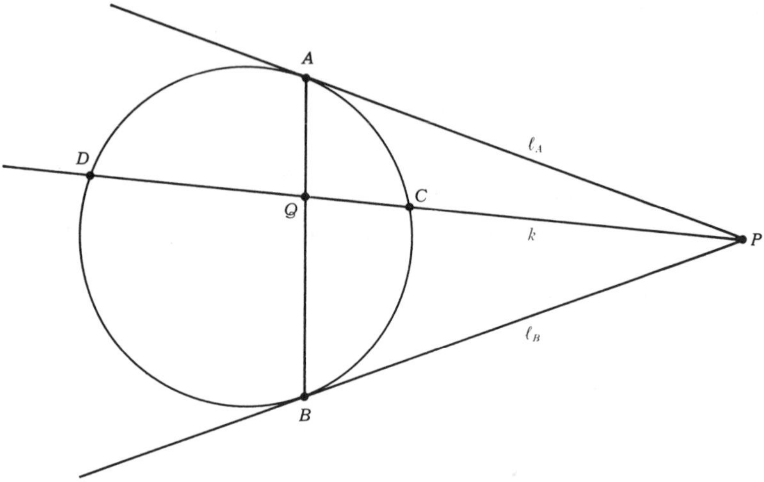

Figure 5.12

(b) Let m be a secant of $\mathcal{C}$ that is on P, and suppose that m intersects $\mathcal{C}$ in the distinct points A, B. Let ℓ_A, ℓ_B be the tangent lines to $\mathcal{C}$ at A, B, respectively, and let $H = \ell_A \cap \ell_B$. Assume first that $k \neq m$. (Since P is an interior point of $\mathcal{C}$, and since $\mathcal{C}$ has at least four points, there are at least two different secants of $\mathcal{C}$ that lie on P.) Construct $U = (A \cup D) \cap (C \cup B)$, $V = (A \cup C) \cap (B \cup D)$, $G = (U \cup V) \cap m$, and $X = (U \cup V) \cap k$. (See Figure 5.13.) Lemma 5.6.1 shows that H, U, V are collinear. The quadrangle $CDVU$ exhibits $\mathcal{H}(A, B; P, G)$, and the quadrangle $ABUV$ demonstrates that $\mathcal{H}(C, D; P, X)$. Since $\mathcal{H}(P, Q; C, D)$, which implies that $\mathcal{H}(C, D; P, Q)$, it follows that $Q = X$. The line $H \cup G$ is determined by the secant m and the condition $\mathcal{H}(A, B; P, G)$, and we have proved that Q lies on $H \cup G$ for every choice of $k \neq m$. If $k = m$, then $Q = G$, and Q lies on $H \cup G$ in this case, too. Thus, $H \cup G$ is the required line ℓ_P. The existence of at least two different secants of $\mathcal{C}$ on P implies the existence of at least two different points (like Q) on which ℓ_P *must* lie; therefore, ℓ_P is unique. ∎

We now define the *polar* of a point P with respect to the complete conic $\mathcal{K}$.

Definition 5.8.2. With $\mathcal{P}$, $\mathcal{C}$, $\mathcal{K}$ having the meanings stated at the beginning of this section, let P be any point of $\mathcal{P}$. Then:

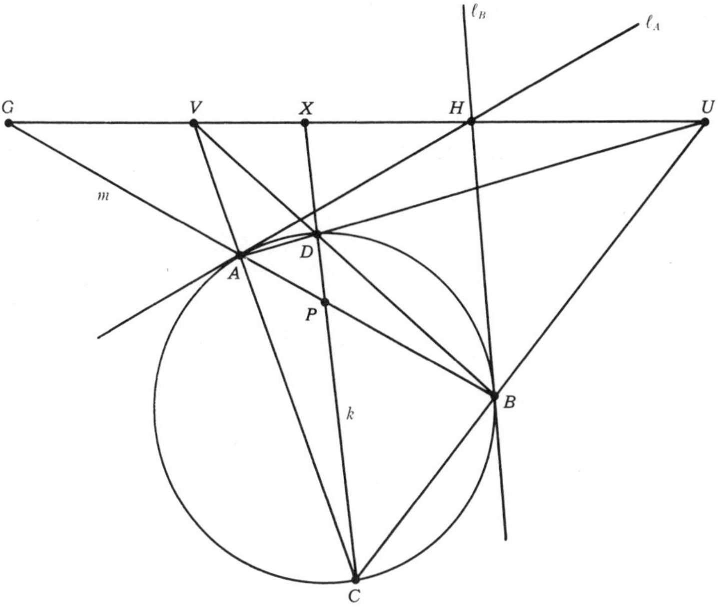

Figure 5.13

(a) If P is an exterior point of $\mathcal{C}$, the *polar* of P with respect to $\mathcal{K}$ is the line $\ell_P = A \cup B$, where A and B are the points of contact of the tangent lines to $\mathcal{C}$ that lie on P.

(b) If P is an interior point of $\mathcal{C}$, the *polar* of P with respect to $\mathcal{K}$ is the line ℓ_P given by part (b) of Theorem 5.8.1.

(c) If P is a point of $\mathcal{C}$, the *polar* of P with respect to $\mathcal{K}$ is the tangent line ℓ_P to $\mathcal{C}$ at P. ∎

If $\mathcal{P}$ is not a 13-point plane, and if P is not a point of $\mathcal{C}$, the polar of P with respect to $\mathcal{K}$ is determined in the manner of (b) of the above definition, whether P is interior or exterior to $\mathcal{C}$, according to Theorem 5.8.1. However, if $\mathcal{P}$ *is* a 13-point plane, and if P is an exterior point of $\mathcal{C}$, there is only one secant of $\mathcal{C}$ on P, therefore only one point Q of the kind mentioned in Theorem 5.8.1; hence, in this case, it takes at least one of the points A, B of (a) to determine the polar of P, and this is the reason for giving (a) separately in Definition 5.8.2. The concept dual to polar of a point is that of *pole* of a line with respect to a complete conic, and the two are related by the next theorem.

Theorem 5.8.3. With $\mathcal{P}$, $\mathcal{C}$, $\mathcal{C}'$, $\mathcal{K}$ having the meanings stated at the beginning of this section, let P be any point of $\mathcal{P}$. If ℓ_P is the polar of P with respect to $\mathcal{K}$, then P is the pole of ℓ_P with respect to $\mathcal{K}$.

Proof: (a) If P is an exterior point of $\mathcal{C}$, then ℓ_P intersects $\mathcal{C}$ in distinct points A, B. By the dual of Definition 5.8.2 (a), the pole of ℓ_P with respect to $\mathcal{K}$ is the point $\ell_A \cap \ell_B$, where ℓ_A and ℓ_B are the tangent lines to $\mathcal{C}$ at A and B. Since $\ell_A \cap \ell_B = P$, the pole of ℓ_P is P.

(b) If P is an interior point of $\mathcal{C}$, let A be any point of $\mathcal{C}$, let ℓ_A be the tangent line to $\mathcal{C}$ at A, and let $H = \ell_P \cap \ell_A$. Since H is an exterior point of $\mathcal{C}$ (it lies on ℓ_A), there is a point B of $\mathcal{C}$ such that $B \neq A$ and the tangent line ℓ_B to $\mathcal{C}$ at B lies on H. Since ℓ_P does not intersect $\mathcal{C}$ (exercise 1), and H is a point on ℓ_P that lies on two distinct lines of $\mathcal{C}'$, the pole of ℓ_P is on the line m such that $\mathcal{H}(\ell_P, m; \ell_A, \ell_B)$, by the dual of Definition 5.8.2 (b). (See exercise 2 for basic facts about harmonic sets of lines.) Refer to Figure 5.13, where ℓ_P is the line $G \cup H$. Because $\mathcal{H}(A, B; P, G)$ from the proof of Theorem 5.8.1 (b), it follows (exercise 2b) that $\mathcal{H}(H \cup A, H \cup B; H \cup P, H \cup G)$, or $\mathcal{H}(\ell_A, \ell_B, H \cup P, \ell_P)$, which implies that $\mathcal{H}(\ell_P, H \cup P; \ell_A, \ell_B)$ (exercise 2c). Therefore, $H \cup P = m$ (exercise 2d); hence P lies on every line m determined in the manner detailed above. Since there are at least two such lines (why?), P is the pole of ℓ_P with respect to $\mathcal{K}$.

(c) If P is a point of $\mathcal{C}$, then ℓ_P is a line of $\mathcal{C}'$. The pole of ℓ_P with respect to $\mathcal{K}$ is the point of contact on ℓ_P, by the dual of Definition 5.8.2 (c). Thus, the pole of ℓ_P is P. ▌

Corollary: Let $\mathcal{P}$ be a Pappian plane of characteristic different from 2, and let $\mathcal{K}$ be a complete conic in $\mathcal{P}$. The function ω on $\mathcal{P}$ that maps each point of $\mathcal{P}$ into its polar with respect to $\mathcal{K}$, and each line of $\mathcal{P}$ into its pole with respect to $\mathcal{K}$, is an involution on $\mathcal{P}$.

Proof: The simple proof of this corollary is left for exercise 3. ▌

The function ω of the preceding corollary is called the ***polarity*** induced by the complete conic $\mathcal{K}$, and it is a very useful tool for the study of conics, as we shall learn. The next theorem gives an important relation between ω and certain harmonic homologies associated with $\mathcal{K}$.

Theorem 5.8.4. With $\mathcal{P}$, $\mathcal{C}$, $\mathcal{K}$ having the meanings stated at the beginning of this section, let P be any point not on $\mathcal{C}$, and let ℓ_P be the polar of P with respect to $\mathcal{K}$. If η is the harmonic homology with center P, axis ℓ_P, then η transforms $\mathcal{K}$ into $\mathcal{K}$, and η commutes with the polarity ω induced by $\mathcal{K}$.

Proof: (1) To show that η maps $\mathcal{K}$ onto itself, let A be any point of $\mathcal{K}$ (that is, of $\mathcal{C}$). If $P \cup A$ is a tangent line to $\mathcal{C}$, then A is on ℓ_P, and is therefore fixed by η. If $P \cup A$ is not a tangent line to $\mathcal{C}$, it intersects $\mathcal{C}$ in another point B, and $\mathcal{H}(P, Q; A, B)$, where $Q = (P \cup A) \cap \ell_P$. Since η is harmonic and fixes P and Q, it exchanges A and B. Thus, the points of $\mathcal{K}$ are mapped onto points of $\mathcal{K}$, and a dual argument shows that lines of $\mathcal{K}$ are mapped onto lines of $\mathcal{K}$.

(2) To prove that η commutes with ω, let X be any point of $\mathcal{P}$. If X is an exterior point of $\mathcal{C}$, and if ℓ_A, ℓ_B are tangent lines to $\mathcal{C}$ at the distinct points A, B, respectively, that lie on X, then $\ell_A\eta$ and $\ell_B\eta$ are tangent lines to $\mathcal{C}$ at $A\eta$, $B\eta$ (Exercise 5.5.6), and $\ell_A\eta$, $\ell_B\eta$ lie on $X\eta$. Therefore, $(X\eta)\omega = A\eta \cup B\eta = (A \cup B)\eta = (X\omega)\eta$. If X is an interior point of $\mathcal{C}$, let m and n be distinct secants of $\mathcal{C}$ on X, intersecting $\mathcal{C}$ at C_1, D_1 and C_2, D_2, respectively. Let Q_1, Q_2 be such that $\mathcal{H}(X, Q_1; C_1, D_1)$ and $\mathcal{H}(X, Q_2; C_2, D_2)$. Then, $m\eta$ and $n\eta$ intersect $\mathcal{C}$ at $C_1\eta$, $D_1\eta$ and $C_2\eta$, $D_2\eta$, respectively, $m\eta$ and $n\eta$ lie on $X\eta$, and $\mathcal{H}(X\eta, Q_i\eta; C_i\eta, D_i\eta)$ for $i = 1, 2$. Therefore, $(X\eta)\omega = Q_1\eta \cup Q_2\eta = (Q_1 \cup Q_2)\eta = (X\omega)\eta$. Finally, if X is a point of $\mathcal{C}$, then $X\omega = \ell_X$, the tangent line to $\mathcal{C}$ at X. Also, $X\eta$ is on $\mathcal{C}$, and $\ell_X\eta$ is the tangent line to $\mathcal{C}$ at $X\eta$ (Exercise 5.5.6). Hence, $(X\eta)\omega = \ell_X\eta = (X\omega)\eta$.

Thus, for every point X in $\mathcal{P}$, $X\eta\omega = X\omega\eta$. A dual argument shows that $\ell\eta\omega = \ell\omega\eta$ for every line ℓ of $\mathcal{P}$. Therefore, $\eta\omega = \omega\eta$. Actually, more has been proved, for the above argument is valid for *any* collineation ρ of $\mathcal{P}$ that maps $\mathcal{K}$ onto $\mathcal{K}$, so that $\rho\omega = \omega\rho$ for any such collineation of $\mathcal{P}$. ∎

Corollary 1: With $\mathcal{P}$, $\mathcal{C}$, $\mathcal{K}$ having the meanings stated at the beginning of this section, let P and Q be points of $\mathcal{P}$. If Q is on the polar of P with respect to $\mathcal{K}$, then P is on the polar of Q with respect to $\mathcal{K}$.

Proof: If P is a point of $\mathcal{K}$, then the polar of P is ℓ_P, the tangent line to $\mathcal{C}$ at P. If Q is on ℓ_P, the polar of Q is on P by Definition 5.8.2 (a) if $Q \neq P$ and is ℓ_P, which is on P, if $Q = P$. If P is not a point of $\mathcal{K}$, let η be the harmonic homology with center P, axis $P\omega$, where ω is the polarity induced by $\mathcal{K}$. If Q is on $P\omega$ (the polar of P), then $Q\eta = Q$, and therefore $(Q\omega)\eta = (Q\eta)\omega = Q\omega$. Thus, $Q\omega$ is an invariant line of η; hence, either $Q\omega$ lies on P, or $Q\omega$ is the axis of η. But, the axis of η is $P\omega$, and $Q\omega = P\omega$ implies that $Q = P$, which is impossible, because P is not on $P\omega$, since P is not a point of $\mathcal{K}$ (exercise 4). Therefore, $Q\omega$ is on P, as required. ∎

Corollary 2: Let ω be the polarity induced by a complete conic $\mathcal{K}$ in a Pappian plane $\mathcal{P}$ of characteristic different from 2. Then, ω maps any pencil of points onto a pencil of lines and any pencil of lines onto a pencil of points.

Proof: Let ℓ be any line of $\mathcal{P}$. If X is on ℓ, then X is on $(\ell\omega)\omega$, the polar of $\ell\omega$ with respect to $\mathcal{K}$. Therefore, by Corollary 1, $\ell\omega$ is on $X\omega$, the polar of X with respect to $\mathcal{K}$. Thus, for every X on ℓ, $X\omega$ is on $\ell\omega$; hence ω maps the pencil $\mathcal{I}(\ell)$ onto the pencil $\mathcal{I}(\ell\omega)$. The second statement of this corollary follows by a dual argument. ▮

Definition 5.8.5. Let $\mathcal{P}$, $\mathcal{K}$ have the meanings stated at the beginning of this section. The point Q of $\mathcal{P}$ is *conjugate* to the point P, with respect to $\mathcal{K}$, if and only if Q lies on the polar of P with respect to $\mathcal{K}$. Dually, the line m of $\mathcal{P}$ is conjugate to the line n, with respect to $\mathcal{K}$, if and only if m lies on the pole of n with respect to $\mathcal{K}$. ▮

Because of Corollary 1 of Theorem 5.8.4, conjugacy with respect to $\mathcal{K}$ is a symmetric relation on the set of points of $\mathcal{P}$. In view of Theorem 5.8.3, it is also a symmetric relation on the set of lines of $\mathcal{P}$. Observe that a point is *self-conjugate* with respect to $\mathcal{K}$ if and only if it lies on its own polar, and is thus a point of $\mathcal{K}$ (exercise 4). Note also that the present use of the word conjugate is quite different from that of Definition 3.5.2.

Exercise 5.8.A

1. With $\mathcal{P}$, $\mathcal{C}$, $\mathcal{K}$ having the meanings stated at the beginning of this section, let P be any interior point of $\mathcal{C}$. Prove that the polar of P with respect to $\mathcal{K}$ does not intersect $\mathcal{C}$.

2. (a) Define a harmonic set of lines. (See Exercise 3.4.11a.)

(b) If $\mathcal{P}$ is a Desarguesian plane, and if $\mathcal{H}(A, B; C, D)$ in $\mathcal{P}$, prove that $\mathcal{H}(P \cup A, P \cup B; P \cup C, P \cup D)$ for any point P that is not on $A \cup B$. (Use the result of Exercise 3.3.8b.)

(c) Suppose that $\mathcal{H}(k, \ell; m, n)$ in a Desarguesian plane of characteristic different from 2. Prove that $\mathcal{H}(k, \ell; n, m)$, $\mathcal{H}(\ell, k; m, n)$, and $\mathcal{H}(m, n; k, \ell)$.

(d) If $\mathcal{P}$ is a Desarguesian plane of characteristic different from 2, prove that the first, third, and fourth lines of a harmonic set of lines in $\mathcal{P}$ uniquely determine the second line of the set.

3. Prove the corollary to Theorem 5.8.3.

In exercises 4 through 11, $\mathcal{P}$, $\mathcal{C}$, $\mathcal{K}$ have the meanings stated at the beginning of this section.

4. Prove that a point P of $\mathcal{P}$ is on its own polar with respect to $\mathcal{K}$ if and only if P is a point of $\mathcal{K}$.

5. Let ω be the polarity of $\mathcal{P}$ induced by $\mathcal{K}$.
   (a) Prove that ω preserves incidence.
   (b) Prove that $(P \cup Q)\omega = P\omega \cap Q\omega$, and $(k \cap \ell)\omega = k\omega \cup \ell\omega$, where P, Q are any distinct points of $\mathcal{P}$, and k, ℓ are any distinct lines of $\mathcal{P}$.

6. Prove that k and ℓ are conjugate lines with respect to $\mathcal{K}$ if and only if their poles with respect to $\mathcal{K}$ are conjugate points with respect to $\mathcal{K}$.

7. Let k be a line that intersects $\mathcal{C}$ in the distinct points P and Q. Prove that the distinct points A, B on k are conjugate points with respect to $\mathcal{K}$ if and only if $\mathcal{H}(P, Q; A, B)$.

Exercise 5.8.B

See the instructions for exercises 8 through 11 preceding exercise 4.

8. Let A and B be distinct points that are conjugate with respect to $\mathcal{K}$, and let k be a secant of $\mathcal{C}$ that lies on A but not on B. Suppose that k intersects $\mathcal{C}$ in Q and R, and that $B \cup Q$ and $B \cup R$ meet $\mathcal{C}$ again in S and P, respectively. Prove that A, S, P are collinear.

9. Given a point P of $\mathcal{P}$, show how to construct the polar of P with respect to $\mathcal{K}$.

10. If a quadrangle is inscribed in $\mathcal{C}$, prove that each side of its diagonal triangle is the polar (with respect to $\mathcal{K}$) of the opposite vertex of the diagonal triangle.

11. Let κ_1, κ_2 be different generalized projectivities on $\mathcal{C}$, both of which are involutions. (See Exercises 5.7.9 and 5.7.10.) For $i = 1, 2$, let O_i, ℓ_i be the center and axis of κ_i.
   (a) Prove that ℓ_i is the polar of O_i with respect to $\mathcal{K}$.
   (b) Prove that $\kappa_1\kappa_2 = \kappa_2\kappa_1$ if and only if O_1 and O_2 are conjugate points with respect to $\mathcal{K}$.

12. Let $\mathcal{C}$ be a point-conic in $\mathcal{E}_2^*$, and let $\mathcal{C}'$ be the set of points of

$\mathcal{C}$ in $\mathcal{E}_2$. Prove that either the ideal line is a tangent line to $\mathcal{C}$, or the Euclidean conic $\mathcal{C}'$ is centrally symmetric.

13. In this exercise, use the information saved from Exercises 2.5.11 and 5.4.12.

(a) Show that the homology of Exercise 2.5.11 maps the complete conic of Exercise 5.4.12 onto itself.

(b) Construct the polarity of the 31-point plane induced by the complete conic of Exercise 5.4.12.

(c) Verify that the polarity of part (b) commutes with the homology of Exercise 2.5.11.

5.9. Polarities

We commence with a definition suggested by the work of the last section.

Definition 5.9.1. Let $\mathcal{P}$ be an arbitrary projective plane.

(a) A *correlation* of $\mathcal{P}$ is a bijection on $\mathcal{P}$ that maps points into lines, lines into points, and an incident point and line into an incident line and point.

(b) A *projective correlation* of $\mathcal{P}$ is a correlation of $\mathcal{P}$ whose restriction to every pencil is a projectivity from that pencil to its image. ▮

Just as for collineations, a simpler criterion for projective correlations is the following (exercise 1): A correlation of $\mathcal{P}$ is projective if its restriction to a single pencil is a projectivity from that pencil to its image. By Exercise 5.8.5a, the polarity induced by a complete conic in a Pappian plane of characteristic different from 2 is a correlation, and the next theorem shows that it is a projective correlation.

Theorem 5.9.2. Let $\mathcal{C}$ be a point-conic in a Pappian plane $\mathcal{P}$ of characteristic different from 2, let $\mathcal{K}$ be the complete conic consisting of $\mathcal{C}$ and its set of tangent lines, and let ω be the polarity induced by $\mathcal{K}$. Then, ω is a projective correlation.

Proof: By the remarks immediately preceding the theorem, it is enough to prove that ω is projective for a single pencil of lines. Let P be an exterior point of $\mathcal{C}$, lying on the tangent lines ℓ_A, ℓ_B to $\mathcal{C}$ at the distinct points A, B, respectively. (See Figure 5.14.) Let η be the harmonic homology of $\mathcal{P}$ with center A, axis ℓ_B, and let π be the restriction of η to $\mathcal{G}(A \cup B)$. Then, $A\pi = A$, $B\pi = B$, and, for any other point X on $A \cup B$, $\mathcal{H}(A, B; X, X\pi)$. Construct the elementary correspondence $\delta = P \circ (A \cup B)$. Now, let k be any line on P, and set $Q = k\delta = k \cap (A \cup B)$. If $Q \neq A$ or B, let R be the point such that $\mathcal{H}(A, B; Q, R)$; then, R is on $Q\omega$ (why?), so that $R = Q\omega \cap (A \cup B) = Q\omega \cap P\omega = (Q \cup P)\omega = k\omega$. (See Exercise 5.8.5b.) But, also, $R = Q\pi$; hence $k\delta\pi = Q\pi = R$. Thus, $k\delta\pi = k\omega$ whenever $Q \neq A$ or B. If $Q = A$, then $k = \ell_A$, and $k\delta\pi = Q\pi = A\pi = A = \ell_A\omega = k\omega$; similarly, if $Q = B$, then $k\delta\pi = B = k\omega$. Therefore, the restriction of ω to $\mathcal{g}(P)$ is the projectivity $\delta\pi$. ∎

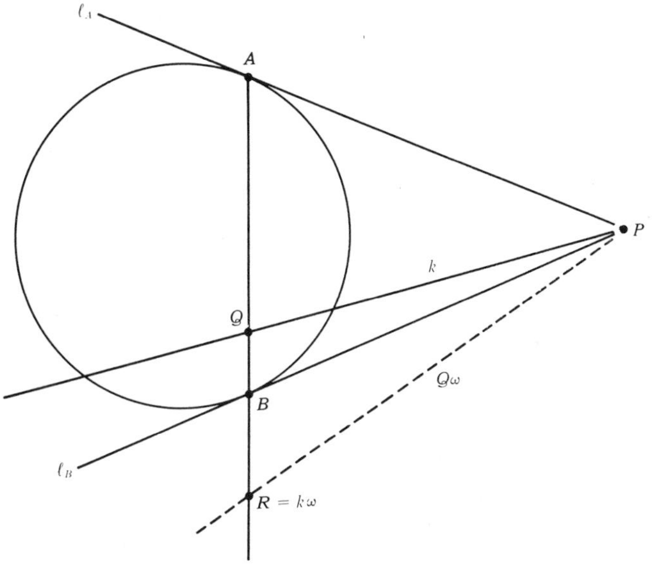

Figure 5.14

A polarity induced by a complete conic in a Pappian plane $\mathcal{P}$ of characteristic different from 2 is an involution in addition to being a projective correlation. This observation suggests the following generalization of the concept of polarity.

Definition 5.9.3. Let $\mathcal{P}$ be a projective plane.

(a) A ***polarity*** of $\mathcal{P}$ is a projective correlation of $\mathcal{P}$ of period two.

(b) If ω is a polarity of $\mathcal{P}$, and if P and ℓ are any point and line of $\mathcal{P}$, then $P\omega$ is the *polar* of P, and $\ell\omega$ the *pole* of ℓ, with respect to ω.

(c) If ω is a polarity of $\mathcal{P}$, and if Q is on $P\omega$, and ℓ is on $k\omega$, then Q is *conjugate* to P, and ℓ is conjugate to k, with respect to ω. ∎

The conjugacy relation of the above definition is symmetric; for, if Q is on $P\omega$, then $Q\omega$ is on $P\omega^2 = P$, and, if ℓ is on $k\omega$, then $\ell\omega$ is on $k\omega^2 = k$, since ω preserves incidence. If a point P lies on its own polar $P\omega$, it is *self-conjugate* with respect to the polarity ω, and dually for lines. The principle aim of this section is to show that every polarity with self-conjugate points in a Pappian plane of characteristic different from 2 is induced by a complete conic. We proceed to establish some of the properties of the self-conjugate points of a polarity.

Lemma 5.9.4. Let ω be a polarity of the projective plane $\mathcal{P}$. Then, each self-conjugate line of ω is incident with precisely one self-conjugate point of ω.

Proof: Let ℓ be any self-conjugate line of ω, and let $P = \ell\omega$; then, P is a self-conjugate point of ω (why?) and is on ℓ. *Suppose* that Q is a self-conjugate point of ω that lies on ℓ and is different from P. Since Q is on $P\omega$, P is on $Q\omega$; but, Q is also on $Q\omega$, by our assumption. Therefore, $Q\omega = P \cup Q = \ell = P\omega$, contradicting the fact that ω is one-to-one. Therefore, ℓ is incident with just one self-conjugate point of ω. ∎

Lemma 5.9.5. Let $\mathcal{P}$ be a Pappian plane of characteristic different from 2. Let ω be a polarity of $\mathcal{P}$, and suppose that P is a self-conjugate point of ω. Then, every line on P *except* $P\omega$ is incident with exactly two distinct self-conjugate points of ω.

Proof: Let ℓ be any line on P except $P\omega$. By the dual of the preceding lemma, ℓ is not self-conjugate with respect to ω (why?). Therefore, $\ell\omega$ is not on ℓ. Define $\delta = \ell\omega \circ \ell$, and let π be the function on $\mathcal{I}(\ell)$ defined by $Q\pi = Q\omega\delta = Q\omega \cap \ell$ for each Q on ℓ. Since the restriction of ω to $\mathcal{I}(\ell)$ is a projectivity, π is a projectivity on ℓ. If Q is on ℓ, and $Q\pi = Q$, then $Q = Q\omega \cap \ell$; hence Q is on $Q\omega$, or Q is self-conjugate with respect to ω. Conversely, if Q is on ℓ, and Q is self-conjugate with respect to ω, then $Q\omega \cap \ell = Q$, or $Q\pi = Q$. Thus, the self-conjugate points of ω on ℓ are precisely the fixed points of π, and we must show that π has exactly two distinct fixed points.

Since P is self-conjugate with respect to ω, $P\pi = P$; hence π is a Π_2 on ℓ, by Exercise 5.1.5. If Q is any point on ℓ, $Q\pi^2 = [(Q\omega \cap \ell)\omega] \cap \ell = (Q\omega^2 \cup \ell\omega) \cap \ell = (Q \cup \ell\omega) \cap \ell = Q$. (See Exercise 5.8.5b.) Therefore, $\pi^2 = \iota$, the identity projectivity on ℓ, so that either $\pi = \iota$, or π is an involution on ℓ. If π is an involution, it has exactly two distinct fixed points, because it is a Π_2, and because the characteristic of $\mathcal{P}$ is not 2. (Furnish details.) Thus, it only remains to be proved that $\pi \neq \iota$.

Suppose that $\pi = \iota$. Let k be any line on $\ell\omega$, and set $Q = k \cap \ell$; then, $k = Q \cup \ell\omega$. Since $Q = Q\pi = Q\omega \cap \ell$, it follows that $Q\omega = Q \cup \ell\omega = k$, and k is the self-conjugate line $Q\omega$. Hence, every line k on $\ell\omega$ is self-conjugate with respect to ω and, by Lemma 5.9.4, is incident with just one self-conjugate point of ω, which is evidently $k \cap \ell$. Because every point of $\mathcal{P}$ is on some line on $\ell\omega$, we see that all the self-conjugate points of ω lie on ℓ, which contradicts the fact (implicit in the argument of the first two paragraphs of this proof) that *every* line on P except $P\omega$ lies on at least one self-conjugate point of ω other than P. Therefore, it is not true that every point on ℓ is self-conjugate. Hence $\pi \neq \iota$, and the lemma is established. ▌

Lemma 5.9.6. Let $\mathcal{P}$ be a Desarguesian plane of characteristic different from 2. Let ω be a polarity of $\mathcal{P}$, and let O be a point of $\mathcal{P}$ that is not self-conjugate with respect to ω. Let η be the harmonic homology of $\mathcal{P}$ with center O, axis $O\omega$. Then, $\omega\eta = \eta\omega$. Furthermore, if P is any self-conjugate point of ω, then $P\eta$ is also a self-conjugate point of ω.

Proof: The bijection $\omega\eta\omega$ sends points into points, lines into lines, and preserves incidence. It is therefore a collineation of $\mathcal{P}$. If k is any line on O, then $k\omega$ is on $O\omega$; thus, $k\omega\eta = k\omega$, and $k\omega\eta\omega = k\omega^2 = k$. Hence, $\omega\eta\omega$ is central with center O, and a dual argument shows that its axis is $O\omega$. Also, $(\omega\eta\omega)^2 = \omega\eta\omega^2\eta\omega = \omega\eta^2\omega = \omega^2 = \iota$, so that either $\omega\eta\omega = \iota$, or $\omega\eta\omega$ is a harmonic homology of $\mathcal{P}$. But, $\omega\eta\omega = \iota$ implies that $\eta = \omega^2 = \iota$, which is not true, since the characteristic of $\mathcal{P}$ is not 2. Therefore, $\omega\eta\omega$ is the harmonic homology of $\mathcal{P}$ with center O, axis $O\omega$. It follows that $\omega\eta\omega = \eta$, or $\omega\eta = \eta\omega$. Finally, if P is any self-conjugate point of ω, then P lies on $P\omega$. Therefore, $P\eta$ lies on $(P\omega)\eta = (P\eta)\omega$, proving that $P\eta$ is also self-conjugate with respect to ω. ▌

The preceding lemmas show that if a polarity of a Pappian plane of characteristic different from 2 has any self-conjugate points, then its behavior is very much like that of a polarity induced by a complete conic. Thus, the stage is set for the main theorem of this section.

Theorem 5.9.7. Let $\mathcal{P}$ be a Pappian plane of characteristic different from 2, and let ω be a polarity of $\mathcal{P}$ with at least one self-conjugate point. Then, the self-conjugate points and lines of ω constitute a complete conic $\mathcal{K}$, and ω is the polarity induced by $\mathcal{K}$.

Proof: Let A be a self-conjugate point of ω, and let k be a line on A that is not self-conjugaee with respect to ω; such a line k exists by the dual of Lemma 5.9.4. Let B be the second self-conjugate point of ω on k, whose existence and uniqueness are guaranteed by Lemma 5.9.5. Let $H = A\omega \cap B\omega$; then, $H\omega = A \cup B = k$. Let C be a self-conjugate point of ω besides A and B; such a point C exists by Lemma 5.9.5, since there must be other non-self-conjugate lines on A besides k, and each one has another self-conjugate point on it besides A. Construct the harmonic homology η of $\mathcal{P}$, with center H, axis k, and set $D = C\eta$. Then, $D \neq C$, and D is also a self-conjugate point of ω, by Lemma 5.9.6. (Refer to Figure 5.15.)

Let $k' = C \cup D$, $H' = C\omega \cap D\omega = (C \cup D)\omega = k'\omega$. Since k' is on H $(= k\omega)$, H' $(= k'\omega)$ is on k. Let η' be the harmonic homology of $\mathcal{P}$ with center H', axis k'. Then, $A\eta'$ is on k, is different from A, and is a self-conjugate point of ω, by Lemma 5.9.6. Therefore, $A\eta' = B$. Let $M = k \cap k'$; then, $\mathcal{H}(H', M; A, B)$.

Since A, B, C are noncollinear and are self-conjugate with respect to ω, there is a unique point-conic $\mathcal{C}$ of $\mathcal{P}$ that contains A, B, C and has $A\omega$ and $B\omega$ as tangent lines (exercise 2). Thus, the complete conic $\mathcal{K}$ of $\mathcal{P}$ that $\mathcal{C}$ determines is the unique complete conic containing A, B, C, $A\omega$, and $B\omega$. Let ω_1 be the polarity of $\mathcal{P}$ induced by $\mathcal{K}$. Then, $A\omega_1 = A\omega$, and $B\omega_1 = B\omega$; hence, $k\omega_1 = (A \cup B)\omega_1 = A\omega \cap B\omega = H$, and $H\omega_1 = k = H\omega$. It follows that $k'\omega_1$ is on k, since $k\omega_1$ is on k'. Also, $k'\omega_1$ must be such that $\mathcal{H}(k'\omega_1, M; A, B)$; therefore, $k'\omega_1 = H'$. Now, $C\omega_1$ is on C (because C is a point of $\mathcal{C}$) and is also on $k'\omega_1 = H'$. Hence, $C\omega_1 = C \cup H' = C\omega$. We have learned that ω_1 agrees with ω on the triply noncollinear points A, B, C, and H. Thus, $\omega_1\omega^{-1}$ $(= \omega_1\omega)$ is a projective collineation (exercise 3b) that fixes A, B, C, and H, from which it follows (by the corollary to Theorem 5.1.1) that $\omega_1\omega^{-1} = \iota$ or $\omega_1 = \omega$.

It has been proved that ω is the polarity induced by the complete conic $\mathcal{K}$, and this implies that the self-conjugate elements of ω are precisely the elements of $\mathcal{K}$. ∎

There exist Pappian planes of characteristic different from 2 in which every polarity has self-conjugate points and is thus induced by a complete conic; examples are the complex projective plane and any finite Pappian plane of characteristic different from 2. There also exist

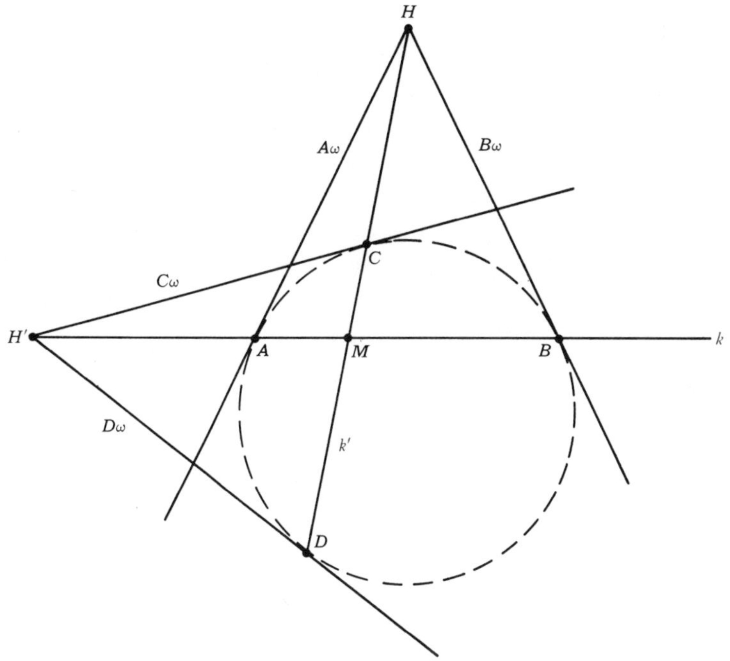

Figure 5.15

Pappian planes of characteristic different from 2 in which some polarities have no self-conjugate points; an example is $\mathcal{E}_2^*$ (Exercise 5.10.5). Thus, the hypothesis in the preceding theorem that ω have self-conjugate points is not redundant.

Exercise 5.9.A

1. Prove that a correlation of a projective plane is a projective correlation if its restriction to a single pencil is a projectivity from that pencil to its image.

2. Let ω be a polarity of a Pappian plane $\mathcal{P}$ of characteristic different from 2, and let A, B, C be distinct self-conjugate points of ω. Prove that there is a unique point-conic $\mathcal{C}$ of $\mathcal{P}$ that contains A, B, C and has $A\omega$ and $B\omega$ as tangent lines.

3. (a) Prove that the inverse of any projective correlation is a projective correlation.

(b) Prove that the composite of any two projective correlations of a projective plane $\mathcal{P}$ is a projective collineation of $\mathcal{P}$.

4. Let ω be a polarity of the projective plane $\mathcal{P}$, and let k, ℓ be any lines of $\mathcal{P}$ that are not conjugate with respect to ω. (Thus, if Q is on k, $Q\omega \neq \ell$.) Let a function π, from $\mathcal{I}(k)$ to $\mathcal{I}(\ell)$, be defined as follows: $Q\pi = Q\omega \cap \ell$ for each point Q on k. Prove that π is a projectivity.

5. Let ω be a polarity of the projective plane $\mathcal{P}$, and let ρ be any collineation of $\mathcal{P}$ that commutes with ω. If A and k are any self-conjugate point and line of ω, prove that $A\rho$ and $k\rho$ are also self-conjugate with respect to ω.

6. Let $\mathcal{C}$ be a point-conic in a Pappian plane $\mathcal{P}$. Prove that the image of $\mathcal{C}$ under any correlation of $\mathcal{P}$ is a line-conic.

Exercise 5.9.B

In exercises 7 through 11, $\mathcal{P}$ is a Pappian plane of characteristic different from 2.

7. Let ω be a polarity of $\mathcal{P}$. Prove that there is a triangle ABC (called a *self-polar triangle* for ω) such that $A\omega = B \cup C$, $B\omega = C \cup A$, and $C\omega = A \cup B$. (It follows that $(B \cup C)\omega = A$, $(C \cup A)\omega = B$, and $(A \cup B)\omega = C$.)

8. Let $\mathcal{Q}$ be any quadrangle, and $\mathcal{Q}'$ any quadrilateral, in $\mathcal{P}$. Prove that there is a unique projective correlation of $\mathcal{P}$ that maps the vertices of $\mathcal{Q}$ onto the sides of $\mathcal{Q}'$ in a specified order.

9. Let $\mathcal{C}$ be any point-conic, and $\mathcal{C}'$ any line-conic, in $\mathcal{P}$. Prove that there is a projective correlation of $\mathcal{P}$ that maps $\mathcal{C}$ onto $\mathcal{C}'$.

10. Let ω_1 and ω_2 be distinct polarities of $\mathcal{P}$, and put $\sigma = \omega_1\omega_2$. Prove that σ is a harmonic homology if and only if $\omega_1\omega_2 = \omega_2\omega_1$.

11. Prove Seydewitz's theorem for $\mathcal{P}$: If A, B, C are distinct self-conjugate points of a polarity ω of $\mathcal{P}$, then any line that is conjugate (with respect to ω) to a side of triangle ABC meets the other two sides in points that are conjugate with respect to ω.

5.10. Equations of Polarities

Suppose that $\mathcal{P}$ is a Pappian plane in which a coordinate system has been established (as in Section 4.2). Let X be any point of $\mathcal{P}$, and suppose that $[x, y, z]$ is a triple for X in the given coordinate system. Let x be the line of $\mathcal{P}$ such that

$$[x] = \begin{bmatrix} x \\ y \\ z \end{bmatrix}.$$

Since any triple for X has the form $[rx, ry, rz]$ for some $r \neq 0$, and because the commutativity of multiplication in $\mathcal{R}$ (the field associated with $\mathcal{P}$) ensures that

$$\begin{bmatrix} rx \\ ry \\ rz \end{bmatrix} = \begin{bmatrix} xr \\ yr \\ zr \end{bmatrix} = \begin{bmatrix} x \\ y \\ z \end{bmatrix} r ,$$

the line x is independent of the choice of a triple for X. Thus, the equation $X\alpha = x$, where $[X] = [x, y, z]$, and x is the line such that

$$[x] = \begin{bmatrix} x \\ y \\ z \end{bmatrix},$$

describes a well-defined function α from the points of $\mathcal{P}$ to the lines of $\mathcal{P}$, and α is clearly a bijection. Dually, the equation $x\beta = X$, where

$$[x] = \begin{bmatrix} x \\ y \\ z \end{bmatrix},$$

and X is the point such that $[X] = [x, y, z]$, describes a well-defined bijection β from the lines of $\mathcal{P}$ to the points of $\mathcal{P}$.

Let Ω be the function on $\mathcal{P}$ that extends both α and β; that is, $X\Omega = X\alpha$, and $x\Omega = x\beta$, for every point X and line x of P. Then, Ω is a bijection on P that maps points into lines and lines into points. Furthermore, Ω preserves incidence; for, if P and k are an incident point and line, with $[P] = [p, q, r]$ and

$$[k] = \begin{bmatrix} k \\ m \\ n \end{bmatrix},$$

then $pk + qm + rn = 0$; thus $kp + mq + nr = 0$, implying that $k\Omega$ and $P\Omega$ are incident. Therefore, Ω is a correlation of $\mathcal{P}$, and it is easily proved to be projective (exercise 1). It is also clear that $\Omega^2 = \iota$, the identity function on $\mathcal{P}$. Hence, Ω is a polarity, called the *coordinate polarity* determined by the given coordinate system in $\mathcal{P}$. (Observe that different coordinate systems may determine different coordinate polarities.)

In order to give analytic expression to the coordinate polarity Ω, we evidently need a symbolic way of indicating the operation of converting a row-triple into a column-triple, or a column-triple into a row-triple. Accordingly, we define $[x, y, z]^\dagger$ to be

$$\begin{bmatrix} x \\ y \\ z \end{bmatrix}, \quad \text{and} \quad \begin{bmatrix} x \\ y \\ z \end{bmatrix}^\dagger$$

to be $[x, y, z]$. Then, Ω can be represented by the equations $[X\Omega] = [X]^\dagger$, $[x\Omega] = [x]^\dagger$. More generally, if $\boldsymbol{\beta}$ is any matrix with elements in $\mathcal{R}$, we define $\boldsymbol{\beta}^\dagger$ to be the matrix obtained by *transposing* $\boldsymbol{\beta}$; that is, the element in row j, column i of $\boldsymbol{\beta}^\dagger$ is the element in row i, column j of $\boldsymbol{\beta}$. Because of the commutativity of multiplication in $\mathcal{R}$, $(\boldsymbol{\beta\gamma})^\dagger = \boldsymbol{\gamma}^\dagger\boldsymbol{\beta}^\dagger$ whenever the product of the matrices $\boldsymbol{\beta}$, $\boldsymbol{\gamma}$ is defined (exercise 2a). In particular, if $\mathbf{X}$ is a row-triple (a one-by-three matrix), $\mathbf{x}$ a column-triple (a three-by-one matrix), and $\boldsymbol{\sigma}$ a nonsingular, three-by-three matrix, $(\mathbf{X}\boldsymbol{\sigma})^\dagger = \boldsymbol{\sigma}^\dagger\mathbf{X}^\dagger$, and $(\boldsymbol{\sigma}^{-1}\mathbf{x})^\dagger = \mathbf{x}^\dagger(\boldsymbol{\sigma}^{-1})^\dagger$. These observations lead to the analytic characterization of projective correlations of Pappian planes provided by the next theorem.

Theorem 5.10.1. Let $\mathcal{P}$ be a Pappian plane with a given coordinate system, and let χ be any projective correlation of $\mathcal{P}$. Then, χ is described by the equations $[X\chi] = \boldsymbol{\sigma}^\dagger[X]^\dagger$, $[x\chi] = [x]^\dagger(\boldsymbol{\sigma}^\dagger)^{-1}$, where $\boldsymbol{\sigma}$ is some nonsingular three-by-three matrix, and X, x are an arbitrary point and line of $\mathcal{P}$.

Proof: Let Ω be the coordinate polarity of $\mathcal{P}$ determined by the given coordinate system, and let $\sigma = \chi\Omega$. Then, σ is a projective collineation of $\mathcal{P}$; hence, by Theorem 4.6.5, $[X\sigma] = [X]\boldsymbol{\sigma}$, and $[x\sigma] = \boldsymbol{\sigma}^{-1}[x]$ for some nonsingular three-by-three matrix $\boldsymbol{\sigma}$. Because $\chi = \chi\Omega^2 = \sigma\Omega$, it follows that $[X\chi] = [X\sigma\Omega] = [X\sigma]^\dagger = ([X]\boldsymbol{\sigma})^\dagger = \boldsymbol{\sigma}^\dagger[X]^\dagger$, and $[x\chi] = [x\sigma\Omega] = [x\sigma]^\dagger = (\boldsymbol{\sigma}^{-1}[x])^\dagger = [x]^\dagger(\boldsymbol{\sigma}^{-1})^\dagger$. Since $(\boldsymbol{\sigma}^{-1})^\dagger = (\boldsymbol{\sigma}^\dagger)^{-1}$ (exercise 2b), the theorem is proved. ∎

The results of Section 4.7 make it possible to write equations for all correlations of any Pappian plane (exercise 3). However, the information of the above theorem is ample for our present purpose, which is to give an analytic characterization of the class of polarities of a Pappian plane. Suppose that $\mathcal{P}$ is a Pappian plane with a given coordinate system, and that χ is a projective correlation of $\mathcal{P}$, described by $[X\chi] = \boldsymbol{\sigma}^\dagger[X]^\dagger$, $[x\chi] = [x]^\dagger(\boldsymbol{\sigma}^\dagger)^{-1}$. (We call $\boldsymbol{\sigma}$ a point-matrix for χ.) Then, χ^2 is a collineation that is (partially) described by $[X\chi^2] = [(X\chi)\chi] = [X\chi]^\dagger(\boldsymbol{\sigma}^\dagger)^{-1} = (\boldsymbol{\sigma}^\dagger[X]^\dagger)^\dagger(\boldsymbol{\sigma}^\dagger)^{-1} = [X]\boldsymbol{\sigma}(\boldsymbol{\sigma}^\dagger)^{-1}$. Now, χ is a polarity if and only if $\chi^2 = \iota$, and, from the equation in the preceding sentence, the necessary and sufficient condition for $\chi^2 = \iota$ is that $\boldsymbol{\sigma}(\boldsymbol{\sigma}^\dagger)^{-1} = s\boldsymbol{\iota}$ for some $s \neq 0$, or, equivalently, $\boldsymbol{\sigma} = s\boldsymbol{\sigma}^\dagger$. The only possible value of s, however, is $s = 1$ (exercise 4), and the condition is therefore that of the next theorem.

Theorem 5.10.2. Let $\mathcal{P}$ be a Pappian plane, χ a projective correlation of $\mathcal{P}$. Then χ is a polarity if and only if a (point-) matrix for χ (relative to a given coordinate system in $\mathcal{P}$) is *symmetric*. That is, if $\boldsymbol{\sigma}$ is a point-matrix for χ, χ is a polarity if and only if $\boldsymbol{\sigma} = \boldsymbol{\sigma}^\dagger$. ▮

Suppose that ω is a polarity of the Pappian plane $\mathcal{P}$. What does it mean for the point P of $\mathcal{P}$ to be self-conjugate with respect to ω? It means simply that P lies on $P\omega$. Thus, if a coordinate system is given in $\mathcal{P}$, and if $\boldsymbol{\omega}$ is a (point-) matrix for ω relative to this coordinate system, the point P is self-conjugate with respect to ω if and only if $[P]\cdot[P\omega] = 0$, or $[P]\cdot(\boldsymbol{\omega}^\dagger[P]^\dagger) = 0$, or (since $\boldsymbol{\omega}^\dagger = \boldsymbol{\omega}$) $[P]\cdot(\boldsymbol{\omega}[P]^\dagger) = 0$.

Theorem 5.10.3. Let $\mathcal{P}$ be a Pappian plane with a given coordinate system. Suppose that ω is a polarity of $\mathcal{P}$, and that

$$\boldsymbol{\omega} = \begin{bmatrix} a & f & g \\ f & b & h \\ g & h & c \end{bmatrix}$$

is a point-matrix for ω relative to this coordinate system. Then, if X is any point of $\mathcal{P}$, with $[X] = [x, y, z]$, X is a self-conjugate point of ω if and only if $[X]\cdot(\boldsymbol{\omega}[X]^\dagger) = 0$. Written in full, this condition is the following.

5.10.4. $ax^2 + by^2 + cz^2 + 2fxy + 2gxz + 2hyz = 0.$ ▮

Corollary: In a Pappian plane $\mathcal{P}$ of characteristic different from 2, any point-conic has an equation of the form of 5.10.4. Conversely, 5.10.4 is an equation of a point-conic in $\mathcal{P}$ provided that it has at least one solution point in $\mathcal{P}$, and provided that the matrix

$$\boldsymbol{\omega} = \begin{bmatrix} a & f & g \\ f & b & h \\ g & h & c \end{bmatrix}$$

is nonsingular.

Proof: Let $\mathcal{C}$ be a point-conic in $\mathcal{P}$, let $\mathcal{K}$ be the complete conic that $\mathcal{C}$ determines, and let ω be the polarity induced by $\mathcal{K}$. Since $\mathcal{C}$ is precisely the set of self-conjugate points of ω, $\mathcal{C}$ has an equation of the form 5.10.4, by the theorem. Conversely, if $\boldsymbol{\omega}$ is a nonsingular matrix, it is a point-matrix for a polarity ω of $\mathcal{P}$; if, further, Equation 5.10.4 has a solution point in $\mathcal{P}$, ω has a self-conjugate point. Hence the self-conjugate points of ω constitute a point-conic $\mathcal{C}$ (by Theorem 5.9.7), and 5.10.4 is an equation for $\mathcal{C}$. ∎

The above theorem and its corollary provide extremely powerful analytic tools for the investigation of correlations and collineations of Pappian planes and for the investigation of conics in Pappian planes of characteristic different from 2. This book ends with a collection of exercises in which some of the possibilities are explored.

Exercise 5.10.A

1. Prove that any coordinate polarity of a Pappian plane is a *projective* correlation.

2. (a) If $\boldsymbol{\beta}$ and $\boldsymbol{\gamma}$ are matrices over the field $\mathcal{R}$ such that the product $\boldsymbol{\beta\gamma}$ is defined, prove that $(\boldsymbol{\beta\gamma})^{\dagger} = \boldsymbol{\gamma}^{\dagger}\boldsymbol{\beta}^{\dagger}$. (The product $\boldsymbol{\beta\gamma}$ is defined in the way that we have learned in Section 4.5 provided that the number of columns of $\boldsymbol{\beta}$ is equal to the number of rows of $\boldsymbol{\gamma}$.)
(b) If $\boldsymbol{\beta}$ is a nonsingular matrix over the field $\mathcal{R}$, prove that $(\boldsymbol{\beta}^{-1})^{\dagger} = (\boldsymbol{\beta}^{\dagger})^{-1}$.

3. If χ is any correlation of the Pappian plane $\mathcal{P}$, prove that χ is described (relative to a given coordinate system in $\mathcal{P}$) by the equations $[X\chi] = \boldsymbol{\sigma}^{\dagger}([X]^{\dagger}\Theta)$, $[x\chi] = ([x]^{\dagger}\Theta)(\boldsymbol{\sigma}^{\dagger})^{-1}$ where $\boldsymbol{\sigma}$ is some nonsingular three-by-three matrix, and Θ is some automorphism of $\mathcal{R}$. Also, prove that χ is projective if and only if Θ is the identity automorphism.

4. Suppose that $\boldsymbol{\sigma}$ is a three-by-three matrix over the field $\mathcal{R}$, that $\boldsymbol{\sigma}$ has at least one nonzero element, and that $\boldsymbol{\sigma} = s\boldsymbol{\sigma}^{\dagger}$ for some $s \neq 0$ in $\mathcal{R}$. Prove that $s = 1$ or -1. Further, if $\boldsymbol{\sigma}$ is nonsingular, prove that $s = 1$.

5. Let any coordinate system be given in $\mathcal{E}_2{}^*$. Prove that the coordinate polarity determined by this coordinate system has no self-conjugate points.

6. Let $\mathcal{P}$ be a Pappian plane. Prove that any projective correlation of $\mathcal{P}$ that maps the vertices of a certain triangle onto the respectively opposite sides is a polarity.

7. Let $\mathcal{P}$ be any Pappian plane.

(a) Establish the result given in Exercise 5.9.8 for $\mathcal{P}$. (In Exercise 5.9.8, the conclusion is asserted only for Pappian planes of characteristic different from 2.)

(b) Use the results of part (a) and exercise 6 to prove that there is a unique polarity of $\mathcal{P}$ that has a given triangle as a self-polar triangle and that maps a given point, not on any side of the triangle, into a prescribed line, not on any vertex of the triangle.

Exercise 5.10.B

8. Prove Chasles' theorem: Let ω be a polarity of the Pappian plane $\mathcal{P}$, and suppose that ABC is a triangle in $\mathcal{P}$ that is not self-polar with respect to ω. Then, ABC and its polar triangle (with respect to ω) are perspective from a point.

9. Let $\mathcal{C}$ be a point-conic in a Pappian plane $\mathcal{P}$ of characteristic different from 2, and let P, Q, R, S be distinct points of $\mathcal{C}$. Prove that a coordinate system can be constructed in $\mathcal{P}$ in which $[P] = [1, 1, 1]$, $[Q] = [1, -1, 1]$, $[R] = [1, 1, -1]$, and $[S] = [1, -1, -1]$. Also, show that, relative to this coordinate system, $\mathcal{C}$ has the equation $ax^2 + by^2 + cz^2 = 0$, where a, b, c are some numbers of $\mathcal{R}$, all different from 0, and $a + b + c = 0$.

10. Let $\mathcal{P}$ be a Pappian plane of characteristic different from 2. Let P, Q, R, S be triply noncollinear points of $\mathcal{P}$, and suppose that $\mathcal{C}_1$ and $\mathcal{C}_2$ are point-conics of $\mathcal{P}$, both containing P, Q, R, S. Finally, assume that the tangent lines to $\mathcal{C}_1$ at P and Q intersect at a point of $\mathcal{C}_2$. Prove that the tangent lines to $\mathcal{C}_1$ at R and S also meet at a point of $\mathcal{C}_2$. (Use the result of exercise 9.)

11. (a) Let $\mathcal{R}$ be the field of four elements associated with $\mathfrak{A}_5$. Prove that every element of $\mathcal{R}$ has a unique square root.

(b) Use the result of part (a) to show that if ω is a polarity of a 21-point plane, the self-conjugate points of ω are collinear.

12. Let $\mathcal{C}$ be a point-conic in a Pappian plane $\mathcal{P}$ of characteristic 2, and suppose that a coordinate system in $\mathcal{P}$ is given. Use Theorem 5.5.2 and the result of Exercise 5.5.8 to prove that $\mathcal{C}$ has a homogeneous quadratic equation relative to the given coordinate system.

5. Pappian Planes

13. Let $\mathcal{P}$ be any Pappian plane. Prove that every central collineation of $\mathcal{P}$ is a composite of two polarities. Deduce that every projective collineation of $\mathcal{P}$ is a composite of polarities.

14. Suppose that ω is a polarity of the Pappian plane $\mathcal{P}$, and that two coordinate systems, related by a linear transformation, are given in $\mathcal{P}$. Let $\boldsymbol{\omega}_i$ $(i = 1, 2)$ denote a point-matrix for ω in the ith coordinate system, and let the coordinate transformation be described by $[\boldsymbol{X}]_1 = [\boldsymbol{X}]_2\boldsymbol{\beta}$, where $\boldsymbol{\beta}$ is a certain nonsingular three-by-three matrix, and $[\boldsymbol{X}]_i$ denotes a triple for X in the ith coordinate system. Prove that $\boldsymbol{\omega}_2 = s\boldsymbol{\beta}\boldsymbol{\omega}_1\boldsymbol{\beta}^{\dagger}$ for some $s \neq 0$ in $\mathcal{R}$.

15. Let $\mathcal{P}$ be a Pappian plane of characteristic different from 2 in which a coordinate system is given. Suppose that $\mathcal{C}$ is a point-conic of $\mathcal{P}$, and that 5.10.4 is an equation for $\mathcal{C}$. If $[p, q, r]$ is a triple for a certain point P of $\mathcal{C}$, find a triple for ℓ_P, the tangent line to $\mathcal{C}$ at P.

BIBLIOGRAPHY

[1] Artin, E., *Geometric Algebra,* Interscience, New York, 1957.

[2] Baer, R., *Linear Algebra and Projective Geometry,* Academic Press, New York, 1952.

[3] ———, "Polarities in Finite Projective Planes," *Bull. Amer. Math. Soc.* **52** 77–93 (1946).

[4] Blumenthal, L. M., *A Modern View of Geometry,* W. H. Freeman, San Francisco, 1961.

[5] Coxeter, H. S. M., *Introduction to Geometry,* Wiley, New York, 1961.

[6] ———, *Projective Geometry,* Blaisdell, Boston, 1964.

[7] ———, *The Real Projective Plane,* Cambridge University Press, Cambridge, 1960.

[8] Dorwart, H. L., *The Geometry of Incidence,* Prentice-Hall, Englewood Cliffs, N.J., 1966.

[9] Eves, H., *A Survey of Geometry,* Vol. 1, Allyn and Bacon, Boston, 1963.

[10] Fishback, W. T., *Projective and Euclidean Geometry,* Wiley, New York, 1962.

[11] Hall, Marshall, Jr., "Cyclic Projective Planes," *Duke Math. J.* **14** 1079–1090 (1947).

[12] ———, "Finite Projective Planes," *Amer. Math. Monthly Suppl.* **62** 18–24 (1955).

[13] ———, *The Theory of Groups,* Macmillan, New York, 1959.

[14] ———, "Uniqueness of the Projective Plane with 57 Points," *Proc. Amer. Math. Soc.* **4** 912–916 (1953); "Correction to: 'Uniqueness of the Projective Plane with 57 Points,'" *Proc. Amer. Math. Soc.* **5** 994–997 (1954).

[15] Hausner, M., *A Vector Space Approach to Geometry,* Prentice-Hall, Englewood Cliffs, N.J., 1965.

[16] Herstein, I. N., *Topics in Algebra,* Blaisdell, Boston, 1964.

[17] Heyting, A., *Axiomatic Projective Geometry,* Interscience, New York, 1963.

[18] Hilbert, D. and S. Cohn-Vossen, *Geometry and the Imagination,* Chelsea, New York, 1952.

[19] Jenner, W. E., *Rudiments of Algebraic Geometry,* Oxford University Press, New York, 1963.

[20] Levenberg, K., "A Class of Non-Desarguesian Plane Geometries," *Amer. Math. Monthly,* **57** 381–387 (1950).

[21] Maxwell, E. A., *The Methods of Plane Projective Geometry,* Cambridge University Press, Cambridge, 1960.

[22] Pedoe, D., *An Introduction to Projective Geometry,* Macmillan, New York, 1963.

[23] Pickert, G., *Projective Ebenen,* Springer-Verlag, Berlin, 1955.

[24] Prenowitz, W. and M. Jordan, *Basic Concepts of Geometry,* Blaisdell, Boston, 1965.

[25] Ryser, H. J., "Geometries and Incidence Matrices," *Amer. Math. Monthly Suppl.* **62** 25–31 (1955).

[26] Seidenberg, A., *Lectures in Projective Geometry,* Van Nostrand, Princeton, N.J., 1962.

[27] Singer, J., "A Theorem in Finite Projective Geometry and Some Applications to Number Theory," *Trans. Amer. Math. Soc.* **43** 377–385 (1938).

[28] Swift, J. D., "Existence and Construction of Non-Desarguesian Projective Planes," *Seminari dell' Instituto Nazionale di Alta Matematica 1962–63,* Rome 153–163 (1964).

[29] Veblen, O. and W. H. Bussey, "Finite Projective Geometries," *Trans. Amer. Math. Soc.* **7** 241–259 (1906).

[30] Veblen, O. and J. H. M. Wedderburn, "Non-Desarguesian and Non-Pascalian Geometries," *Trans. Amer. Math. Soc.* **8** 379–388 (1907).

[31] Veblen, O. and J. W. Young, *Projective Geometry,* 2 vol., Ginn, Boston, 1910.

[32] Yaglom, I., *Geometric Transformations,* Random House, New York, 1962.

[33] Young, J. W., *Projective Geometry,* Open Court, Chicago, 1930.

SUGGESTIONS FOR THE EXERCISES

Section 1.1.

6. (b) The statement is true for $n = 3$. Assume that it is true for all $n \leqq k$, and consider the case of $n = k + 1$. In a given composite of the $k + 1$ α_i's, the *final* composition combines two functions, each of which is a composite of k or fewer α_i's. By repeated use of the induction assumption, this composite can be written $(\alpha_1 \cdots \alpha_r)(\alpha_{r+1} \cdots \alpha_{k+1}) = [(\alpha_1 \cdots \alpha_r)(\alpha_{r+1} \cdots \alpha_k)]\alpha_{k+1} = (\alpha_1 \cdots \alpha_k)\alpha_{k+1}$, where the association of factors inside parentheses is immaterial. Since any two composites of the $k + 1$ α_i's can be expressed in this form, the result follows.

10. (a) Three distinct points of $\mathcal{E}_2$ are collinear if and only if the sum of the two smaller distances between pairs is equal to the largest distance between pairs. Therefore, an isometry of $\mathcal{E}_2$ maps collinear points into collinear points. To see that all points on ℓ' are images of points on ℓ, observe that any point on ℓ' is uniquely determined by its distances from two distinct points on ℓ' that are known to be images of points on ℓ.

Section 1.2.

2. To establish 1.2.1a, consider separately the cases in which the two points are ordinary, ideal, or one ordinary and one ideal.

7. The fixed points of $\pi\pi'$ are the point of intersection of k and ℓ and the point in which the line through O and O' intersects k.

Section 1.3.

8. Use Theorem 1.3.2 if $k \neq \ell$.

9. Otherwise ℓ would intersect the sides of $\mathcal{Q}$ in distinct points.

Suggestions for the Exercises

Section 1.4.

2. (a) All 13 points are on the sides of any quadrangle.

5. If the perfect difference set has $n + 1$ elements, there are just $(n + 1)n$ different ordered pairs of these elements; hence there are $n^2 + n$ different nonzero differences.

6. (b) 234.

7. If ℓ were incident with fewer than two diagonal points of $\mathcal{Q}$, it would intersect the sides of $\mathcal{Q}$ in at least five distinct points. If ℓ were incident with all the diagonal points of $\mathcal{Q}$, there would be 14 different lines incident with the vertices and diagonal points of $\mathcal{Q}$.

8. (a) The number of (unordered) pairs of distinct points in each plane is equal to the number of (unordered) pairs of distinct points in a column of the incidence table multiplied by the number of columns. Thus, if every pair appears in some column, no pair can appear in two different columns.

9. Let P_i, P_j be any distinct points of the constructed plane. If i, j both belong to $\mathfrak{D}$, P_i and P_j are on the first constructed line. In any case, $j - i$ (modulo $n^2 + n + 1$) is obtainable in one and only one way as a difference $s - r$ (modulo $n^2 + n + 1$) of elements r, s of $\mathfrak{D}$. Then, for some k between 0 and $n^2 + n$, inclusive, $s + k = j$, and $r + k = i$ (both modulo $n^2 + n + 1$). Hence P_i and P_j lie on the line constructed at the $(k + 1)$th step.

10. If P_i lies on ℓ_j, then P_j lies on the line constructed $j - i$ (modulo $n^2 + n + 1$) steps after, or $i - j$ (modulo $n^2 + n + 1$) steps before, ℓ_j, and this line is ℓ_i.

Section 1.5.

6. Imitate the construction of $\mathcal{E}_2^*$ in Section 1.2. You will need to show that if k, ℓ, m are lines of an affine plane such that ℓ is parallel to k, and m is parallel to ℓ, then either $m = k$, or m is parallel to k.

8. Any theorem for $\mathcal{P}$ translates into the dual theorem for $\mathcal{P}^\delta$, and conversely.

9. Start with an arbitrary quadrilateral. Draw a figure.

Section 1.6.

3. (b) If ψ is such that $\phi\psi = \iota_1$, then $\phi^{-1}(\phi\psi) = (\phi^{-1}\phi)\psi = \iota_2\psi = \psi$, and $\phi^{-1}(\phi\psi) = \phi^{-1}\iota_1 = \phi^{-1}$. Hence $\psi = \phi^{-1}$.

7. Calculate what each projectivity does to each point on ℓ_0 before you decide. Note that the *number* of elementary correspondences that are composed to produce a given projectivity is not unique.

9. (a) For each Y in $\mathcal{S}_2$, define $Y\beta$ to be one particular X in $\mathcal{S}_1$ such that $X\alpha = Y$. (This requires the axiom of choice if $\mathcal{S}_2$ is infinite and α is not one-to-one.) (b) If Y in $\mathcal{S}_2$ is not in the range of α, $Y\gamma$ can be defined as any (definite) point of $\mathcal{S}_1$.

11. Any point of $\mathcal{E}_2$ is uniquely determined by its distances from three noncollinear points that are known to be in the range of the isometry.

12. See the suggestion for exercise 9b.

Section 1.7.

2. Construct the elementary correspondence from ℓ to K, where K is any point different from L, then use the dual of Theorem 1.7.2.

6. Since there are only four points on a line, a projectivity that transforms three points correctly must also map the fourth point correctly.

8. See the suggestion for exercise 6.

9. See the suggestion for Exercise 1.6.7.

Section 1.8.

7. There are 19 points on the sides of $\mathcal{Q}$, only three of which lie on the line joining the diagonal points.

8. In doing this problem, remember that a line of a projective plane is not just a set of points, so that points and lines can be independently deleted from the plane. To do part (c), observe that a presumed 13-point subplane could not be enlarged to the 21-point plane without adding at least one more point for *each* line of the subplane.

9. Regardless of whether $\mathcal{Q}$ has collinear diagonal points, there are fewer than 31 different lines incident with its vertices and diagonal points.

11. First prove by induction that, for any positive integer n, $\mathcal{S}_n = \{1, 2, \ldots, n\}$ is not equipotent with any proper subset of itself.

12. (a) Choose a point X_1 in $\mathcal{S}$. Proceed by induction. If points X_1, $X_2, \ldots, X_n$, all different, have been found in $\mathcal{S}$, they do not exhaust $\mathcal{S}$, for $\mathcal{S}$ is infinite. Choose X_{n+1} among the remaining points of $\mathcal{S}$. Take the subset containing all the X_i's. (This requires the countable axiom of choice.) (b) If $\mathcal{S}$ is an infinite set, let $\mathfrak{J}$ be a subset of $\mathcal{S}$ constructed as in part (a). Define a function on $\mathcal{S}$ that fixes the points not in $\mathfrak{J}$ and does an obvious thing to the points of $\mathfrak{J}$.

Section 2.1.

9. Start with an arbitrary quadrangle $\mathcal{Q}$ in $\mathcal{P}_2$. If θ is an isomorphism of $\mathcal{P}_1$ onto $\mathcal{P}_2$, the image of $\mathcal{Q}$ under θ^{-1} is a quadrangle in $\mathcal{P}_1$.

Section 2.2.

3. If $\mathcal{P}_1$ is a 7-point plane, no three *distinct* points of $\mathcal{S}_1$ are collinear.

5. Use the Extension Theorem.

6. Use the Extension Theorem.

7. (b) In Example 2.1.5, if $Q \neq P$, the elation is completely determined by ℓ and O. How many choices of ℓ and O are there? (Don't forget to add 1 for the identity elation.)

9. An argument similar to, though much simpler than, the one in the proof of Step 2 of the Extension Theorem will suffice.

10. Imitate the proof of the Extension Theorem, using only Steps 1, 2 (exercise 9), 3, 6, and 7.

11. Use the Extension Theorem.

Section 2.3.

9. (a) If $P = [p_1, p_2]$, $Q = [q_1, q_2]$, $P\delta = [p_1', p_2']$, $Q\delta = [q_1', q_2']$, use Equation 2.3.4 to show that $q_i' - p_i' = r(q_i - p_i)$ for $i = 1, 2$.

Section 2.4.

1. Prove that any fixed point not on the axis of μ is a center for μ.

3. The central collineation $\mu\nu^{-1}$ has two distinct centers.

8. Clearly, σ is central with center H.

Section 2.5.

2. (b) See the suggestion for Exercise 1.7.6, which implies that every bijection between two pencils in a 13-point plane can be realized by a projectivity.

7. If $\pi = \ell \circ M \circ k \circ N \circ \ell$, then $\rho^{-1}\pi\rho = \ell\rho \circ M\rho \circ k\rho \circ N\rho \circ \ell\rho$.

8. This is easy if $m = k$. If $m \neq k$, Figure 2.6 suggests what π should be.

10. Draw a figure showing the construction of $X\epsilon\epsilon$ from X, $X\epsilon$, and the center and axis of ϵ.

Section 2.6.

1. Let A, B, C be distinct elements of $\mathcal{S}$. Define bijections that permute A, B, C and fix all other elements of $\mathcal{S}$.

2. See the suggestion for Exercise 1.6.3b.

9. If η is the homology, η^2 is also a homology, and η^2 has enough centers to be the identity.

13. Use the results of Exercises 1.1.4, 1.1.9, and 1.6.10.

Section 2.7.

8. The cycles of ϕ are unique because the decomposition of $\mathcal{S}$ into equivalence classes (***orbits***) under ϕ, given in the proof of Theorem 2.7.2, is unique.

10. Let ϕ be a transposition on $\mathcal{S}$. If ψ is any even permutation on $\mathcal{S}$, $\psi\phi$ is odd. Thus, ϕ induces a bijection of the set of even permutations onto the set of odd permutations on $\mathcal{S}$.

Section 2.8.

5. The projectivity π must effect an *even* permutation.

6. (a) $P_0\rho = P_{18}$. (b) Nonprojective. (c) The collineation ρ^2 is an elation with axis ℓ_0, center P_1. Use the result in Theorem 2.8.1.

7. Look ahead to step (1) in the proof of Theorem 2.9.1.

8. If σ, τ are projective collineations that meet the conditions, $\sigma\tau^{-1}$ is a projective collineation that fixes A, B, C, D, and the diagonal points of the quadrangle $ABCD$. Then, use Theorem 2.8.5 and the result of Exercise 2.1.7.

9. Two nonprojective collineations ρ_1, ρ_2 fulfilling the conditions must agree on A, B, C, D, and on the diagonal points of the quadrangle $ABCD$. For the other two points on $A \cup B$, ρ_1 and ρ_2 also agree, since each must transform these points in just the reverse of the way that the (unique) projective collineation of exercise 8 transforms them.

11. (a) 60. (b) Use Theorem 2.8.5 and the result of Exercise 2.7.10.

Section 2.9.

3. To prove that η fixes H, let m be a line, other than k, on H, let $R = m \cap \ell$, and let X be a point on m different from H and R. Then, $X\alpha$ is on m. Since $H = m \cap k = (X \cup R) \cap k$, $H\eta = (X\alpha \cup R) \cap k = m \cap k = H$.

4. (a) 118.

5. It is clear that σ also fixes the diagonal points of the quadrangle. Hence, by the Fundamental Theorem, σ fixes every point on each side of the quadrangle.

6. The projectivity π^3 on k fixes A, B, C.

7. Use Theorem 1.7.2.

8. Duplicate the proof of Theorem 2.9.2.

9. First prove the dual of the Fundamental Theorem. To do so, note that if ϕ is a projectivity on a point P that fixes three distinct lines, and if $\delta = k \circ P$, then $\delta\phi\delta^{-1}$ is a projectivity on k that fixes three distinct points.

Section 2.10.

3. Let P be a point of the space; exercises 1 and 2 imply that there are $n^2 + n + 1$ lines on P, and that each of these lines has n points on it besides P.

6. (a) Let A be a point of $\mathcal{E}_3$. To each line ℓ on A adjoin a single ideal point I_l; also adjoin I_l to all lines of $\mathcal{E}_3$ that are parallel to ℓ, but to no other lines. To each plane $\mathcal{P}$ on A adjoin one ideal line, containing all the ideal points of the lines on A that lie in $\mathcal{P}$. The same ideal line will necessarily be adjoined to all planes parallel to $\mathcal{P}$, since all such planes share the ideal points of $\mathcal{P}$.

9. Imitate the proof of Theorem 2.10.4.

Section 3.1.

4. Count the number of elations other than the identity that have each point on ℓ as center, multiply by the number of points on ℓ, and add 1 (for the identity elation).

7. Use Theorem 3.1.4 and the First (or Second) Commuting Theorem.

8. The problem is to construct the center of the collineation.

9. Enough information is given to construct both the center and axis of the elation.

10. (a) A homology different from the identity induces a permutation on the points that is a composite of five disjoint three-cycles. An elation different from the identity induces a permutation on the points that is a composite of eight disjoint transpositions.

11. As long as the ratios of the central dilatations are 2 and 1/2, the composite will surely be a translation, in view of Exercise 2.3.9a. Thus, the only problem is to choose the centers of the central dilatations so that the composite sends $\mathcal{P}$ into $\mathcal{P}'$.

Section 3.2.

1. If ℓ is on B, then B, P, Q cannot be distinct. But, $P \neq Q$ by assumption; $B = P$ requires that $B' = B$, and $Q = P$, a contradiction. Similarly, $B \neq Q$. Thus, ℓ is not on B, and the argument is symmetric in B and B'.

4. Use Figure 3.4.

5. The line ℓ is determined by $k \cap k'$ and one other point of the form $(X \cup Y\pi) \cap (Y \cup X\pi)$. All the rest of the points of this form are on ℓ by exercise 4.

7. Use a central collineation.

8. The result is trivial if $M = N$. If $M \neq N$, let $E = k \cap m$, $P = (M \cup N) \cap k$, and let Q be any point on k other than P and E. Let $O = (Q \cup Q\pi) \cap (M \cup N)$. If X is any point on k other than Q and E, the triangle QXM and the triangle with vertices $Q\pi$, $X\pi$, N are perspective from ℓ. (Draw a figure.) Use Desargues' theorem to conclude that $X \cup X\pi$ lies on O.

9. Duplicate the proof of Theorem 2.9.2.

10. Let $T = (H \cup D) \cap (E \cup F)$, $U = (H \cup E) \cap (D \cup F)$, and $V = (H \cup F) \cap (D \cup E)$. It suffices to prove that A, T, U are collinear, C, T, V are collinear, and B, U, V are collinear.

12. Let μ_1 have center H and the axis of perspective of $\mathfrak{J}_2$ and $\mathfrak{J}_3$ as its axis, and let μ_1 map $\mathfrak{J}_2$ onto $\mathfrak{J}_3$, in the manner of the proof of Desargues' theorem. Similarly, let μ_2 and μ_3 be central collineations with center H, and with suitably chosen axes, respectively mapping $\mathfrak{J}_1$ onto $\mathfrak{J}_3$ and $\mathfrak{J}_1$ onto $\mathfrak{J}_2$. Then, $\mu_3\mu_1 = \mu_2$, and the conclusion follows from the dual of Theorem 2.4.4.

Section 3.3.

3. Refer to Figure 3.4. Let $R_1 = (B \cup C') \cap \ell$, $R_2 = (B' \cup C) \cap \ell$. Use quadrangles $ABB'C'$ and $A'B'BC$ and the line ℓ to prove that $R_1 = R_2$.

6. Construct a Π_2 on ℓ with central invariant point E and axial invariant point B.

8. (b) By Theorem 3.3.2, it may be assumed that P is the first vertex of the determining quadrangle $\mathcal{Q}$. Use the quadrilateral with sides ℓ, $Q_3 \cup Q_4$, $Q_2 \cup Q_4$, $Q_2 \cup Q_3$, where Q_2, Q_3, Q_4 are the other vertices of $\mathcal{Q}$.

12. Imitate the proof of Theorem 3.3.2, using certain Π_2's instead of central collineations.

Section 3.4.

4. Since $\eta_1\eta_2$ fixes every point on the line joining the centers of η_1, η_2, it is central. Also, $\eta_1\eta_2 = \eta_2\eta_1$, by the First Commuting Theorem, so that $(\eta_1\eta_2)^2 = \iota$.

6. If $H \neq M$, π extends to a harmonic homology. If $H = M$, harmonic sets in $\mathcal{P}$ have only three distinct points.

9. (a) Let η have center H, axis ℓ. If μ is an elation, let its center be M, and let $X = H\mu$, so that $H = X\mu^{-1}$. Then, $\mathcal{H}(M, H; X, H\mu^{-1})$. But, also, $\mathcal{H}(M, H; X, X\eta)$. Therefore, $H\mu^{-1} = X\eta$, or $H = X\eta\mu$, or $H = H\mu\eta\mu$; hence $H\eta = H = H\mu\eta\mu\eta = H(\mu\eta)^2$. Since $\mu\eta$ is a homology with center different from H, $(\mu\eta)^2 = \iota$, so that $\mu\eta$ is harmonic. Conversely, if $\sigma = \mu\eta$ is a harmonic homology, then $\mu = \sigma\eta$; hence $\eta\mu\eta = \eta\sigma = \mu^{-1}$. Thus, μ^{-1} is the conjugate of μ by η. But, μ and μ^{-1} have the same center M; hence, M is fixed by η. Therefore, either M is on ℓ, in which case μ is an elation, or $M = H$. If $M = H$, σ has center H; hence, $\sigma = \eta$, and $\mu = \iota$, an elation.

10. Let X be a point different from H and not on ℓ, and let $M = (H \cup X) \cap \ell$. Then, $\mathcal{H}(H, M; X, X\eta_1)$; hence $\mathcal{H}(H, M; X\eta_2, X\eta_1\eta_2)$. But, $\mathcal{H}(H, M; X\eta_2, X\eta_2\eta_1)$, implying that $X\eta_1\eta_2 = X\eta_2\eta_1$, and $\eta_1\eta_2 = \eta_2\eta_1$.

12. Let η be the harmonic homology with center A, axis $B \cup C$. Then, $Y\eta = Y'$, and $Z\eta = Z'$; therefore $(Z' \cup Y') \cap (Z \cup Y)$ is on $B \cup C$. But, $X' = (B \cup C) \cap (Z \cup Y)$.

Section 3.5.

2. To prove the symmetry of the relation, let Φ be an isomorphism from $\mathcal{H}$ to $\mathcal{K}$, and let K_1, K_2 be any elements of $\mathcal{K}$. Set $H_1 = K_1\Phi^{-1}$, $H_2 = K_2\Phi^{-1}$, so that $K_1 = H_1\Phi$, and $K_2 = H_2\Phi$. Then, $(H_1 \cdot H_2)\Phi = K_1 \cdot K_2$; hence $H_1 \cdot H_2 = (K_1 \cdot K_2)\Phi^{-1}$. Therefore, $(K_1 \cdot K_2)\Phi^{-1} = (K_1\Phi^{-1}) \cdot (K_2\Phi^{-1})$, and Φ^{-1} is an isomorphism from $\mathcal{K}$ to $\mathcal{H}$.

4. Imitate the proof of Theorem 3.5.4.

7. Calculate what $\psi^{-1}\phi\psi$ does to $P_i\psi$.

8. The two groups are conjugate under transformation by ρ.

11. Use the basic property of the logarithm function.

12. (c) Imitate the proof of Theorem 3.5.1.

Section 3.6.

4. (b) Construct a collineation that maps the center and axis of one of the harmonic homologies into the center and axis of the other.

6. The two groups are conjugate under transformation by any collineation that maps H_1 onto H_2 and ℓ_1 onto ℓ_2; construct such a collineation.

7. (a) Since p is a prime, and $k < p$, integers r, s can be found such that $kr + ps = 1$. Then, $(\epsilon_2^k)^r = (\epsilon_2)^{1-ps} = \epsilon_2$, so that $\epsilon_2 = \epsilon_1^{mr}$, and the exponent on ϵ_1 can be made positive by the addition of a suitable multiple of p. (b) Suppose that $\epsilon_1^i\epsilon_2^j = \epsilon_1^{i'}\epsilon_2^{j'}$, with i, j, i', j' all between 0 and $p - 1$, inclusive, and suppose that $j \geqq j'$. Then, $\epsilon_2^{j-j'} = \epsilon_1^{i'-i}$. The result of part (a) then implies that $j = j'$. Hence, also, $i = i'$. (d) Eventually one of the sets constructed as in (b) and (c) must exhaust the elations with the given center and axis.

8. (a) If θ is an isomorphism of $\mathcal{P}$ onto $\mathcal{P}'$, and if $\mathfrak{D}$ is any determining set in $\mathcal{P}'$, then $\mathfrak{D}\theta^{-1}$ is a determining set in $\mathcal{P}$.

9. Let π be any projectivity on a line k that fixes three distinct points. Construct a collineation σ that sends k into ℓ. Then, $\sigma^{-1}\pi\sigma$ is a projectivity on ℓ that fixes three distinct points.

10. Let I be the ideal point on $A \cup B$, J the ideal point on $A \cup C$, I' the ideal point on $A' \cup B'$, and J' the ideal point on $A' \cup C'$. Construct a collineation of $\mathcal{P}$ that maps B, C, I, J into B', C', I', J', respectively.

Section 3.7.

5. (b) For one part, note that $0 = a \cdot 0 = a[b + (-b)] = ab + a(-b)$. Hence, $a(-b) = -(ab)$.

6. (c) The function γ_B is the restriction to $\mathcal{G}(k)$ of the homology η^B of Lemma 3.7.3.

7. There is a point $R \neq 0$ in $\mathcal{S}$ such that $X\eta = R \cdot X$. Since $\eta^2 = \iota$, $R \cdot R = 1$. Hence $R \cdot R - 1 = (R - 1) \cdot (R + 1) = 0$, and $R = 1$ or -1, by exercise 5a.

Section 3.8.

1. (a) See the suggestion for Exercise 3.5.2.

2. Let the notation be that of Section 3.7. By Exercise 3.7.2, the function Φ, from the multiplicative group of nonzero elements of S to $\mathcal{H}(\infty, m)$ (where m is a line on 0 different from k), defined by $X\Phi = \eta^X$, is a group isomorphism.

3. If Θ is a division ring isomorphism, then $(x + 0)\Theta = x\Theta + 0\Theta$, but is also $x\Theta$. Therefore, 0Θ is the additive identity in the second division ring.

4. By exercise 3, $1\Phi = 1$. Then, $(xx^{-1})\Phi = (x\Phi)[(x^{-1})\Phi] = 1$.

7. (a) An automorphism of $\mathcal{R}$ must fix 1, 1 + 1, etc., and these are all the elements of $\mathcal{R}$.

8. (a) It is easy to see that an automorphism must fix all the integers; thus, it must fix all the reciprocals of nonzero integers. Every rational is a product of an integer and the reciprocal of a nonzero integer. (b) By the argument of (a), an automorphism Φ fixes all the rational numbers. If $x > 0$, then $x = y^2$ for some $y \neq 0$. Therefore, $x\Phi = (y\Phi)^2 > 0$. Thus, Φ preserves order, and it is easy to deduce that Φ is the identity.

9. (a) The collineation $\mu = \eta'_A \eta_A^{-1}$ is central with center 0, axis on ∞. Since μ fixes 1, either $\mu = \iota$, or the axis of μ is k. In either case, η'_A agrees with η_A on $\mathcal{G}(k)$.

11. (a) Extend π to a homology, and use the result of exercise 9a.

Section 4.1.

7. (a) Let c, f be numbers of $\mathcal{R}$ such that $cf \neq fc$. Take $k = c$, $m = 1$, $n = 0$, $x = 1$, $y = -c$, $z = 0$, and $r = f$.

9. If Φ is the coordinatization of $\mathcal{S}$, assign to $x\Phi$ the class of pairs $[rx, r]$ for $r \neq 0$. Assign to ∞ the class of pairs $[r, 0]$ for $r \neq 0$.

Section 4.2.

7. (a) If $[P] = [p, q, 1]$, then $[P\eta] = [ap, aq, 1]$, as in the development of Phase 2. Thus, also, $[P\eta] = [p, q, a^{-1}]$.

10. If P is in $\mathcal{S}$, with $P = p\Phi$ and, also, $P = p'\Psi$, then $p' = p\Phi\Psi^{-1} = p\Theta$. If $[X]_1 = [x, y, z]$, with $z \neq 0$, then, also, $[X]_1 = [z^{-1}x, z^{-1}y, 1]$. Hence, from the previous sentence, $[X]_2 = [(z^{-1}x)\Theta, (z^{-1}y)\Theta, 1]$. It follows that $[X]_2 = [x\Theta, y\Theta, z\Theta]$ when $z \neq 0$.

11. Take ℓ_∞ as the ideal line. Then, if X is in A, it has a unique coordinate triple $[x, y, 1]$ with third member 1. Assign to X the pair $[x, y]$.

12. It is clear that α is a bijection. If P_1, P_2, P_3 are collinear, let k be a line on which they lie, and suppose that

$$[k] = \begin{bmatrix} k \\ m \\ n \end{bmatrix}.$$

Then, $P_1\alpha$, $P_2\alpha$, $P_3\alpha$ lie on the line k', where

$$[k'] = \begin{bmatrix} k\Phi \\ m\Phi \\ n\Phi \end{bmatrix}.$$

Now, use the extension theorem of Exercise 2.2.10.

Section 4.3.

4. (a) The given conditions imply that $\mathbf{A}' + \mathbf{D}' = s(\mathbf{A} + \mathbf{D})$, $\mathbf{A}' = r_1\mathbf{A}$, and $\mathbf{D}' = r_2\mathbf{D}$. Therefore, $\mathbf{A}' - s\mathbf{A} = s\mathbf{D} - \mathbf{D}'$; hence $(r_1 - s)\mathbf{A} = (s - r_2)\mathbf{D}$. Since $\mathbf{A}$, $\mathbf{D}$ are inequivalent, $r_1 - s = s - r_2 = 0$.

5. If $u \neq 0$, for example, then $\mathbf{A} = -(u^{-1}v)\mathbf{B} - (u^{-1}w)\mathbf{C}$, contradicting the noncollinearity of A, B, C.

7. (a) If $z \neq 0$,

$$[X \cup O_1] = \begin{bmatrix} 1 \\ z^{-1}x \\ -z^{-1}x \end{bmatrix};$$

hence $[X\pi_1] = [z^{-1}x, -1, 0]$.

8. (a) Since O_1 is on $O \cup J$, $O_1 = (O \cup J) \cap (O_1 \cup I)$; therefore, $O_1\epsilon = (A \cup J) \cap (O_1 \cup I)$. Now,

$$[A \cup J] = \begin{bmatrix} 1 \\ 0 \\ -a \end{bmatrix}, \text{ and } [O_1 \cup I] = \begin{bmatrix} 0 \\ 1 \\ -1 \end{bmatrix},$$

from which it follows that $[O_1\epsilon] = [a, 1, 1]$. (b) The result is obvious if $z = 0$. If $z \neq 0$, let $P = (X \cup J) \cap \ell_I$. Then, $[P] = [z^{-1}x, 0, 1]$, and $[P\epsilon] = [z^{-1}x + a, 0, 1]$. Since $X = (P \cup J) \cap (X \cup I)$, $X\epsilon = (P\epsilon \cup J) \cap (X \cup I)$, and a triple for $X\epsilon$ can be computed from this information.

9. (b) Observe that $\epsilon_2 = \epsilon\epsilon_1$, where ϵ is the elation of exercise 8, and ϵ_1 is the elation of part (a) of this exercise.

Section 4.4.

1. Find an equation for ϕ in an induced coordinate system on k with A and D as first and second base points. Then use Lemma 4.4.3.

2. With the notation of Section 4.2, choose an induced coordinate system on ℓ_U with base points ∞, O, U. The corollary to Lemma 4.4.3 implies that the restriction of α to ℓ_U is a projectivity.

6. If ϕ is described by $[P\phi] = u[e, f] + v[g, h]$, the given conditions imply that $[e, f] = r[a', d']$, $[g, h] = s[a'', d'']$, and $[e, f] + [g, h] = t([a', d'] + [a'', d''])$ for some r, s, t, all different from zero. It follows that $r = s = t$; then, Θ is defined by $x\Theta = s^{-1}xs$.

7. If the characteristic of $\mathcal{P}$ is not 2, $d_2 = -a_1$ is necessary and sufficient. If the characteristic of $\mathcal{P}$ is 2, the condition is that $d_2 = a_1$ $(= -a_1)$, and not both a_2, d_1 are zero.

8. For $P \neq A$ or D, $P\phi_2 = G\phi_1\phi_2 = G\phi_2\phi_1$. But, $[G\phi_2] = [t, 1]$; hence $[G\phi_2\phi_1] = [t, u^{-1}v]$, which is equivalent to $[ut, v]$. For $P = A$ or D, a separate verification is necessary.

9. Let $\phi_s = \pi_1\pi_2$, with $\pi_1 = k \circ H_1 \circ \ell$, $\pi_2 = \ell \circ H_2 \circ k$. Let $\mathbf{D}'$ be the triple for $D\pi_1$ such that $[H_1] = \mathbf{D} + \mathbf{D}'$. Then, successively show that $s\mathbf{A} + \mathbf{D} + \mathbf{D}'$ is a triple for H_2, $u\mathbf{A} - v\mathbf{D}'$ is a triple for $P\pi_1$, and $(u + vs)\mathbf{A} + v\mathbf{D}$ is a triple for $P\phi_s$.

10. (a) To prove that Φ is multiplicative, let x, y be any numbers of $\mathcal{R}$, with $x \neq 0$, and let $\eta_{x\Phi}$ be the homology that generates the left-multiplication by $x\Phi$ in $\mathcal{S}$. Then, the restriction of $\eta_{x\Phi}$ to $\mathcal{g}(k)$ is a Π_2 on k with central invariant point 0, axial invariant point ∞, sending 1 into $x\Phi$. Now, $[y\Phi] = [y, 1]$, and $[x\Phi] = [1, x^{-1}]$. By Lemma 4.4.3 (a), $[(y\Phi)\eta_{x\Phi}] = [y, x^{-1}]$, which is equivalent to $[xy, 1]$. Therefore, $(y\Phi)\eta_{x\Phi} = (xy)\Phi$. But, also, $(y\Phi)\eta_{x\Phi} = (x\Phi)\cdot(y\Phi)$ (in $\mathcal{S}$).

Section 4.5.

1. Let $\mathbf{Z}$, $\mathbf{W}$ be any vectors in the domain of λ^{-1}, and let z, w be any numbers of $\mathcal{R}$. Set $\mathbf{X} = \mathbf{Z}\lambda^{-1}$, $\mathbf{Y} = \mathbf{W}\lambda^{-1}$. Then, $(z\mathbf{X} + w\mathbf{Y})\lambda = z(\mathbf{X}\lambda) + w(\mathbf{Y}\lambda) = z\mathbf{Z} + w\mathbf{W}$. Hence, $(z\mathbf{Z} + w\mathbf{W})\lambda^{-1} = z\mathbf{X} + w\mathbf{Y} = z(\mathbf{Z}\lambda^{-1}) + w(\mathbf{W}\lambda^{-1})$.

6. The statements in this exercise are implicitly contained in the proofs of Theorems 4.5.1 and 4.5.5.

8. (b) Let A, D, G be the base points of the induced coordinate system on k, let ι be the identity projectivity on k, and let

$$\begin{bmatrix} a & b \\ c & d \end{bmatrix}$$

be a matrix for ι in the given coordinate system. Since $A\iota = A$, $b = 0$. Since $D\iota = D$, $c = 0$. Since $G\iota = G$, $d = a$. If x is any number of $\mathcal{R}$, let X be the point on k represented by $[x, 1]$. Since $X\iota = X$, $[xa, a] =$

s[x, 1] for some s $\neq 0$. Thus, xa = sx, and a = s; hence xa = ax, and a is in $\mathcal{C}(\mathcal{R})$.

9. (b) $[P\phi]_2 = [P\phi]_1\beta = [P]_1[\phi]_1\beta = [P]_2\beta^{-1}[\phi]_1\beta$. Thus, $\beta^{-1}[\phi]_1\beta$ is a matrix for ϕ in the second coordinate system.

10. (a) A linear transformation on $\mathcal{E}_2$ transforms a locus defined by a quadratic equation into another locus defined by a quadratic equation; it also transforms a bounded locus into a bounded locus.

Section 4.6.

6. (b) $\begin{bmatrix} 1 & 0 & 0 \\ 0 & 1 & 0 \\ -b & -b & 1 \end{bmatrix}$.

8. The number of nonsingular matrices is twice the number of collineations, since there are two nonzero elements in the center of the field, and every collineation of the plane is projective.

9. A matrix for σ must have the form $r\iota$ for some $r \neq 0$. Then, Φ is defined by $x\Phi = r^{-1}xr$.

10. $\begin{bmatrix} a & a-1 & 0 \\ 0 & 1 & 0 \\ 0 & 0 & 1 \end{bmatrix}$.

11. $\begin{bmatrix} r & 0 & 0 \\ 0 & r & 0 \\ h(1-r) & k(1-r) & 1 \end{bmatrix}$.

12. Be sure to prove that the multiplicative inverse of any nonzero element of $\mathcal{C}(\mathcal{R})$ is in $\mathcal{C}(\mathcal{R})$.

Section 4.7.

1. (c) If Y is any point of $\mathcal{P}$, let X be the point such that $[X] = ([Y]\sigma^{-1})\Theta^{-1}$. Then, $X\rho = Y$.

3. Note that $(\sigma\sigma^{-1})\Theta = (\sigma\Theta)(\sigma^{-1}\Theta)$, and, also, $(\sigma\sigma^{-1})\Theta = \iota\Theta = \iota$.

5. $[k\rho] = \sigma^{-1}([k]\Theta)$.

7. The given conditions imply that $[X] = ([X]\Theta_2\Theta_1^{-1})\{(\sigma_2\sigma_1^{-1})\Theta_1^{-1}\}$.

Section 4.8.

6. Suppose that θ is an isomorphism of $\mathcal{P}_1$ onto $\mathcal{P}_2$, and construct coordinate systems in $\mathcal{P}_1$ and $\mathcal{P}_2$, as in Section 4.2. Let Φ_1 and Φ_2 be the coordinatizations of $\mathcal{S}_1$ and $\mathcal{S}_2$, respectively, that are used in establishing these coordinate systems. Then, the restriction of θ to $\mathcal{S}_1$ is an isomorphism of $\mathcal{S}_1$ onto $\mathcal{S}_2$, as in the first three paragraphs of Section 3.8. It follows that $\Phi_1\theta\Phi_2^{-1}$ is an isomorphism of $\mathcal{R}_1$ onto $\mathcal{R}_2$.

8. (a) A projective affinity of an affine plane $\mathcal{A}$ is the restriction to $\mathcal{A}$ of a projective collineation of $\mathcal{P}$ (the projective extension of $\mathcal{A}$) that fixes the ideal line.

Section 5.1.

4. In Proof 3, R would not have been on $P \cup Q$ if c had not commuted with f. With suitable choices of C and C', c and f could be any numbers of $\mathcal{R}$.

5. If π is a projectivity on k with a fixed point, a Π_2 on k can be constructed (Exercise 1.7.11) that agrees with π on three distinct points.

6. If the projectivity has a fixed point, it is a Π_2 (by exercise 5), and it extends to a homology, since no elation has period 2.

7. Two Π_2's with inversely matched invariant points are equal if they agree on one other point, by the Fundamental Theorem.

8. Use the result of Exercise 3.7.9 and the fact that $\mathcal{R}$ is a field.

9. Let Q_1, Q_2, Q_3, Q_4 be the vertices of $\mathcal{Q}$. Let $Q_1' = Q_3$ and $Q_2' = Q_4$. Locate Q_3' and Q_4' so that $\mathcal{Q}'$ $(D, E, F; X, B, C)$. If $B \neq E$, use Pappus' theorem.

10. Let $\delta_1 = A \circ m$ and $\delta_2 = k \circ A\pi$, where A is on k, but $A \neq k \cap m$, and $A\pi \neq k \cap m$. Then, $\delta_1\pi^{-1}\delta_2$ is a perspectivity from A to $A\pi$, since it fixes $A \cup A\pi$. Let ℓ be the axis of this perspectivity.

12. Use Theorem 1.7.3 to construct a projectivity on k that is an involution and agrees with π on three distinct points.

14. (a) Let A, B be nonfixed points of σ such that B is not on $A \cup A\sigma$. Let $H = (A \cup A\sigma) \cap (B \cup B\sigma)$, $M = (A \cup B\sigma) \cap (A\sigma \cup B)$, $N = (A \cup B) \cap (A\sigma \cup B\sigma)$. Then, H is a center, and $M \cup N$ is an axis, for σ.

Section 5.2.

4. Construct a coordinate system in $\mathcal{P}$ in which W, X, Y play the roles of ∞, O, U, respectively, and let η be the harmonic homology with center $X\,(= O)$, axis ℓ_∞. Then, $Y\eta = Z$ if and only if $\mathcal{R}(W, X; Y, Z) = -1$.

7. Use the induced coordinate system on k with base points W, X, Y.

12. (c) If r is a solution, then $1/r$ is also a solution, and $1/r \neq r$ if the characteristic of $\mathcal{R}$ is not 3. (f) The subfield contains 0, 1, r (a solution of the equation), and $r + 1$.

13. (c) Compare the multiplication tables.

Section 5.3.

1. These points determine the ideal points I and J, hence all the base points of a coordinate system for $\mathcal{P}$ constructed as in Section 4.2.

3. $[d, e, 1]$, $[g, h, 1]$, and $[g - d, h - e, 0]$ are triples for D, G, A, respectively, and $[p, q, 1] = u[g - d, h - e, 0] + [d, e, 1]$.

4. Solve the equation $(p - b)/(c - p) = r$ for p.

7. Use Corollary 2 of Theorem 5.2.2.

8. Find a matrix that transforms $[h + 1, k, 1]$ into $[h + r, k, 1]$ and multiplies $[1, 0, 0]$ and $[0, 1, 0]$ by the same nonzero number.

9. If $A \cup Q$, $B \cup R$, $C \cup P$ are concurrent at S, apply Menelaus' theorem successively to triangle ABQ, points P, C, S, and triangle CAQ, points R, S, B; multiply the resulting equations and rearrange. For the converse, prove that if any two of the lines intersect, the three lines are concurrent.

10. (b) Use Ceva's theorem (exercise 9).

Section 5.4.

4. (c) Let A, B, C, D, E be any triply noncollinear points in a 21-point plane. There is a unique projectivity π from A to B that sends $A \cup C$ into $B \cup C$, $A \cup D$ into $B \cup D$, and $A \cup E$ into $B \cup E$; π is not a perspectivity because C, D, E are not collinear. Hence, $(A \cup B)\pi$ is the line on B that doesn't lie on A, C, D, or E; also, if k is the line on A that doesn't lie on B, C, D, or E, then $k\pi = B \cup A$. Thus, A, B, π

determine the point-conic consisting of the five given points. In this argument, A and B could have been any two of the given points.

8. See the suggestion for exercise 9, to follow.

9. Let $\mathcal{C}$ be determined by A, C, and π. Let $S = \ell_A \cap (D \cup E)$, $T = (A \cup E) \cap (D \cup C)$, $\delta_1 = (D \cup E) \circ A$, $\delta_2 = C \circ (A \cup E)$. Then, $\delta_1 \pi \delta_2$ sends P into Q, D into T, S into A, and E into E.

10. Let the distinct points be A, B, C, D, and let ℓ_A be the tangent line at A. The conic is determined by A, B, and π, where $(A \cup C)\pi = B \cup C$, $(A \cup D)\pi = B \cup D$, and $\ell_A\pi = B \cup A$.

11. See the suggestion for exercise 10.

13. Count the number of different sets of five triply noncollinear points and divide by six (since each point-conic contains six such sets). The answer is 3100.

Section 5.5.

5. Use Theorem 5.4.2.

6. If $\mathcal{C}$ is determined by A, B, and π, then $\mathcal{C}\rho$ is the point-conic determined by $A\rho$, $B\rho$, and $\rho^{-1}\pi\rho$.

7. If k is a tangent line, the characteristic of the plane is 2. Otherwise, use the analytic method of this section, and show that $\mathcal{R}(P, Q; C, D) = -1$. Then use the result of Exercise 5.2.4.

8. Refer to Figure 5.6. The point-conic of that figure is determined by the triply noncollinear points A, B, C, J. (See Exercise 5.4.11.)

9. (b) If $\mathcal{P}$ has order n, there are $n + 1$ tangent lines to $\mathcal{C}$, and each has n exterior points on it. But, each of these exterior points lies on two tangent lines. Thus, there are $(1/2)(n^2 + n)$ exterior points, and $n + 1$ points of $\mathcal{C}$, leaving $(1/2)(n^2 - n)$ interior points.

10. (a) Use the coordinate system in $\mathcal{P}$ suggested by Figure 5.6. (b) Use a coordinate system in $\mathcal{P}$ like that of Figure 5.6, except with $[A] = [0, 1, 0]$ and $[J] = [0, 0, 1]$.

Section 5.6.

5. Let $\mathcal{P}$ be the point of concurrency of $M \cup A$, $N \cup B$, $U \cup C$ (exercise 4). Use quadrangle $APNC$ to deduce that $\mathcal{H}(M, U; D, B)$.

6. There is a unique line-conic containing k, m, n and having A and B

as the points of contact on k, m. Use the dual of Theorem 5.6.2. (The principle of duality is valid for the class of Pappian planes of characteristic different from 2.)

8. Choose a coordinate system in which a given point-conic has equation $y^2 = xz$. If P is such that $[P] = [1, 0, 1]$, then P is an interior point.

9. Let ℓ be a line on P that intersects $\mathcal{C}$. By taking the points of intersection of ℓ with $\mathcal{C}$ as the points O, I, a coordinate system can be constructed in $\mathcal{P}$ in which $\mathcal{C}$ has equation $y^2 = xz$, and $[P] = [a, 0, 1]$ for some $a \neq 0$. Since P is interior, $a + v^2 = 0$ has no solution for v. Hence, $a > 0$. If k is any line on P other than ℓ, then

$$[k] = \begin{bmatrix} 1 \\ k \\ -a \end{bmatrix}$$

for some k. To prove that k intersects $\mathcal{C}$ in two distinct points, it suffices to show that the equation $v^2 + kv - a = 0$ has two distinct solutions for v.

Section 5.7.

2. Imitate part of the proof of Theorem 5.7.4, taking π to be the identity projectivity on ℓ.

4. (b) If $\kappa = \delta\pi\epsilon$ and $\kappa' = \delta'\pi'\epsilon'$, then $\kappa\kappa' = \delta\phi\epsilon'$, where $\phi = \pi\epsilon\delta'\pi'$ is a projectivity, in view of Theorem 5.7.2.

5. Let A be a point of $\mathcal{C}$, let $\delta = \mathcal{C}\circ A$, $\epsilon = A\sigma\circ\mathcal{C}$, and let π be the projectivity from A to $A\sigma$ that is the restriction of σ to $\mathcal{J}(A)$. The restriction of σ to $\mathcal{C}$ is $\delta\pi\epsilon$.

6. (a) If $\kappa = \delta\pi\epsilon$, then $\phi = \delta^{-1}\kappa\delta = \pi\epsilon\delta$ is a (strict) projectivity that fixes three distinct elements of the domain of π. (b) Let P be any point of $\mathcal{C}$, let $\delta = \mathcal{C}\circ P$, and let π be the projectivity on P such that $(P \cup A)\pi = P \cup A'$, $(P \cup B)\pi = P \cup B'$, and $(P \cup C)\pi = P \cup C'$. (If $P = X$, $P \cup X$ is to be interpreted as the tangent line to $\mathcal{C}$ at X.) Take $\kappa = \delta\pi\delta^{-1}$, then use the result of part (a).

7. Let A, B, C be distinct points of $\mathcal{C}$, let $P = (A \cup B\kappa) \cap (A\kappa \cup B)$, $Q = (A \cup C\kappa) \cap (A\kappa \cup C)$, $R = (B \cup C\kappa) \cap (B\kappa \cup C)$, where $X \cup Y$ is to be interpreted as the tangent line to $\mathcal{C}$ at X if $X = Y$. Let $\ell = P \cup Q$; then, R is on ℓ by Pascal's theorem, or by one of Exercises

5.4.8, 5.4.9, 5.5.4. Not all of A, B, C lie on ℓ; if A is not on ℓ, show that $\kappa = \mathcal{C}\circ A\circ\ell\circ A\kappa\circ\mathcal{C}$.

9. (c) Let $O = (A \cup A') \cap (B \cup B')$. If X is any point of $\mathcal{C}$ other than A, A', B, B', the triangle ABX and the triangle with vertices A', B', $X\kappa$ are perspective from the axis of κ.

10. (a) Let A be a point of $\mathcal{C}$ different from X and $X\kappa$ and such that A is not fixed by κ. Let $P = (A \cup X) \cap (A\kappa \cup X\kappa)$, and let $Q = (A \cup X\kappa) \cap (A\kappa \cup X)$. Then, $\ell = P \cup Q$, and the quadrangle with vertices $A\kappa$, Q, P, A gives the conclusion.

Section 5.8.

1. Prove that if the polar of a point P not on $\mathcal{C}$ intersects $\mathcal{C}$, then P is an exterior point.

3. By Theorem 5.8.3 and its dual, $\omega^2 = \iota$; hence ω is a bijection. (The principle of duality is valid for the class of Pappian planes of characteristic different from 2.)

8. Let η be the harmonic homology with center A and axis ℓ_A (the polar of A). Then, η exchanges Q and R; hence it exchanges $B \cup Q$ and $B \cup R$. Since η maps $\mathcal{C}$ into itself, it must exchange P and S.

9. If P is not a point of $\mathcal{C}$, and if $\mathcal{P}$ has more than 13 points, draw two secants through P, intersecting $\mathcal{C}$ at Q, R and at P, S. Then, the polar of P joins $(Q \cup S) \cap (R \cup P)$ and $(R \cup S) \cap (P \cup Q)$. If P is a point of $\mathcal{C}$, let k be any secant on P, and let A, B be distinct points on k that are not points of $\mathcal{C}$. Construct the polars ℓ_A, ℓ_B of A, B, as explained above; then, $\ell_P = P \cup (\ell_A \cap \ell_B)$.

12. If the ideal line is not tangent to $\mathcal{C}$, let H be the pole of the ideal line with respect to the complete conic determined by $\mathcal{C}$. The harmonic homology with center H, axis the ideal line, restricts to a central dilatation of $\mathcal{E}_2$ with ratio -1.

Section 5.9.

1. Imitate the proof of Theorem 2.5.4.

2. $\mathcal{C}$ is determined by A, B, and π, where $(A\omega)\pi = A \cup B$, $(A \cup B)\pi = B\omega$, and $(A \cup C)\pi = B \cup C$.

3. (a) You will need to show that a correlation maps a nonincident point and line into a nonincident line and point. See the paragraph in the text immediately following Definition 2.1.1.

6. See the suggestion for Exercise 5.5.6.

8. First construct the polarity ω induced by some complete conic. Then, $\mathcal{Q}\omega$ is a quadrilateral and can be mapped onto $\mathcal{Q}'$ by a suitable projective collineation.

9. Use the results of exercise 8 and Exercise 5.5.8.

10. The only hard part of this problem is handled by Exercise 5.1.14.

11. Let k be conjugate to $A \cup B$. Then, $k = D\omega$ for some D on $A \cup B$. If $D = A$ or B, the conclusion is trivial. If $D \cup C$ is self-conjugate, then k is on C. In all other cases, $D \cup C$ intersects the point-conic determined by ω in a second point E. Let $F = (A \cup C) \cap (B \cup E)$ and $G = (A \cup E) \cap (B \cup C)$. Then, k intersects $A \cup C$ and $B \cup C$ in F, G, respectively.

Section 5.10.

1. Let the notation be as in Section 4.2. Construct the induced coordinate system on ℓ_∞ with base points I, J, ∞. Let π be the projectivity on ℓ_∞ described, relative to this induced coordinate system, by $[P\pi] = [v, -u]$, where $[P] = [u, v]$. Let $\delta = O \circ \ell_\infty$. Then, the restriction of Ω to $\mathcal{J}(O)$ is $\delta\pi$.

3. If χ is projective, $\chi\Omega$ is a projective collineation.

6. Construct a coordinate system in which the vertices of the triangle are O, I, J, and calculate a matrix for the correlation in this coordinate system.

7. (a) See the suggestion for Exercise 5.9.8. For the present problem, use a coordinate polarity of $\mathcal{P}$.

8. Construct a coordinate system with A, B, C playing the roles of O, I, J. A matrix for ω is symmetric, from which it is easy to prove that $(A \cup B) \cap C\omega$, $(B \cup C) \cap A\omega$, and $(C \cup A) \cap B\omega$ are collinear.

9. It is easy to calculate where the base points of the coordinate system must be. For instance, $O = (P \cup R) \cap (Q \cup S)$. Putting the given coordinates of P, Q, R, S into Equation 5.10.4 yields four equations whose simultaneous solution shows that $f = g = h = a + b + c = 0$.

10. Construct a coordinate system as described in exercise 9. For $i = 1, 2$, let ω_i be the polarity induced by the complete conic determined by $\mathcal{C}_i$. By exercise 9,

$$\boldsymbol{\omega}_i = \begin{bmatrix} a_i & 0 & 0 \\ 0 & b_i & 0 \\ 0 & 0 & c_i \end{bmatrix}$$

is a matrix for ω_i in the chosen coordinate system. Calculate coordinates for $P\omega_1 \cap Q\omega_1$ and $R\omega_1 \cap S\omega_1$, and show that if one of these points is on $\mathcal{C}_2$, then so is the other.

11. (b) Equation 5.10.4 reduces to $ax^2 + by^2 + cz^2 = 0$, which is equivalent to $(a'x + b'y + c'z)^2 = 0$, where a', b', c' are the respective square roots of a, b, c.

12. There is a projective collineation σ that transforms $\mathcal{C}$ into the conic $\mathcal{C}'$ with equation $y^2 = xz$. The point P is on $\mathcal{C}$ if and only if $P\sigma$ is on $\mathcal{C}'$. When σ is represented by a matrix $\boldsymbol{\sigma}$, the condition for P to be on $\mathcal{C}$ is that $[P]\boldsymbol{\sigma}$ satisfy $y^2 = xz$, and this translates into a homogeneous quadratic equation in the coordinates of P.

13. If η is a homology of $\mathcal{P}$, construct a coordinate system for $\mathcal{P}$ with O, ℓ_∞ as the center and axis of η. Then,

$$\boldsymbol{\eta} = \begin{bmatrix} r & 0 & 0 \\ 0 & r & 0 \\ 0 & 0 & 1 \end{bmatrix}$$

is a matrix for η, and η is the composite of the polarity with this same matrix and the coordinate polarity. If ϵ is an elation of $\mathcal{P}$, construct a coordinate system for $\mathcal{P}$ with I, ℓ_∞ as the center and axis of ϵ, and such that $O\epsilon$ is represented by $[1, 0, 1]$. Then,

$$\boldsymbol{\epsilon} = \begin{bmatrix} 1 & 0 & 0 \\ 0 & 1 & 0 \\ 1 & 0 & 1 \end{bmatrix}$$

is a matrix for ϵ. Let ω be the polarity with matrix

$$\boldsymbol{\omega} = \begin{bmatrix} 0 & 0 & 1 \\ 0 & 1 & 0 \\ 1 & 0 & 0 \end{bmatrix},$$

and ω' the polarity with matrix

$$\omega' = \begin{bmatrix} 0 & 0 & 1 \\ 0 & 1 & 0 \\ 1 & 0 & -1 \end{bmatrix}.$$

Since $\boldsymbol{\omega}(\boldsymbol{\omega}')^{-1}$ is a matrix for $\omega\omega'$, $\omega\omega' = \epsilon$.

15. The elements of the required triple are (in order): $pa + qf + rg$, $pf + qb + rh$, and $pg + qh + rc$.

INDEX

Index

Index

Index

Index

Index